Teacher Edition

Eureka Math
Grade 6
Module 6

Special thanks go to the Gordon A. Cain Center and to the Department of Mathematics at Louisiana State University for their support in the development of *Eureka Math*.

Published by the non-profit Great Minds

Copyright © 2015 Great Minds. No part of this work may be reproduced, sold, or commercialized, in whole or in part, without written permission from Great Minds. Non-commercial use is licensed pursuant to a Creative Commons Attribution-NonCommercial-ShareAlike 4.0 license; for more information, go to http://greatminds.net/maps/math/copyright. "Great Minds" and "Eureka Math" are registered trademarks of Great Minds.

Printed in the U.S.A.

This book may be purchased from the publisher at eureka-math.org

10 9 8 7 6 5 4 3 2

ISBN 978-1-63255-611-0

***Eureka Math: A Story of Ratios* Contributors**

Michael Allwood, Curriculum Writer
Tiah Alphonso, Program Manager—Curriculum Production
Catriona Anderson, Program Manager—Implementation Support
Beau Bailey, Curriculum Writer
Scott Baldridge, Lead Mathematician and Lead Curriculum Writer
Bonnie Bergstresser, Math Auditor
Gail Burrill, Curriculum Writer
Beth Chance, Statistician
Joanne Choi, Curriculum Writer
Jill Diniz, Program Director
Lori Fanning, Curriculum Writer
Ellen Fort, Math Auditor
Kathy Fritz, Curriculum Writer
Glenn Gebhard, Curriculum Writer
Krysta Gibbs, Curriculum Writer
Winnie Gilbert, Lead Writer / Editor, Grade 8
Pam Goodner, Math Auditor
Debby Grawn, Curriculum Writer
Bonnie Hart, Curriculum Writer
Stefanie Hassan, Lead Writer / Editor, Grade 8
Sherri Hernandez, Math Auditor
Bob Hollister, Math Auditor
Patrick Hopfensperger, Curriculum Writer
Sunil Koswatta, Mathematician, Grade 8
Brian Kotz, Curriculum Writer
Henry Kranendonk, Lead Writer / Editor, Statistics
Connie Laughlin, Math Auditor
Jennifer Loftin, Program Manager—Professional Development
Nell McAnelly, Project Director
Ben McCarty, Mathematician
Stacie McClintock, Document Production Manager
Saki Milton, Curriculum Writer
Pia Mohsen, Curriculum Writer
Jerry Moreno, Statistician
Ann Netter, Lead Writer / Editor, Grades 6–7
Sarah Oyler, Document Coordinator
Roxy Peck, Statistician, Lead Writer / Editor, Statistics
Terrie Poehl, Math Auditor
Kristen Riedel, Math Audit Team Lead
Spencer Roby, Math Auditor
Kathleen Scholand, Math Auditor
Erika Silva, Lead Writer / Editor, Grade 6–7
Robyn Sorenson, Math Auditor
Hester Sutton, Advisor / Reviewer Grades 6–7
Shannon Vinson, Lead Writer / Editor, Statistics
Allison Witcraft, Math Auditor

Julie Wortmann, Lead Writer / Editor, Grade 7
David Wright, Mathematician, Lead Writer / Editor, Grades 6–7

Board of Trustees

Lynne Munson, President and Executive Director of Great Minds

Nell McAnelly, Chairman, Co-Director Emeritus of the Gordon A. Cain Center for STEM Literacy at Louisiana State University

William Kelly, Treasurer, Co-Founder and CEO at ReelDx

Jason Griffiths, Secretary, Director of Programs at the National Academy of Advanced Teacher Education

Pascal Forgione, Former Executive Director of the Center on K-12 Assessment and Performance Management at ETS

Lorraine Griffith, Title I Reading Specialist at West Buncombe Elementary School in Asheville, North Carolina

Bill Honig, President of the Consortium on Reading Excellence (CORE)

Richard Kessler, Executive Dean of Mannes College the New School for Music

Chi Kim, Former Superintendent, Ross School District

Karen LeFever, Executive Vice President and Chief Development Officer at ChanceLight Behavioral Health and Education

Maria Neira, Former Vice President, New York State United Teachers

Mathematics Curriculum

Table of Contents[1]

Statistics

Module Overview 3

Topic A: Understanding Distributions (**6.SP.A.1, 6.SP.A.2, 6.SP.B.4, 6.SP.B.5b**) 9

    Lesson 1: Posing Statistical Questions 11

    Lesson 2: Displaying a Data Distribution 20

    Lesson 3: Creating a Dot Plot 31

    Lesson 4: Creating a Histogram 40

    Lesson 5: Describing a Distribution Displayed in a Histogram 54

Topic B: Summarizing a Distribution That Is Approximately Symmetric Using the Mean and Mean Absolute Deviation (**6.SP.A.2, 6.SP.A.3, 6.SP.B.4, 6.SP.B.5**) 64

    Lesson 6: Describing the Center of a Distribution Using the Mean 66

    Lesson 7: The Mean as a Balance Point 77

    Lesson 8: Variability in a Data Distribution 89

    Lesson 9: The Mean Absolute Deviation (MAD) 98

    Lessons 10–11: Describing Distributions Using the Mean and MAD 110

Mid-Module Assessment and Rubric 130
Topics A through B (assessment 1 day)

Topic C: Summarizing a Distribution That Is Skewed Using the Median and the Interquartile Range (**6.SP.A.2, 6.SP.A.3, 6.SP.B.4, 6.SP.B.5**) 146

    Lesson 12: Describing the Center of a Distribution Using the Median 148

    Lesson 13: Describing Variability Using the Interquartile Range (IQR) 161

    Lesson 14: Summarizing a Distribution Using a Box Plot 171

    Lesson 15: More Practice with Box Plots 181

    Lesson 16: Understanding Box Plots 193

Topic D: Summarizing and Describing Distributions (**6.SP.B.4, 6.SP.B.5**) 203

    Lesson 17: Developing a Statistical Project 205

    Lesson 18: Connecting Graphical Representations and Numerical Summaries 213

---

[1]Each lesson is ONE day, and ONE day is considered a 45-minute period.

Lesson 19: Comparing Data Distributions 225

Lesson 20: Describing Center, Variability, and Shape of a Data Distribution from a Graphical
              Representation 237

Lesson 21: Summarizing a Data Distribution by Describing Center, Variability, and Shape 246

Lesson 22: Presenting a Summary of a Statistical Project 255

End-of-Module Assessment and Rubric 260
Topics A through D (assessment 1 day, remediation or further applications 1 day)

EUREKA MATH

©2015 Great Minds eureka-math.org
G6-M6-TE-B3-1.3.1-01.2016

Grade 6 • Module 6

Statistics

OVERVIEW

In Grade 5, students used bar graphs and line plots to represent data and then solved problems using the information presented in the plots (**5.MD.B.2**). In this module, students move from simply representing data into analyzing data. In Topic A, students begin to think and reason statistically by first recognizing a statistical question as one that can be answered by collecting data (**6.SP.A.1**). Students learn that the data collected to answer a statistical question have a distribution that is often summarized in terms of center, variability, and shape (**6.SP.A.2**). Beginning in Topic A, and throughout the module, students see and represent data distributions using dot plots and histograms (**6.SP.B.4**).

In Topics B and C, students study quantitative ways to summarize numerical data sets in relation to their context and to the shape of the distribution. The mean and mean absolute deviation (MAD) are used for data distributions that are approximately symmetric, and the median and interquartile range (IQR) are used for distributions that are skewed. Students apply their experience in writing, reading, and evaluating expressions in which letters stand for numbers (**6.EE.A.2**) as they learn to compute and interpret these statistical measures for center and spread (**6.SP.A.5**).

In Topic B, students study *mean* as a measure of center and *mean absolute deviation* as a measure of variability. Students learn that these measures are preferred when the shape of the distribution is roughly symmetric. Then, in Topic C, students study *median* as a measure of center and *interquartile range* as a measure of variability. Students learn that these measures are preferred when the shape of the distribution is skewed. Students develop in Topic B, and reinforce in Topic C, the idea that a measure of center provides a summary of all values in a data distribution in a single number, while a measure of variation describes how values in a data distribution vary, also with a single number (**6.SP.A.3**).

Measures of center and variability for distributions that are approximately symmetric (mean and MAD) are covered before measures for skewed data distributions (median and IQR). This choice was made because it is easier for students to understand measuring center and variability in the context of symmetric distributions.

For students, box plots are the most difficult of the graphical displays covered in this module. This is because they differ from dot plots and histograms in that they are not really a display of the data but rather a graph of five summary measures (minimum, lower quartile, median, upper quartile, and maximum). This graph conveys information on center and variability but is more difficult for students to interpret because, unlike histograms, where large area corresponds to many observations, in a box plot, large area indicates spread, and small area indicates a large number of observations in a small interval. Box plots also require the calculation of quartiles and are best covered after quartiles have been introduced and used to calculate the IQR. For these reasons, box plots are introduced late in the module after the IQR and after students have already developed some fundamental understanding of data distributions, which is easier to do in the context of dot plots and histograms.

Module 6:   Statistics

3

©2015 Great Minds eureka-math.org
G6-M6-TE-B3-1.3.1-01.2016

In Topic D, students synthesize what they have learned as they connect the graphical, verbal, and numerical summaries to each other within situational contexts, culminating with a major project (**6.SP.B.4**, **6.SP.B.5**). Students implement the four-step investigative process with their projects by stating their statistical questions, explaining the plan they used to collect data, analyzing data numerically and with graphs, and interpreting their results to answer their statistical questions.

The 25-day module consists of 22 lessons; 3 days are reserved for administering the Mid- and End-of-Module Assessments, returning assessments, and remediating or providing further applications of the concepts. The Mid-Module Assessment follows Topic B, and the End-of-Module Assessment follows Topic D.

Focus Standards

Develop understanding of statistical variability.

6.SP.A.1   Recognize a statistical question as one that anticipates variability in the data related to the question and accounts for it in the answers. *For example, "How old am I?" is not a statistical question, but "How old are the students in my school?" is a statistical question because one anticipates variability in students' ages.*

6.SP.A.2   Understand that a set of data collected to answer a statistical question has a distribution which can be described by its center, spread, and overall shape.

6.SP.A.3   Recognize that a measure of center for a numerical data set summarizes all of its values with a single number, while a measure of variation describes how its values vary with a single number.

Summarize and describe distributions.

6.SP.B.4   Display numerical data in plots on a number line, including dot plots, histograms, and box plots.

6.SP.B.5   Summarize numerical data sets in relation to their context, such as by:

    a.   Reporting the number of observations.

    b.   Describing the nature of the attribute under investigation, including how it was measured and its units of measurement.

    c.   Giving quantitative measures of center (median and/or mean) and variability (interquartile range and/or mean absolute deviation), as well as describing any overall pattern and any striking deviations from the overall pattern with reference to the context in which the data were gathered.

    d.   Relating the choice of measures of center and variability to the shape of the data distribution and the context in which the data were gathered.

©2015 Great Minds eureka-math.org
G6-M6-TE-B3-1.3.1-01.2016

Foundational Standards

Perform operations with multi-digit whole numbers and with decimals to hundredths.

5.NBT.B.5   Fluently multiply multi-digit whole numbers using the standard algorithm.

5.NBT.B.6   Find whole-number quotients of whole numbers with up to four-digit dividends and two-digit divisors, using strategies based on place value, the properties of operations, and/or the relationship between multiplication and division. Illustrate and explain the calculation by using equations, rectangular arrays, and/or area models.

5.NBT.B.7   Add, subtract, multiply, and divide decimals to hundredths, using concrete models or drawings and strategies based on place value, properties of operations, and/or the relationship between addition and subtraction; relate the strategy to a written method and explain the reasoning used.

Represent and interpret data.

5.MD.B.2   Make a line plot to display a data set of measurements in fractions of a unit ($1/2$, $1/4$, $1/8$). Use operations on fractions for this grade to solve problems involving information presented in line plots. *For example, given different measurements of liquid in identical beakers, find the amount of liquid each beaker would contain if the total amount in all the beakers were redistributed equally.*

Apply and extend previous understandings of arithmetic to algebraic expressions.

6.EE.A.2   Write, read, and evaluate expressions in which letters stand for numbers.

    a.   Write expressions that record operations with numbers and with letters standing for numbers. *For example, express the calculation "Subtract y from 5" as $5 - y$.*

    b.   Identify parts of an expression using mathematical terms (sum, term, product, factor, quotient, coefficient); view one or more parts of an expression as a single entity. *For example, describe the expression $2(8 + 7)$ as a product of two factors; view $(8 + 7)$ as both a single entity and a sum of two terms.*

    c.   Evaluate expressions at specific values of their variables. Include expressions that arise from formulas used in real-world problems. Perform arithmetic operations, including those involving whole-number exponents, in the conventional order when there are no parentheses to specify a particular order (Order of Operations). *For example, use the formulas $V = s^3$ and $A = 6s^2$ to find the volume and surface area of a cube with sides of length $s = 1/2$.*

Focus Standards for Mathematical Practice

MP.1 **Make sense of problems and persevere in solving them.** Students make sense of problems by defining them in terms of a statistical question and then determining what data might be collected in order to provide an answer to the question and therefore a solution to the problem.

MP.2 **Reason abstractly and quantitatively.** Students pose statistical questions and reason about how to collect and interpret data in order to answer these questions. Students use graphs to summarize the data and to answer statistical questions.

MP.3 **Construct viable arguments and critique the reasoning of others.** Students examine the shape, center, and variability of a data distribution. They communicate the answer to a statistical question in the form of a poster presentation. Students also have an opportunity to critique poster presentations made by other students.

MP.4 **Model with mathematics.** Students create graphs of data distributions. They select an appropriate measure of center to describe a typical data value for a given data distribution. They also calculate and interpret an appropriate measure of variability based on the shape of the data distribution.

MP.6 **Attend to precision.** Students interpret and communicate conclusions in context based on graphical and numerical data summaries. Students use statistical terminology appropriately.

Terminology

New or Recently Introduced Terms

- **Absolute Deviation** (An *absolute deviation* is the distance of a data value from the mean of the data set.)
- **Box Plot** (A *box plot* is a graphical representation of five numerical summary measures: the minimum, lower quartile, median, upper quartile, and the maximum. It conveys information about center and variability in a data set.)
- **Dot Plot** (A *dot plot* is a plot of numerical data along a number line. Data values are represented by a dot placed in a column directly above where the data value is located on the number line.)
- **Frequency** (A *frequency* associated with an interval used to construct a summary table or a histogram is the number of data values that are included in the interval.)
- **Frequency Table** (A *frequency table* summarizes a data distribution. The table includes the data values (sometimes grouped into intervals) and the associated frequencies.)
- **Histogram** (A *histogram* is a graphical representation of a numerical data set that has been grouped into intervals. Each interval is represented by a bar drawn above that interval that has a height corresponding to the number of observations in that interval or the relative frequency corresponding to that interval.)

©2015 Great Minds eureka-math.org
G6-M6-TE-B3-1.3.1-01.2016

- **Interquartile Range (IQR)** (*Interquartile range* is a measure of variability appropriate for data distributions that are skewed. It is the difference between the upper quartile and the lower quartile of a data set and describes how spread out the middle 50% of the data are.)

- **Mean** (The *mean* is a measure of center appropriate for data distributions that are approximately symmetric. It is the average of the values in the data set. Two common interpretations of the mean are as a "fair share" and as the balance point of the data distribution.)

- **Mean Absolute Deviation (MAD)** (The *mean absolute deviation* of a numerical data set is the mean of all the distances from the mean for that data set.)

- **Median** (The *median* is a measure of center appropriate for skewed data distributions. It is the middle value when the data are ordered from smallest to largest if the number of observations is odd and half way between the middle two observations if the number of observations is even.)

- **Relative Frequency** (A *relative frequency* associated with an interval used to construct a summary table or a histogram is equal to the number of data values that are included in the interval divided by the total number of values in the data set. It is the proportion of the data values that are included in the interval.)

- **Relative Frequency Histogram** (A *relative frequency histogram* is a histogram that is constructed using relative frequencies rather than frequencies to determine the heights of the bars.)

- **Relative Frequency Table** (A *relative frequency table* is a frequency table that displays relative frequency in addition to frequency for each data value or interval.)

- **Statistical Question** (A *statistical question* is a question that can be answered by collecting data and that anticipates variability in the data collected.)

- **Variability** (*Variability* of a data set is the extent to which data values differ from each other. Variability occurs when the observations in the data set are not all the same.)

Familiar Terms and Symbols[2]

- Line Plot or Dot Plot

---

[2]These are terms and symbols students have seen previously.

Suggested Tools and Representations

- Dot Plots
- Histograms
- Box Plots

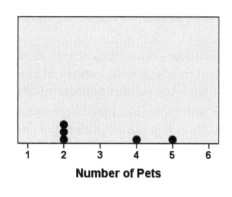

Dot Plot

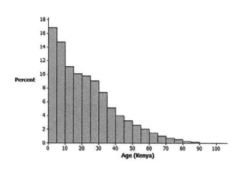

Histogram

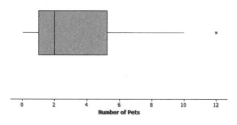

Box Plot

Assessment Summary

Assessment Type	Administered	Format	Standards Addressed
Mid-Module Assessment Task	After Topic B	Constructed response with rubric	6.SP.A.1, 6.SP.A.2, 6.SP.A.3, 6.SP.B.4, 6.SP.B.5
End-of-Module Assessment Task	After Topic D	Constructed response with rubric	6.SP.A.1, 6.SP.A.2, 6.SP.A.3, 6.SP.B.4, 6.SP.B.5
Project	Topic D: Lessons 17 and 22	Poster or other form of presentation	6.SP.A.1, 6.SP.A.2, 6.SP.A.3, 6.SP.B.4, 6.SP.B.5

EUREKA MATH

©2015 Great Minds eureka-math.org
G6-M6-TE-B3-1.3.1-01.2016

Mathematics Curriculum

Topic A

Understanding Distributions

6.SP.A.1, 6.S.AP.2, 6.SP.B.4, 6.SP.B.5b

Focus Standards:	6.SP.A.1	Recognize a statistical question as one that anticipates variability in the data related to the question and accounts for it in the answers. *For example, "How old am I?" is not a statistical question, but "How old are the students in my school?" is a statistical question because one anticipates variability in students' ages.*
	6.SP.A.2	Understand that a set of data collected to answer a statistical question has a distribution that can be described by its center, spread, and overall shape.
	6.SP.B.4	Display numerical data in plots on a number line, including dot plots, histograms, and box plots.
	6.SP.B.5	Summarize numerical data sets in relation to their context, such as by: b. Describing the nature of the attribute under investigation, including how it was measured and its units of measurement.
Instructional Days:	5	
	Lesson 1:	Posing Statistical Questions (P)[1]
	Lesson 2:	Displaying a Data Distribution (P)
	Lesson 3:	Creating a Dot Plot (P)
	Lesson 4:	Creating a Histogram (P)
	Lesson 5:	Describing a Distribution Displayed in a Histogram (P)

In Topic A, students begin a study of statistics by learning to recognize a statistical question. They develop an understanding of what data could be collected to answer a statistical question and to anticipate variability in the data collected to answer the question. Lesson 1 introduces statistical questions in the context of a four-step process for posing and answering questions based on data. As students begin to explore data, they see the need to organize and summarize the data. Lesson 2 introduces students to the idea that a data distribution can be represented graphically and that there are several types of graphs, including dot plots and histograms, commonly used to represent a distribution of numerical data. This lesson then builds on

---

[1]Lesson Structure Key: **P**-Problem Set Lesson, **M**-Modeling Cycle Lesson, **E**-Exploration Lesson, **S**-Socratic Lesson

students' previous work with line plots and introduces them to dot plots (i.e., line plots, but in a data context where students consider the distribution of data rather than think of individual points plotted on a number line). In Lesson 3, students construct dot plots and begin to describe data distributions. Lesson 4 introduces students to histograms as another way of representing a data distribution graphically and discusses the advantages and disadvantages of histograms relative to dot plots. Additionally, this lesson asks students to consider the shape of a data distribution (symmetric versus skewed). Lesson 4 then goes on to introduce the idea that the numerical summary measures of center and variability used to describe data distributions that are approximately symmetric are different from the ones that are used to describe data distributions that are skewed. This is an important distinction and is the basis for the content introduced in Topics B and C. Lesson 5 gives students additional practice in constructing and describing histograms and introduces relative frequency histograms (i.e., histograms where relative frequency rather than frequency is used for the vertical scale).

©2015 Great Minds eureka-math.org
G6-M6-TE-B3-1.3.1-01.2016

Lesson 1: Posing Statistical Questions

Student Outcomes

- Students distinguish between statistical questions and those that are not statistical.
- Students formulate a statistical question and explain what data could be collected to answer the question.
- Students distinguish between categorical data and numerical data.

Classwork

Example 1 (5 minutes): Using Data to Answer Questions

Have students read Example 1, and then pose the following questions:

- What questions was the beekeeper trying to answer?
  - *The beekeeper wanted to know if beekeepers have fewer hives this year than last year. The beekeeper also wanted to know about how many fewer hives beekeepers have this year.*

- Did the beekeeper collect data to answer his questions?
  - *Yes. He collected data on whether there were fewer hives this year and on how many fewer hives there were.*

- What did the beekeeper conclude?
  - *The beekeeper concluded that most beekeepers had fewer hives this year and that a typical decrease was about 4 hives.*

Example 1: Using Data to Answer Questions

Honeybees are important because they produce honey and pollinate plants. Since 2007, there has been a decline in the honeybee population in the United States. Honeybees live in hives, and a beekeeper in Wisconsin notices that this year, he has 5 fewer hives of bees than last year. He wonders if other beekeepers in Wisconsin are also losing hives. He decides to survey other beekeepers and ask them if they have fewer hives this year than last year, and if so, how many fewer. He then uses the data to conclude that most beekeepers have fewer hives this year than last and that a typical decrease is about 4 hives.

Next, have students read the information below. Then, point out how these steps relate to the beekeeper example (Example 1). Step 3 is not visible in the paragraph students read, but point out that the beekeeper would have had to summarize the information he collected in order to draw his conclusions.

Statistics is about using data to answer questions. In this module, you will use the following four steps in your work with data:

Step 1: Pose a question that can be answered by data.

Step 2: Determine a plan to collect the data.

Step 3: Summarize the data with graphs and numerical summaries.

Step 4: Answer the question posed in Step 1 using the data and summaries.

You will be guided through this process as you study these lessons. This first lesson is about the first step: What is a statistical question, and what does it mean that a question can be answered by data?

©2015 Great Minds eureka-math.org
G6-M6-TE-B3-1.3.1-01.2016

Example 2 (15 minutes): What Is a Statistical Question?

Introduce the situation described in Example 2 to the class. Consider showing students an example of a baseball card so that they can see the different kinds of information that appears on the card.

Example 2: What Is a Statistical Question?

Jerome, a sixth grader at Roosevelt Middle School, is a huge baseball fan. He loves to collect baseball cards. He has cards of current players and of players from past baseball seasons. With his teacher's permission, Jerome brought his baseball card collection to school. Each card has a picture of a current or past major league baseball player, along with information about the player. When he placed his cards out for the other students to see, they asked Jerome all sorts of questions about his cards. Some asked:

- What is Jerome's favorite card?

- What is the typical cost of a card in Jerome's collection? For example, what is the average cost of a card?

- Are more of Jerome's cards for current players or for past players?

- Which card is the newest card in Jerome's collection?

Then, consider the questions posed in Example 2, and ask students the following:

- Which of these questions do you think might be statistical questions?

    □ *Answers will vary. Some students do not know how to answer this question, but some may go back to the definition of Step 1 in the process described earlier to look for questions that can be answered by data. Even so, they still might think at this point that all of the questions are statistical questions.*

- What do you think I mean when I say *a statistical question?*

    □ *Answers will vary. If no one relates the idea of a statistical question to the need for data, consider asking students to go back and look at the four-step process described earlier in this lesson.*

Students do not yet understand what a statistical question is. Allow them to discuss and make conjectures about what it might mean before guiding them to the following:

- A *statistical question* is one that can be answered with data and for which it is anticipated that the data (information) collected to answer the question will vary.

- The second and third questions are statistical questions because the data collected to answer the questions would vary. To decide on a typical value (i.e., to describe what is typical for values in a data set using a single number) for the cost of a card, you would collect data on what each card cost. You would expect variability in the costs because some cards probably cost more than others. For the third question, you would need to collect data on whether or not each card was for a current player or for a past player. There would be variability in the data collected because some cards would be for current players, and some would be for past players. The first question—"What is Jerome's favorite card?"—is not a statistical question because there is no variability in the data collected to answer this question. There is only one data value and no variability. The same is true for the fourth question.

Convey the main idea that a question is statistical if it can be answered with data that vary. Point out that the concept of variability in the data means that not all data values have the same value.

- The question "How old am I?" is not a statistical question because it is not answered by collecting data that vary. The question "How old are the students in my school?" is a statistical question because to answer it, you would collect data on the ages of students at the school, and the ages will vary—not all students are the same age.

Lesson 1:   Posing Statistical Questions

©2015 Great Minds eureka-math.org
G6-M6-TE-B3-1.3.1-01.2016

- Would the following questions be answered by collecting data that vary?

How tall is your sixth-grade math teacher?

  □ *This question would not be answered by collecting data that vary because my sixth-grade math teacher can only be one height.*

- What is your handspan (measured from the tip of the thumb to the tip of the small finger)?

  □ *This question is not a statistical question because I would just measure my handspan. It would not be answered by collecting data that vary.*

- Which of these data sets would have the most variability?

The number of minutes students in your class spend getting ready for school or the number of pockets on the clothes of students in your class

  □ *The number of minutes students spend getting ready for school would vary the most because some students take a long time to get ready, and some students only require a short time to get ready for school. The number of pockets will vary from student to student, but most values will be 0, 1, or 2.*

After arriving at this understanding as a class, write the informal definition of *statistical question* on the board so that students may refer to it for the remainder of the class.

Exercises 1–5 (10 minutes)

These question sets are designed to reinforce the definition of a statistical question. The main focus is on whether there is variability in the data that would be used to answer the question. Consider having students share their answers to Exercise 3 with a partner and having the partner decide whether or not the question is a statistical question.

Exercises 1–5

1. For each of the following, determine whether or not the question is a statistical question. Give a reason for your answer.

    a. Who is my favorite movie star?

    This is not a statistical question because it is not answered by collecting data that vary.

    b. What are the favorite colors of sixth graders in my school?

    This is a statistical question because to answer this question, you would collect data by asking students about their favorite colors, and there would be variability in the data. The favorite color would not be the same for every student.

    c. How many years have students in my school's band or orchestra played an instrument?

    This is a statistical question because to answer this question, you would collect data by asking students in the band about how many years they have played an instrument, and there would be variability in the data. The number of years would not be the same for every student.

    d. What is the favorite subject of sixth graders at my school?

    This is a statistical question because to answer this question, you would collect data by asking students about their favorite subjects, and there would be variability in the data. The favorite subject would not be the same for every student.

    e. How many brothers and sisters does my best friend have?

    This is not a statistical question because it is not answered by collecting data that vary.

---

2. Explain why each of the following questions is not a statistical question.

    a.   How old am I?

         This is not a statistical question because I only have one age at the time the question is asked.

    b.   What's my favorite color?

         This is not a statistical question because it is not answered by data that vary. I only have one favorite color.

    c.   How old is the principal at our school?

         This is not a statistical question because the principal has just one age at the time I ask the principal's age. Therefore, the question is not answered by data that vary.

3. Ronnie, a sixth grader, wanted to find out if he lived the farthest from school. Write a statistical question that would help Ronnie find the answer.

    Answers will vary. One possible answer is, "What is a typical distance from home to school (in miles) for students at my school?"

4. Write a statistical question that can be answered by collecting data from students in your class.

    Answers will vary. For example, "What is the typical number of pets owned by students in my class?" or "How many hours each day do students in my class play video games?"

5. Change the following question to make it a statistical question: How old is my math teacher?

    What is a typical age for teachers at my school?

Example 3 (5 minutes): Types of Data

To answer statistical questions, we collect data. For example, in the context of baseball cards, we might record the cost of a card for each of 25 baseball cards. This would result in a data set with 25 values. We might also record the age of each card or the team of the player featured on each card.

Example 3: Types of Data

We use two types of data to answer statistical questions: numerical data and categorical data. If you recorded the ages of 25 baseball cards, we would have numerical data. Each value in a numerical data set is a number. If we recorded the team of the featured player for each of 25 baseball cards, you would have categorical data. Although you still have 25 data values, the data values are not numbers. They would be team names, which you can think of as categories.

- What are other examples of categorical data?
  - *Answers will vary. Eye color, the month in which you were born, and your favorite subject are examples of categorical data.*
- What are other examples of numerical data?
  - *Answers will vary. Height, number of pets, and minutes to get to school are all examples of numerical data.*

©2015 Great Minds eureka-math.org
G6-M6-TE-B3-1.3.1-01.2016

To help students distinguish between the two data types, encourage them to think of possible data values. If the possible data values are words or categories, then the variable is categorical.

- Suppose that you collected data on the following. What are some of the possible values that you might get?
  - *Eye color*
  - *Favorite TV show*
  - *Amount of rain that fell during each of 20 storms*
  - *High temperatures for each of 12 days*

Exercises 6–7 (5 minutes)

Have students complete the exercises below to reinforce their understanding of the two types of data.

Exercises 6–7

6. Identify each of the following data sets as categorical (C) or numerical (N).
    a. Heights of 20 sixth graders __N__

    b. Favorite flavor of ice cream for each of 10 sixth graders __C__

    c. Hours of sleep on a school night for each of 30 sixth graders __N__

    d. Type of beverage drunk at lunch for each of 15 sixth graders __C__

    e. Eye color for each of 30 sixth graders __C__

    f. Number of pencils in the desk of each of 15 sixth graders __N__

7. For each of the following statistical questions, identify whether the data Jerome would collect to answer the question would be numerical or categorical. Explain your answer, and list four possible data values.
    a. How old are the cards in the collection?

    The data are numerical data, as I anticipate the data will be numbers.

    Possible data values: 2 years, $2\frac{1}{2}$ years, 4 years, 20 years

    b. How much did the cards in the collection cost?

    The data are numerical data, as I anticipate the data will be numbers.

    Possible data values: $0.20, $1.50, $10.00, $35.00

    c. Where did Jerome get the cards in the collection?

    The data are categorical, as I anticipate the data will represent the names of places or people.

    Possible data values: a store, a garage sale, from my brother, from a friend

---

©2015 Great Minds eureka-math.org
G6-M6-TE-B3-1.3.1-01.2016

Closing (2 minutes)

- What is a statistical question?
    - *A statistical question is one that can be answered by collecting data that vary. All of the data values are not the same.*
- What is the difference between a numerical data set and a categorical data set?
    - *Every value in a numerical data set is a number. The values in a categorical data set are not numerical. They are categories.*

While reviewing the four steps students follow in their work with data, remind students of the opening example about the beekeeper. Consider revisiting that example here to show students how the four steps allow them to pose and answer statistical questions.

Lesson Summary

Statistics is about using data to answer questions. In this module, the following four steps summarize your work with data:

      Step 1: Pose a question that can be answered by data.

      Step 2: Determine a plan to collect the data.

      Step 3: Summarize the data with graphs and numerical summaries.

      Step 4: Answer the question posed in Step 1 using the data and summaries.

A statistical question is one that can be answered by collecting data and where there will be variability in the data.

Two types of data are used to answer statistical questions: numerical and categorical.

Exit Ticket (3 minutes)

©2015 Great Minds eureka-math.org
G6-M6-TE-B3-1.3.1-01.2016

Name _____   Date_____

Lesson 1: Posing Statistical Questions

Exit Ticket

1. Indicate whether each of the following two questions is a statistical question. Explain why or why not.

    a.   How much does Susan's dog weigh?

    b.   How much do the dogs belonging to students at our school weigh?

2. If you collected data on the weights of dogs, would the data be numerical or categorical? Explain how you know the data are numerical or categorical.

Exit Ticket Sample Solutions

1. Indicate whether each of the following two questions is a statistical question. Explain why or why not.

    a. How much does Susan's dog weigh?

    This is not a statistical question. This question is not answered by collecting data that vary.

    b. How much do the dogs belonging to students at our school weigh?

    This is a statistical question. This question would be answered by collecting data on weights of dogs. There is variability in these weights.

2. If you collected data on the weights of dogs, would the data be numerical or categorical? Explain how you know the data are numerical or categorical.

    The data collected would be numerical data because the weight values are numbers.

Problem Set Sample Solutions

1. For each of the following, determine whether the question is a statistical question. Give a reason for your answer.

    a. How many letters are in my last name?

    This is not a statistical question because this question is not answered by collecting data that vary.

    b. How many letters are in the last names of the students in my sixth-grade class?

    This is a statistical question because it would be answered by collecting data on name lengths, and there is variability in the lengths of the last names.

    c. What are the colors of the shoes worn by students in my school?

    This is a statistical question because it would be answered by collecting data on shoe colors, and we expect variability in the colors.

    d. What is the maximum number of feet that roller coasters drop during a ride?

    This is a statistical question because it would be answered by collecting data on the drop of roller coasters, and we expect variability in how many feet different roller coasters drop. They will not all be the same.

    e. What are the heart rates of students in a sixth-grade class?

    This is a statistical question because it would be answered by collecting data on heart rates, and we expect variability. Not all sixth graders have exactly the same heart rate.

    f. How many hours of sleep per night do sixth graders usually get when they have school the next day?

    This is a statistical question because it would be answered by collecting data on hours of sleep, and we do not expect that all sixth graders sleep the same number of hours.

    g. How many miles per gallon do compact cars get?

    This is a statistical question because it would be answered by collecting data on fuel efficiency, and we expect variability in miles per gallon from one car to another.

©2015 Great Minds eureka-math.org
G6-M6-TE-B3-1.3.1-01.2016

2.   Identify each of the following data sets as categorical (C) or numerical (N). Explain your answer.

   a.   Arm spans of 12 sixth graders

        N; the arm span can be measured as number of inches, for example, so the data set is numerical.

   b.   Number of languages spoken by each of 20 adults

        N; number of languages is clearly numerical.

   c.   Favorite sport of each person in a group of 20 adults

        C; a sport falls into a category, such as "soccer" or "hockey." Favorite sport is not measured numerically.

   d.   Number of pets for each of 40 third graders

        N; number of pets is clearly numerical.

   e.   Number of hours a week spent reading a book for a group of middle school students

        N; number of hours is clearly numerical.

3.   Rewrite each of the following questions as a statistical question.

     Answers will vary. Sample answers are given below.

   a.   How many pets does your teacher have?

        How many pets do teachers in our school have?

   b.   How many points did the high school soccer team score in its last game?

        What is a typical number of points scored by the high school soccer team in its games this season?

   c.   How many pages are in our math book?

        What is a typical number of pages for the books in the school library?

   d.   Can I do a handstand?

        Can most sixth graders do a handstand?

4.   Write a statistical question that would be answered by collecting data from the sixth graders in your classroom.

     Answers will vary. Check to make sure the question would be answered by collecting data that vary.

5.   Are the data you would collect to answer the question you wrote in Problem 2 categorical or numerical? Explain your answer.

     Answers will vary. Check to make sure that the answer here is consistent with the statistical question from Problem 4. If the possible values for the data collected would be numerical, students should answer numerical here, but if the possible data values are categories rather than numbers, students should answer categorical.

©2015 Great Minds eureka-math.org
G6-M6-TE-B3-1.3.1-01.2016

Lesson 2: Displaying a Data Distribution

Student Outcomes

- Given a dot plot, students begin describing the distribution of the points on the dot plot in terms of center and variability.

Classwork

Example 1 (9 minutes): Heart Rate

MP.1

This example uses the scenario of students' resting heart rates. While discussing the scenario with students, consider demonstrating how a pulse is taken, and (if time permits) have students find their resting heart rates and use that data to make a dot plot. Take a few minutes to go over Example 1, and make sure that students understand what the given numbers represent.

Example 1: Heart Rate

Mia, a sixth grader at Roosevelt Middle School, was thinking about joining the middle school track team. She read that Olympic athletes have lower resting heart rates than most people. She wondered about her own heart rate and how it would compare to other students. Mia was interested in investigating the statistical question: What are the heart rates of students in my sixth-grade class?

Heart rates are expressed as beats per minute (or bpm). Mia knew her resting heart rate was 80 beats per minute. She asked her teacher if she could collect the heart rates of the other students in her class. With the teacher's help, the other sixth graders in her class found their heart rates and reported them to Mia. The following numbers are the resting heart rates (in beats per minute) for the 22 other students in Mia's class.

89 87 85 84 90 79 83 85 86 88 84 81 88 85 83 83 86 82 83 86 82 84

Use the given data values to construct a dot plot. Mia's data point is not included. While making the dot plot, have students follow the steps to make their own dot plots of the data. Emphasize that it is important to think about where to start numbering (need to include the smallest value in the data set) and where to stop numbering (need to include the largest value in the data set) when setting up the number line for the dot plot. Mia's data point is not included.

- To learn about the heart rates, a good place to start is to make a graph of the data. There are several different graphs that could be used, including the three types of graphs that you learn in this module: dot plots, histograms, and box plots. This lesson covers dot plots.

- Mia noticed that there were many different heart rates. She decided to make a dot plot to show the different heart rates. Help Mia construct a dot plot of her classmates' heart rates by drawing a number line. Start numbering at 78, and continue to 92.

- Place a dot above the corresponding number on the number line for each heart rate. If there is already a dot above a number, add another above it. Continue until there is one dot for each heart rate.

©2015 Great Minds eureka-math.org
G6-M6-TE-B3-1.3.1-01.2016

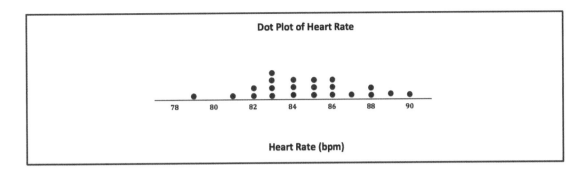

The main purpose of this lesson is to get students to think about a dot plot as a graph of the distribution of the data collected to answer a statistical question. Emphasize thinking about the center of the data and the spread of the data.

At this point, students may differ in what they think *center of the data* means. Record their ideas in order to refer back to their initial ideas throughout the module. Exercise 6 asks students to describe the center. Some students may choose a number that occurs most often, while others may pick a number that is in the middle (i.e., halfway between the highest and lowest data values). Some students may say it is the average. The intent is not to calculate any specific value but to gauge students' thinking about center. Formal measures of center are developed starting in Lesson 6.

Exercise 8 asks students to think about what a typical heart rate is for sixth graders. Similar to the idea of center, students may have different ideas about what they think *typical* means. The idea is to have students begin to discuss where there are clusters of data and where the data center on the number line.

Once students have had a chance to think about the dot plot, ask students the following questions:

- What can you tell me about the heart rates of the sixth-grade students?
    - *Answers will vary. Examples might include "The heart rates ranged from* 79 bpm *to* 90 bpm*" or "There were more students who had a heart rate of* 83 bpm *than any other number."*
- Where do the heart rates tend to center? Why did you choose that number?
    - *Answers will vary. For example, students might say* 83 bpm *because this was the number that occurred most often, or they might say around* 84 bpm *because most of the heart rates are between* 82 bpm *and* 86 bpm.
- How much spread do you see in the heart rates?
    - *Answers will vary. For example, students might say most of the heart rates were between* 82 bpm *and* 86 bpm *or that the heart rates range from* 79 bpm *to* 90 bpm. *This may be the first time students have thought about variability in data, so it may be difficult for them to formulate answers to this question. If they struggle, ask if most of the heart rates were similar or if the heart rates tended to differ quite a bit from one student to another.*

Exercises 1–10 (11 minutes)

The ten exercises that follow are designed to have students recognize the details that can be observed in a dot plot. Students should be able to find the lowest, highest, and most common heart rates. They should also be able to describe the approximate location of the center of the data set.

Allow students about 5–8 minutes to work independently or in small groups. Then, bring the groups together to summarize their answers.

©2015 Great Minds eureka-math.org
G6-M6-TE-B3-1.3.1-01.2016

Exercises 1–10

1. What was the heart rate for the student with the lowest heart rate?

    79 bpm

2. What was the heart rate for the student with the highest heart rate?

    90 bpm

3. How many students had a heart rate greater than 86 bpm?

    5

4. What fraction of students had a heart rate less than 82 bpm?

    $\frac{2}{22}$ *or* $\frac{1}{11}$

5. What heart rate occurred most often?

    83 bpm

6. What heart rate describes the center of the data?

    85 bpm *(Answers will vary, but student responses should be around* 84 bpm *or* 85 bpm.*)*

7. Some students had heart rates that were unusual in that they were quite a bit higher or quite a bit lower than most other students' heart rates. What heart rates would you consider unusual?

    Answers will vary and could include 79 bpm, 81 bpm, 87 bpm, 88 bpm, 89 bpm, *and/or* 90 bpm.

8. If Mia's teacher asked what the typical heart rate is for sixth graders in the class, what would you tell Mia's teacher?

    Answers will vary, but expect answers between 82 bpm *and* 86 bpm.

9. Remember that Mia's heart rate was 80 bpm. Add a dot for Mia's heart rate to the dot plot in Example 1.

    Add a dot above 80 bpm *on the number line.*

10. How does Mia's heart rate compare with the heart rates of the other students in the class?

    Her heart rate is lower than all but one of the students.

©2015 Great Minds eureka-math.org
G6-M6-TE-B3-1.3.1-01.2016

Example 2 (9 minutes): Seeing the Spread in Dot Plots

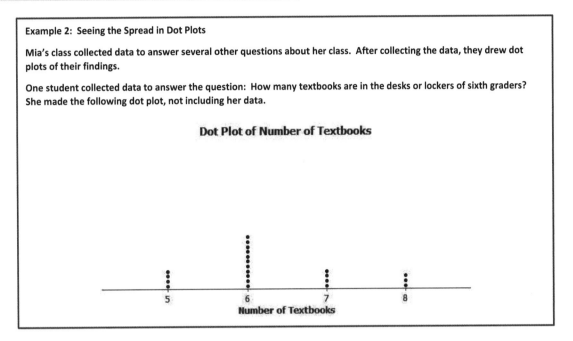

Example 2: Seeing the Spread in Dot Plots

Mia's class collected data to answer several other questions about her class. After collecting the data, they drew dot plots of their findings.

One student collected data to answer the question: How many textbooks are in the desks or lockers of sixth graders? She made the following dot plot, not including her data.

Dot Plot of Number of Textbooks

Number of Textbooks

Before having students look at the dot plot, ask the following:

- Do you think the data responses will be similar, or will the data have a wide range?
    - *The responses should all be about the same since every student takes the same number of subjects in school.*

Have students examine the dot plot.

- Is this represented in the dot plot? Why or why not?
    - *This is represented in the dot plot because there were only four different responses given by students, with most students answering that they had 6 books in their desks or lockers.*
- Another student in Mia's class poses the question: How tall are the sixth graders in our class? Would the data vary more than the data collected about textbooks? Why or why not?
    - *The heights would be spread out since there were some shorter students and some very tall students in class.*

Another student in Mia's class poses the question: How tall are the sixth graders in our class?

This dot plot shows the heights of the sixth graders in Mia's class, not including the datum for the student conducting the survey.

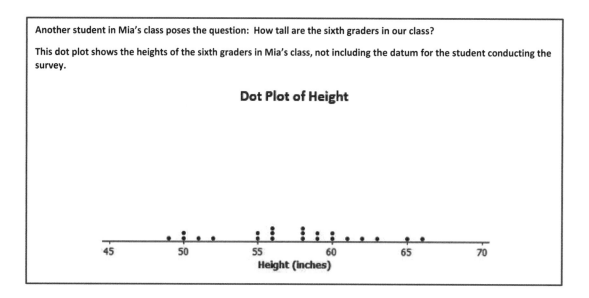

Dot Plot of Height

Height (inches)

In this example, the focus is on the spread of the data. Display the two dot plots (one for the number of textbooks in their desks and the other for the heights of sixth graders). Point out that for the number of textbooks, the data span from 5 to 8, while the heights range from 49 to 66 inches.

Exercises 11–14 (9 minutes)

These exercises represent a matching problem giving students statistical questions to which they should match a dot plot. Stress that students need to explain why they matched each question with a particular dot plot.

Allow students about 3–5 minutes to work independently or in small groups. Bring the groups together to summarize their answers.

Exercises 11–14

Below are four statistical questions and four different dot plots of data collected to answer these questions. Match each statistical question with the appropriate dot plot, and explain each choice.

Statistical Questions:

11.   What are the ages of fourth graders in our school?

Dot plot A because most fourth graders are around 9 or 10 years old.

12.   What are the heights of the players on the eighth-grade boys' basketball team?

Dot plot D because the players on an eighth-grade basketball team can vary in height. Generally, there is a tall player (73 inches), while most others are between 5 feet, or 60 inches, and 5 feet 4 inches, or 64 inches.

13.   How many hours of TV do sixth graders in our class watch on a school night?

Dot plot B; explanations will vary. For example, a student might say, "I think a few of the students may watch a lot of TV. Most students watch two hours or less."

©2015 Great Minds eureka-math.org
G6-M6-TE-B3-1.3.1-01.2016

14. How many different languages do students in our class speak?

Dot plot C because most students know one language, English. Many students in our class also study another language or live in an environment where their families speak another language.

Dot Plot A

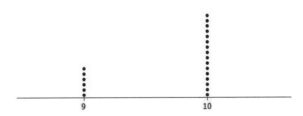

Dot Plot B

Dot Plot C

Dot Plot D

Closing (2 minutes)

- If a number occurs twice in a data set, how do you represent the second one on a dot plot?
    - □ *Place a second dot on top of the first dot at the same value.*
- When examining a dot plot, what information can one gather?
    - □ *We can find the smallest and largest values, gather information about the spread of the data, and see where the center of the data is located.*

Exit Ticket (5 minutes)

©2015 Great Minds eureka-math.org
G6-M6-TE-B3-1.3.1-01.2016

Name _____   Date_____

Lesson 2: Displaying a Data Distribution

Exit Ticket

A sixth-grade class collected data on the number of letters in the first names (name lengths) of all the students in class. Here is the dot plot of the data they collected:

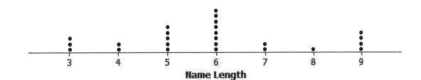

Name Length

1. How many students are in the class?

2. What is the shortest name length?

3. What is the longest name length?

4. What name length occurs most often?

5. What name length describes the center of the data?

©2015 Great Minds eureka-math.org
G6-M6-TE-B3-1.3.1-01.2016

Exit Ticket Sample Solutions

A sixth-grade class collected data on the number of letters in the first names (name lengths) of all the students in class. Here is the dot plot of the data they collected:

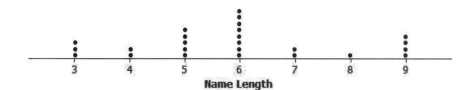

1. How many students are in the class?

   There are 25 students in the class.

2. What is the shortest name length?

   The shortest name length is 3 letters.

3. What is the longest name length?

   The longest name length is 9 letters.

4. What name length occurs most often?

   The most common name length is 6 letters.

5. What name length describes the center of the data?

   The name length that describes the center of the data is 6 letters. (Answers may vary, but student responses should be around 6.)

©2015 Great Minds eureka-math.org
G6-M6-TE-B3-1.3.1-01.2016

EUREKA
MATH™

Problem Set Sample Solutions

1. The dot plot below shows the vertical jump height (in inches) of some NBA players. A vertical jump height is how high a player can jump from a standstill.

Dot Plot of Vertical Jump

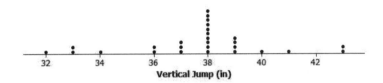

Vertical Jump (in)

a. What statistical question do you think could be answered using these data?

    What are the vertical jump heights of NBA players?

b. What was the highest vertical jump by a player?

    43 inches

c. What was the lowest vertical jump by a player?

    32 inches

d. What is the most common vertical jump height (the height that occurred most often)?

    38 inches

e. How many players jumped the most common vertical jump height?

    10

f. How many players jumped higher than 40 inches?

    3

g. Another NBA player jumped 33 inches. Add a dot for this player on the dot plot. How does this player compare with the other players?

    Add another dot above 33. This player jumped the same as two other players and jumped higher than only one player.

EUREKA MATH™

©2015 Great Minds eureka-math.org
G6-M6-TE-B3-1.3.1-01.2016

2. Below are two statistical questions and two different dot plots of data collected to answer these questions. Match each statistical question with its dot plot, and explain each choice.

Statistical Questions:

a. What is the number of fish (if any) that students in class have in an aquarium at their homes?

A; some students may not have any fish (0 from the dot plot), while another student has 10 fish.

b. How many days out of the week do the children on my street go to the playground?

B; the dot plot displays the values 2, 3, 4, 5, and 6, which are all reasonable within the context of the question.

Dot Plot A

Dot Plot B

3. Read each of the following statistical questions. Write a description of what the dot plot of the data collected to answer the question might look like. Your description should include a description of the spread of the data and the center of the data.

a. What is the number of hours sixth graders are in school during a typical school day?

Most students are in school for the same number of hours, so the spread would be small. Differences may exist for those students who might have doctor's appointments or who participate in a club or an afterschool activity. Student responses vary based on their estimates of the number of hours students spend in school.

b. What is the number of video games owned by the sixth graders in our class?

These data would have a very big spread. Some students might have no video games, while others could have a large number of games. A typical value of 5 (or something similar) would identify a center. In this case, the center is based on the number most commonly reported by students.

EUREKA MATH

©2015 Great Minds eureka-math.org
G6-M6-TE-B3-1.3.1-01.2016

Lesson 3: Creating a Dot Plot

Student Outcomes

- Students create a dot plot of a given data set.
- Students summarize a given data set using equal length intervals and construct a frequency table.
- Based on a frequency table, students describe the distribution.

Classwork

Example 1 (5 minutes): Hours of Sleep

> **Example 1: Hours of Sleep**
>
> Robert, a sixth grader at Roosevelt Middle School, usually goes to bed around 10:00 p.m. and gets up around 6:00 a.m. to get ready for school. That means he gets about 8 hours of sleep on a school night. He decided to investigate the statistical question: How many hours per night do sixth graders usually sleep when they have school the next day?
>
> Robert took a survey of 29 sixth graders and collected the following data to answer the question.
>
> 7 8 5 9 9 9 7 7 10 10 11 9 8 8 8 12 6 11 10 8 8 9 9 9 8 10 9 9 8
>
> Robert decided to make a dot plot of the data to help him answer his statistical question. Robert first drew a number line and labeled it from 5 to 12 to match the lowest and highest number of hours slept. Robert's datum is not included.
>
> **Dot Plot of Number of Hours Slept**
>
>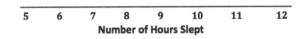
>
> Number of Hours Slept

MP.1 The beginning steps to make a dot plot are presented, and students are asked to complete the plot. It is important to point out to students that as they determine the scale for the number line, they must list the numbers sequentially using the same spacing. A common mistake in the beginning is that students may not list a number if there are no data for that value. Students may also skip numbers if there is a large gap between values that appear in the data set. Emphasize that it is important to keep the vertical spacing between dots at the same value the same to better understand the data distribution. Lined paper can be useful for keeping vertical spacing consistent when constructing a dot plot.

> He then placed a dot above 7 for the first value in the data set. He continued to place dots above the numbers until each number in the data set was represented by a dot.
>
> **Dot Plot of Number of Hours Slept**
>
>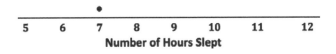
>
> Number of Hours Slept

©2015 Great Minds eureka-math.org
G6-M6-TE-B3-1.3.1-01.2016

This example begins with the statistical question: How many hours per night do sixth graders usually sleep when they have school the next day? The data shown come from a random sample of sixth graders collected from the Census at School website (http://www.amstat.org/censusatschool/).

- Why is the number line labeled from 5 to 12? Could we have labeled the number line from 8 to 16? Could we have labeled the number line from 0 to 15?
  - *The number line is labeled 5 to 12 because that is the range of the data we collected. We cannot label the number line 8 to 16 because not all of the data would be included. We could label the number line 0 to 15 because all of the data fall between those two numbers.*
- If there are no data for a particular value, do you have to show that value on the number line? For example, if your data are 1, 2, 3, 4, 8, 9, and 10, can you skip 5, 6, and 7?
  - *Even if there are no data for a particular value, the value must be included on the number line if it falls in the range of the numbers used to make the scale.*

Exercises 1–9 (13 minutes)

The first five exercises are designed to have students complete the dot plot and to answer questions about the most common value and the center of the distribution. Exercise 6 asks students to make a dot plot without any prompts. Some students may need help with making the number line. For those students, have them find the smallest and largest values, and suggest that they use these values to start and end their number lines. Exercise 9 is designed to have students begin to compare two distributions. Comparison of distributions is a focus of lessons later in this unit.

Allow about 13 minutes for students to work independently or in small groups. Bring the groups together to summarize their answers. If time is an issue, give students the dot plot for Exercise 6 rather than having them construct it themselves. They have another opportunity to create a dot plot in Exercise 12.

Exercises 1–9

1. Complete Robert's dot plot by placing a dot above the corresponding number on the number line for each value in the data set. If there is already a dot above a number, then add another dot above the dot already there. Robert's datum is not included.

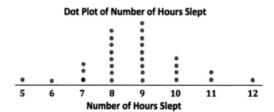

Dot Plot of Number of Hours Slept

Number of Hours Slept

2. What are the least and the most hours of sleep reported in the survey of sixth graders?

   The least number of hours students slept is 5, and the most number of hours slept is 12.

3. What number of hours slept occurred most often in the data set?

   9 is the most common number of hours that students slept.

©2015 Great Minds eureka-math.org
G6-M6-TE-B3-1.3.1-01.2016

4. What number of hours of sleep would you use to describe the center of the data?

    The center is around 8 or 9. (Answers may vary, but students' responses should be around the center of the data distribution.)

5. Think about how many hours of sleep you usually get on a school night. How does your number compare with the number of hours of sleep from the survey of sixth graders?

    Answers will vary. For example, a student might say that the number of hours she sleeps is similar to what these students reported, or she might say that she generally gets less (or more) sleep than the sixth graders who were surveyed.

Here are the data for the number of hours the sixth graders usually sleep when they do not have school the next day.

    7 8 10 11 5 6 12 13 13 7 9 8 10 12 11 12 8 9 10 11 10 12 11 11 11 12 11 11 10

6. Make a dot plot of the number of hours slept when there is no school the next day.

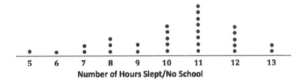

7. When there is no school the next day, what number of hours of sleep would you use to describe the center of the data?

    The center of the data is around 11 hours. (Answers may vary, but student responses should be around the center of the data distribution.)

8. What are the least and most number of hours slept with no school the next day reported in the survey?

    The least number of hours students sleep is 5, and the most number of hours students sleep is 13.

9. Do students tend to sleep longer when they do not have school the next day than when they do have school the next day? Explain your answer using the data in both dot plots.

    Yes, because more of the data points are in the 10, 11, 12, and 13 categories in the no school *dot plot than in the* have school *dot plot.*

Example 2 (10 minutes): Building and Interpreting a Frequency Table

Example 2: Building and Interpreting a Frequency Table

A group of sixth graders investigated the statistical question, "How many hours per week do sixth graders spend playing a sport or an outdoor game?"

Here are the data students collected from a sample of 26 sixth graders showing the number of hours per week spent playing a sport or a game outdoors.

                3 2 0 6 3 3 3 1 1 2 2 8 12 4 4 4 3 3 1 1 0 0 6 2 3 2

To help organize the data, students summarized the data in a frequency table. A frequency table lists possible data values and how often each value occurs.

The data shown come from a random sample of sixth graders collected from the Census at School website (http://www.amstat.org/censusatschool/). The format for the frequency table is presented, and students are directed through the completion of the table. It is important to point out that when listing possible data values, the numbers must be listed sequentially with no missing numbers or gaps in the numbers. Students should be able to draw a dot plot from a frequency table and build a frequency table from a dot plot. After students have completed the frequency table and the dot plot of the data, lead a discussion on what each representation tells about the data distribution.

To build a frequency table, first make three columns. Label one column "Number of Hours Playing a Sport/Game," label the second column "Tally," and label the third column "Frequency." Since the least number of hours was 0 and the most was 12, list the numbers from 0 to 12 in the "Number of Hours" column.

Number of Hours Playing a Sport/Game	Tally	Frequency
0	| | |	3
1	| | | |	4
2	++++	5
3	++++ | |	7
4	| | |	3
5		0
6	| |	2
7		0
8	|	1
9		0
10		0
11		0
12	|	1

Exercises 10–15 (10 minutes)

In Exercises 10 and 11, students complete the frequency table. It may be necessary to explain how to complete the tally mark column before students get started on Exercise 10. Exercise 12 directs students to make a dot plot of the data. Encourage students to use the frequency table to help build the dot plot.

After students have completed Exercise 12, ask the following question:

- What information is available in the frequency table that is not readily available in the dot plot?
  - *The frequency table makes it easier to determine how many people responded with each number. On a dot plot, I would have to count the dots to determine how many people responded with each number.*

Exercise 15 is designed to have students begin to analyze the data as they are presented in two different representations. They should focus on the center and spread of the data as they answer this question.

Exercises 10–15

10. Complete the tally mark column in the table created in Example 2.

    See the table above.

11. For each number of hours, find the total number of tally marks, and place this in the frequency column in the table created in Example 2.

    See the table above.

©2015 Great Minds eureka-math.org
G6-M6-TE-B3-1.3.1-01.2016

12. Make a dot plot of the number of hours playing a sport or playing outdoors.

Dot Plot of Number of Hours

Number of Hours Playing a Sport

13. What number of hours describes the center of the data?

    The center of data is around 3. (Answers may vary, but student responses should be around the center of the data distribution.)

14. How many of the sixth graders reported that they spend eight or more hours a week playing a sport or playing outdoors?

    Only 2 sixth graders reported they spent 8 or more hours a week playing a sport or playing outdoors.

15. The sixth graders wanted to answer the question, "How many hours do sixth graders spend per week playing a sport or playing an outdoor game?" Using the frequency table and the dot plot, how would you answer the sixth graders' question?

    Most sixth graders spend about 2 to 4 hours per week playing a sport or playing outdoors.

Closing (2 minutes)

- Can you skip numbers on the number line used for a dot plot?
    - *All numbers within the range of the smallest and largest numbers must be included on the number line of a dot plot.*
- What are the three columns included in a frequency table?
    - *The first column contains all the possible values of the data between the smallest and the largest data value, the second column is the tally column, and the third column is the frequency, which is the number of tallies for each data value.*

Exit Ticket (5 minutes)

This Exit Ticket is designed to assess if a student can complete a frequency table and draw a dot plot from a given frequency table.

©2015 Great Minds eureka-math.org
G6-M6-TE-B3-1.3.1-01.2016

Name _____   Date _____

Lesson 3: Creating a Dot Plot

Exit Ticket

A biologist collected data to answer the question, "How many eggs do robins lay?"

The following is a frequency table of the data she collected:

Number of Eggs	Tally	Frequency
1	I I	
2	卌 卌 II	
3	卌 卌 卌 III	
4	卌 IIII	
5	I	

1. Complete the frequency column.

2. Draw a dot plot of the data on the number of eggs a robin lays.

3. What number of eggs describes the center of the data?

©2015 Great Minds eureka-math.org
G6-M6-TE-B3-1.3.1-01.2016

Exit Ticket Sample Solutions

A biologist collected data to answer the question, "How many eggs do robins lay?"

The following is a frequency table of the data she collected:

Number of Eggs	Tally	Frequency
1	I I	2
2	HHH HHH II	12
3	HHH HHH HHH III	18
4	HHH IIII	9
5	I	1

1. Complete the frequency column.

    See the table above.

2. Draw a dot plot of the data on the number of eggs a robin lays.

    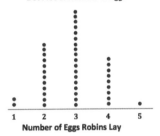

    Dot Plot of Number of Eggs

    1   2   3   4   5

    Number of Eggs Robins Lay

3. What number of eggs describes the center of the data?

    The center of the data is around 3. (Answers may vary, but student responses should be around the center of the data distribution.)

Problem Set Sample Solutions

1. The data below are the number of goals scored by a professional indoor soccer team over its last 23 games.

    8 16 10 9 11 11 10 15 16 11 15 13 8 9 11 9 8 11 16 15 10 9 12

    a. Make a dot plot of the number of goals scored.

    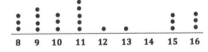

    Dot Plot of Number of Soccer Goals

    8   9   10   11   12   13   14   15   16

    Number of Soccer Goals Scored

b.   What number of goals describes the center of the data?

The center of the data is around 11 or 12. (Answers may vary, but student responses should be around the center of the data distribution.)

c.   What is the least and most number of goals scored by the team?

The least number of goals scored is 8, and 16 is the most.

d.   Over the 23 games played, the team lost 10 games. Circle the dots on the plot that you think represent the games that the team lost. Explain your answer.

Students will most likely circle the lowest 10 scores, but answers may vary. Students need to supply an explanation in order to defend their answers.

2.   A sixth grader rolled two number cubes 21 times. The student found the sum of the two numbers that he rolled each time. The following are the sums for the 21 rolls of the two number cubes.

9 2 4 6 5 7 8 11 9 4 6 5 7 7 8 8 7 5 7 6 6

a.   Complete the frequency table.

Sum Rolled	Tally	Frequency
2	I	1
3		0
4	I I	2
5	I I I	3
6	I I I I	4
7	┼┼┼┼	5
8	I I I	3
9	I I	2
10		0
11	I	1
12		0

b.   What sum describes the center of the data?

7

c.   What sum occurred most often for these 21 rolls of the number cubes?

7

©2015 Great Minds eureka-math.org
G6-M6-TE-B3-1.3.1-01.2016

3. The dot plot below shows the number of raisins in 25 small boxes of raisins.

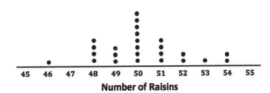

Dot Plot of Number of Raisins

Number of Raisins

a. Complete the frequency table.

Number of Raisins	Tally	Frequency
46	I	1
47		0
48	I I I I	4
49	I I I	3
50	++++ I I I	8
51	I I I I	4
52	I I	2
53	I	1
54	I I	2

b. Another student opened up a box of raisins and reported that it had 63 raisins. Do you think that this student had the same size box of raisins? Why or why not?

I think the student did not have the same size box because the 21 small boxes opened had at most 54 raisins, and 63 is too high.

Lesson 4: Creating a Histogram

Student Outcomes

- Students construct a frequency histogram.
- Students recognize that the number of intervals used may affect the shape of a histogram.

Lesson Notes

This lesson organizes the development of the student outcomes in three examples. Example 1 introduces frequency tables with intervals. Example 2 illustrates how to create a histogram from data that are organized in the interval frequency table from Example 1. Example 3 introduces an important feature of a histogram—its shape. Students are introduced to a mound/symmetric shape and a skewed shape. Following each example is an exercise set designed for independent or small group work to reinforce the main objectives of constructing and interpreting a histogram. Teacher selection of examples and exercises is encouraged. It may be possible to skip a few of the exercises. If all examples and exercises in this lesson are completed, this lesson will probably take longer than one class period.

Classwork

Example 1 (5 minutes): Frequency Table with Intervals

Example 1: Frequency Table with Intervals

The boys' and girls' basketball teams at Roosevelt Middle School wanted to raise money to help buy new uniforms. They decided to sell baseball caps with the school logo on the front to family members and other interested fans. To obtain the correct cap size, students had to measure the head circumference (distance around the head) of the adults who wanted to order a cap. The following data set represents the head circumferences, in millimeters (mm), of the adults.

513, 525, 531, 533, 535, 535, 542, 543, 546, 549, 551, 552, 552, 553, 554, 555, 560, 561, 563, 563, 563, 565,

565, 568, 568, 571, 571, 574, 577, 580, 583, 583, 584, 585, 591, 595, 598, 603, 612, 618

The caps come in six sizes: XS, S, M, L, XL, and XXL. Each cap size covers an interval of head circumferences. The cap manufacturer gave students the table below that shows the interval of head circumferences for each cap size. The interval $510-<530$ represents head circumferences from 510 mm to 530 mm, not including 530.

Cap Sizes	Interval of Head Circumferences (millimeters)	Tally	Frequency
XS	$510-<530$		
S	$530-<550$		
M	$550-<570$		
L	$570-<590$		
XL	$590-<610$		
XXL	$610-<630$		

©2015 Great Minds eureka-math.org
G6-M6-TE-B3-1.3.1-01.2016

This example begins with data on head circumference from the GAISE (Guidelines for Assessment and Instruction in Statistics Education) report published by the American Statistical Association (http://www.amstat.org/education/gaise/index.cfm). Consider using a tape measure to actually measure the head circumference of a student in the class to make the numbers in the data set more meaningful for students. The example summarizes the data in a frequency table with the head circumferences grouped into intervals. Consider displaying a frequency table from Lesson 3 that does not use intervals, and discuss the similarities and differences. It is also important that students understand that each interval should be the same width and that they should not skip intervals when making a frequency table, even if there are no data that fall in that interval. Be sure that students understand the notation used in the Interval column, where, for example, $510 -< 530$ means the interval that includes 510 and all head circumferences up to but not including 530 mm. A head circumference of 530 mm is included in the next interval of $530 -< 550$.

MP.1

- How is the frequency table with intervals similar to the frequency tables from Lesson 3? How is it different?
  - *This frequency table is different from the one in Lesson 3 because this one has intervals, and the other one does not.*
  - *The two frequency tables are similar because they both use tallies and frequencies to summarize the data.*
- What is the width of each interval? Are all the intervals the same width?
  - *The width of each interval is 20 because 20 whole numbers are included in each interval. The intervals are all the same width.*

Exercises 1–4 (6 minutes)

The four exercises that follow are designed to help students understand the idea of grouping data in intervals.

Exercises 1–4

1. What size cap would someone with a head circumference of 570 mm need?

    Someone with a head circumference of 570 mm would need a large.

2. Complete the tally and frequency columns in the table in Example 1 to determine the number of each size cap students need to order for the adults who wanted to order a cap.

Cap Sizes	Interval of Head Circumferences (millimeters)	Tally	Frequency
XS	510–< 530	‖	2
S	530–< 550	＃Ｉ ‖‖	8
M	550–< 570	＃Ｉ ＃Ｉ ＃Ｉ	15
L	570–< 590	＃Ｉ ‖‖‖	9
XL	590–< 610	‖‖‖	4
XXL	610–< 630	‖	2

3. What head circumference would you use to describe the center of the data?

    The head circumferences center somewhere around 550 mm to 570 mm. This corresponds to a cap size of medium. (Answers may vary, but student responses should be around the center of the data distribution.)

4. Describe any patterns that you observe in the frequency column.

    The numbers start small but increase to 15 and then go back down.

Example 2 (8 minutes): Histogram

> **Example 2: Histogram**
>
> One student looked at the tally column and said that it looked somewhat like a bar graph turned on its side. A histogram is a graph that is like a bar graph except that the horizontal axis is a number line that is marked off in equal intervals.
>
> To make a histogram:
>
> - Draw a horizontal line, and mark the intervals.
>
> - Draw a vertical line, and label it Frequency.
>
> - Mark the Frequency axis with a scale that starts at 0 and goes up to something that is greater than the largest frequency in the frequency table.
>
> - For each interval, draw a bar over that interval that has a height equal to the frequency for that interval.
>
> The first two bars of the histogram have been drawn below.
>
>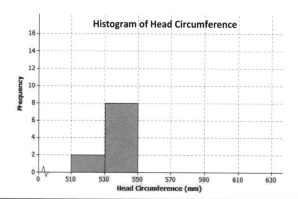

This example introduces students to a histogram. They use the data from Example 1 that were organized in a frequency table with intervals of 20 mm. Consider beginning this lesson by showing students an example of a bar graph. For example, show a bar graph summarizing data on favorite pizza toppings. Point out that the horizontal axis is *not* a number line but contains categories. The vertical axis is the frequency (or count) of how many people chose the particular pizza topping. While presenting the histogram to students, point out that the main difference is that the horizontal axis is a number line, and the intervals are listed in order from smallest to largest. Some students may struggle with the notation for the intervals. Remind students that the interval labeled $510-< 530$ represents any head circumference from 510 mm to 530 mm, not including 530 mm. A head circumference of 530 mm is counted in the bar from 530 to 550 mm and not in the bar from 510 to 530 mm.

- Why should the bars touch each other in the histogram?
    - *In a histogram, the bars touch because where one interval ends is where the next interval begins.*
- How are histograms and bar graphs similar? How are they different?
    - *Histograms and bar graphs are similar because they both have frequency on the y-axis, and both have bars representing a count of data values.*
    - *Histograms and bar graphs are different because histograms have intervals on a number line, while the bar graph has categories. Also, the intervals on a histogram make the bars touch, which does not happen on a bar graph.*

©2015 Great Minds eureka-math.org
G6-M6-TE-B3-1.3.1-01.2016

Exercises 5–9 (6 minutes)

The first exercise asks students to complete the histogram. Emphasize that the bars should touch each other and be the same width. Also, point out the jagged line (or scissor cut), and explain that it is used to indicate a cutting of the horizontal axis. (A scissor cut could also be used on a vertical axis but not on bar graphs or histograms because for these types of graphs, the vertical axis always starts at 0.) The cut is used to shorten the graph by pulling in unused space.

Exercises 5–9

5. Complete the histogram by drawing bars whose heights are the frequencies for the other intervals.

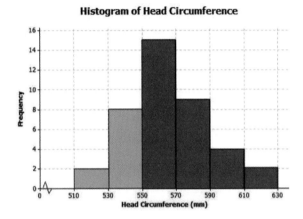

6. Based on the histogram, describe the center of the head circumferences.

    The center of the head circumferences is around 560 mm. (Answers may vary, but student responses should be around the center of the data distribution.)

7. How would the histogram change if you added head circumferences of 551 mm and 569 mm to the data set?

    The bar for the 550 to 570 mm interval would go up to 17.

8. Because the 40 head circumference values were given, you could have constructed a dot plot to display the head circumference data. What information is lost when a histogram is used to represent a data distribution instead of a dot plot?

    In a dot plot, you can see individual values. In a histogram, you only see the total number of values in an interval.

9. Suppose that there had been 200 head circumference measurements in the data set. Explain why you might prefer to summarize this data set using a histogram rather than a dot plot.

    There would be too many dots on a dot plot, and it would be hard to read. A histogram would work for a large data set because the frequency scale can be adjusted.

©2015 Great Minds eureka-math.org
G6-M6-TE-B3-1.3.1-01.2016

Example 3 (5 minutes): Shape of the Histogram

Example 3: Shape of the Histogram

A histogram is useful to describe the shape of the data distribution. It is important to think about the shape of a data distribution because depending on the shape, there are different ways to describe important features of the distribution, such as center and variability.

A group of students wanted to find out how long a certain brand of AA batteries lasted. The histogram below shows the data distribution for how long (in hours) that some AA batteries lasted. Looking at the shape of the histogram, notice how the data mound up around a center of approximately 105 hours. We would describe this shape as mound shaped or symmetric. If we were to draw a line down the center, notice how each side of the histogram is approximately the same, or a mirror image of the other. This means the histogram is approximately symmetrical.

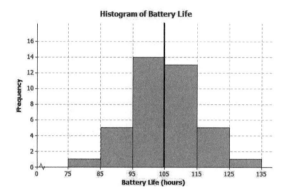

Another group of students wanted to investigate the maximum drop length for roller coasters. The histogram below shows the maximum drop (in feet) of a selected group of roller coasters. This histogram has a skewed shape. Most of the data are in the intervals from 50 feet to 170 feet. But there is one value that falls in the interval from 290 feet to 330 feet and one value that falls in the interval from 410 feet to 450 feet. These two values are unusual (or not typical) when compared to the rest of the data because they are much greater than most of the data.

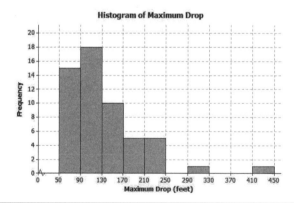

EUREKA
MATH

©2015 Great Minds eureka-math.org
G6-M6-TE-B3-1.3.1-01.2016

MP.4 This example discusses the concept of the shape of a distribution and how it relates to center and variability. Two shapes are introduced: mound shaped (which is also symmetric) and skewed. Below is an example of a symmetric mound-shaped distribution. For histograms, perfect symmetry is rarely seen, but many histograms can be described as approximately symmetric.

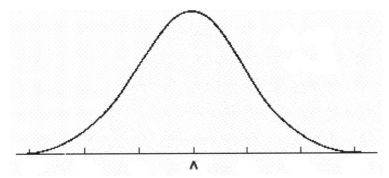

Below are two examples of skewed distributions:

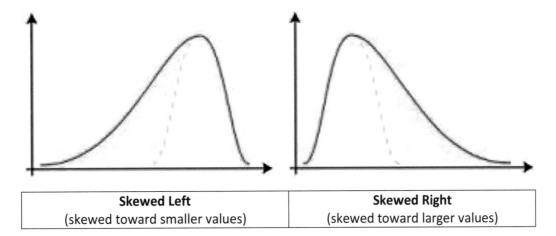

Skewed Left (skewed toward smaller values)	**Skewed Right** (skewed toward larger values)

Point out to students that a skewed distribution has values that are not typical of the rest of the data on either the high end or the low end. This results in a histogram that has a longer *tail* on one side of the distribution than on the other side, meaning that the distribution extends farther from the center of the data distribution on one side than the other.

If there is time, there are a number of interesting questions to ask students about the roller coaster maximum drop histogram. For example, ask the following:

- How many of the roller coasters had a maximum drop between 290 and 330 feet? Is this roller coaster unusual compared to the other roller coasters?

  □ *There is one roller coaster with a drop between 290 and 330 feet. It is unusual because most of the roller coasters had a maximum drop that was much smaller.*

- Are there any other roller coasters that you would consider unusual?

  □ *Yes. There was a roller coaster that had a maximum drop that was even greater than 330 feet. It had a drop that was somewhere between 410 and 450 feet.*

Lesson 4:   Creating a Histogram

45

©2015 Great Minds eureka-math.org
G6-M6-TE-B3-1.3.1-01.2016

Exercises 10–12 (8 minutes)

The next three exercises are designed to help students understand how to classify a distribution as either approximately symmetric or skewed.

Exercises 10–12

10. The histogram below shows the highway miles per gallon of different compact cars.

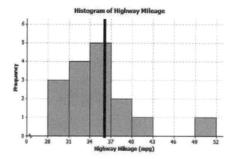

Histogram of Highway Mileage

a. Describe the shape of the histogram as approximately symmetric, skewed left, or skewed right.

Skewed right toward the larger values

b. Draw a vertical line on the histogram to show where the typical number of miles per gallon for a compact car would be.

The vertical line to show the typical number of miles per gallon would be around 36.

c. What does the shape of the histogram tell you about miles per gallon for compact cars?

Most cars get around 31 to 40 mpg. But there was one car that got between 49 and 52 mpg.

11. Describe the shape of the head circumference histogram that you completed in Exercise 5 as approximately symmetric, skewed left, or skewed right.

The shape of the histogram is approximately symmetric.

12. Another student decided to organize the head circumference data by changing the width of each interval to be 10 instead of 20. Below is the histogram that the student made.

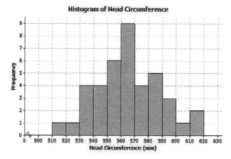

Histogram of Head Circumference

©2015 Great Minds eureka-math.org
G6-M6-TE-B3-1.3.1-01.2016

EUREKA MATH™

a. How does this histogram compare with the histogram of the head circumferences that you completed in Exercise 5?

Answers will vary; both histograms have the same general shape and center.

b. Describe the shape of this new histogram as approximately symmetric, skewed left, or skewed right.

The shape of this new histogram is approximately symmetric.

c. How many head circumferences are in the interval from 570 to 590 mm?

There are 9 head circumferences in the interval from 570 to 590 mm.

d. In what interval would a head circumference of 571 mm be included? In what interval would a head circumference of 610 mm be included?

The head circumference of 571 mm is in the interval from 570 to 580 mm. The head circumference of 610 mm is in the interval from 610 to 620 mm.

Closing (2 minutes)

- Histograms involve intervals. What must be true about the intervals?
  - *All intervals should be the same width.*
- Why do the bars in a histogram touch and not have spaces between them?
  - *The bars in a histogram touch because the next interval begins where the previous interval ends.*

Exit Ticket (5 minutes)

©2015 Great Minds eureka-math.org
G6-M6-TE-B3-1.3.1-01.2016

Name _____   Date _____

Lesson 4: Creating a Histogram

Exit Ticket

The frequency table below shows the length of selected movies shown in a local theater over the past six months.

Length of Movie (minutes)	Tally	Frequency
80–< 90	|	1
90–< 100	||||	4
100–< 110	⊬⊬ ||	7
110–< 120	⊬⊬	5
120–< 130	⊬⊬ ||	7
130–< 140	|||	3
140–< 150	|	1

1. Construct a histogram for the length of movies data.

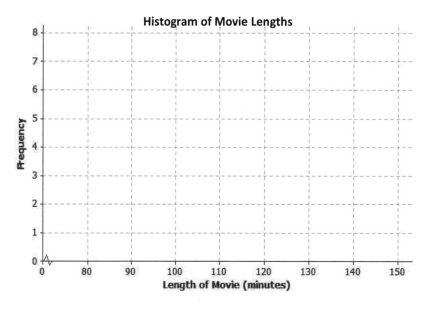

2. Describe the shape of the histogram.

3. What does the histogram tell you about the length of movies?

EUREKA MATH

©2015 Great Minds eureka-math.org
G6-M6-TE-B3-1.3.1-01.2016

Exit Ticket Sample Solutions

The frequency table below shows the length of selected movies shown in a local theater over the past six months.

Length of Movie (minutes)	Tally	Frequency
80−< 90	I	1
90−< 100	IIII	4
100−< 110	⧐⧐⧐ II	7
110−< 120	⧐⧐⧐	5
120−< 130	⧐⧐⧐ II	7
130−< 140	III	3
140−< 150	I	1

1. Construct a histogram for the length of movies data.

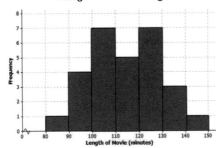

Histogram of Movie Lengths

2. Describe the shape of the histogram.

    The shape of the histogram is mound shaped and approximately symmetric.

3. What does the histogram tell you about the length of movies?

    Most movie lengths were between 100 *and* 130 *minutes.*

Problem Set Sample Solutions

1. The following histogram summarizes the ages of the actresses whose performances have won in the Best Leading Actress category at the annual Academy Awards (i.e., Oscars).

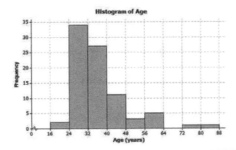

Histogram of Age

©2015 Great Minds eureka-math.org
G6-M6-TE-B3-1.3.1-01.2016

a. Which age interval contains the most actresses? How many actresses are represented in that interval?

The interval 24 to 32 contains the most actresses. There are 34 actresses whose age falls into that category.

b. Describe the shape of the histogram.

The shape of the histogram is skewed to the right.

c. What does the histogram tell you about the ages of actresses who won the Oscar for best actress?

Most of the ages are between 24 and 40, with two ages much larger than the rest.

d. Which interval describes the center of the ages of the actresses?

The interval of 32 to 40 describes the center of the ages. (Answers may vary, but student responses should be around the center of the data distribution.)

e. An age of 72 would be included in which interval?

The age of 72 is in the interval from 72 to 80.

2. The frequency table below shows the seating capacity of arenas for NBA basketball teams.

Number of Seats	Tally	Frequency
$17,000 - < 17,500$	||	2
$17,500 - < 18,000$	|	1
$18,000 - < 18,500$	卌 |	6
$18,500 - < 19,000$	卌	5
$19,000 - < 19,500$	卌	5
$19,500 - < 20,000$	卌	5
$20,000 - < 20,500$	||	2
$20,500 - < 21,000$	||	2
$21,000 - < 21,500$		0
$21,500 - < 22,000$		0
$22,000 - < 22,500$	|	1

©2015 Great Minds eureka-math.org
G6-M6-TE-B3-1.3.1-01.2016

a.   Draw a histogram for the number of seats in the NBA arenas data. Use the histograms you have seen throughout this lesson to help you in the construction of your histogram.

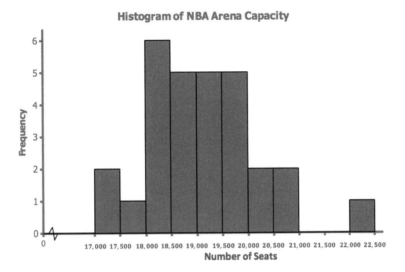

Histogram of NBA Arena Capacity

b.   What is the width of each interval? How do you know?

The width of each interval is 500.

Subtract the values identifying an interval.

c.   Describe the shape of the histogram.

The shape of the histogram is skewed to the right.

d.   Which interval describes the center of the number of seats data?

The interval of 19,000 *to* 19,500 *describes the center. (Answers may vary, but student responses should be around the center of the data distribution.)*

3.   Listed are the grams of carbohydrates in hamburgers at selected fast food restaurants.

       33   40   66   45   28   30   52   40   26   42
       42   44   33   44   45   32   45   45   52   24

a.   Complete the frequency table using the given intervals of width 5.

Number of Carbohydrates (grams)	Tally	Frequency
20−< 25	I	1
25−< 30	II	2
30−< 35	IIII	4
35−< 40		0
40−< 45	IIII I	6
45−< 50	IIII	4
50−< 55	II	2
55−< 60		0
60−< 65		0
65−< 70	I	1

©2015 Great Minds eureka-math.org
G6-M6-TE-B3-1.3.1-01.2016

b. Draw a histogram of the carbohydrate data.

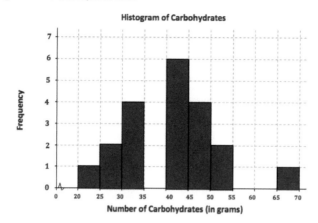

c. Describe the center and shape of the histogram.

The center is around 40; the histogram is mound shaped and approximately symmetric. (Answers may vary, but student responses for describing the center should be around the center of the data distribution.)

d. In the frequency table below, the intervals are changed. Using the carbohydrate data above, complete the frequency table with intervals of width 10.

Number of Carbohydrates (grams)	Tally	Frequency
20–< 30	|||	3
30–< 40	||||	4
40–< 50	##|| ##||	10
50–< 60	||	2
60–< 70			1

e. Draw a histogram.

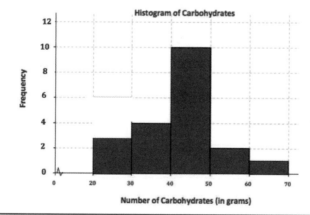

EUREKA
MATH™

©2015 Great Minds eureka-math.org
G6-M6-TE-B3-1.3.1-01.2016

4. Use the histograms that you constructed in Exercise 3 parts (b) and (e) to answer the following questions.

   a. Why are there fewer bars in the histogram in part (e) than the histogram in part (b)?

   There are fewer bars in part (e) because the width of the interval changed from 5 grams to 10 grams, so there are fewer intervals.

   b. Did the shape of the histogram in part (e) change from the shape of the histogram in part (b)?

   Generally, both are approximately symmetric and mound shaped, but the histogram in part (b) has gaps.

   c. Did your estimate of the center change from the histogram in part (b) to the histogram in part (e)?

   The centers of the two histograms are about the same.

Lesson 5: Describing a Distribution Displayed in a Histogram

Student Outcomes

- Students construct a relative frequency histogram.
- Students recognize that the shape of a histogram constructed using relative frequencies is the same as the shape of the histogram constructed using frequencies (provided that the same intervals are used).

Lesson Notes

This lesson may take longer than one class period.

Classwork

Example 1 (5 minutes): Relative Frequency Table

Example 1: Relative Frequency Table

In Lesson 4, we investigated the head circumferences that the boys' and girls' basketball teams collected. Below is the frequency table of the head circumferences that they measured.

Cap Sizes	Interval of Head Circumferences (millimeters)	Tally	Frequency
XS	510−< 530	||	2
S	530−< 550	＋＋＋ |||	8
M	550−< 570	＋＋＋ ＋＋＋ ＋＋＋	15
L	570−< 590	＋＋＋ ||||	9
XL	590−< 610	||||	4
XXL	610−< 630	||	2
		Total:	40

Isabel, one of the basketball players, indicated that most of the caps were small (S), medium (M), or large (L). To decide if Isabel was correct, the players added a relative frequency column to the table.

Relative frequency is the frequency for an interval divided by the total number of data values. For example, the relative frequency for the extra small (XS) cap is 2 divided by 40, or 0.05. This represents the fraction of the data values that were XS.

This example begins with the frequency table of head circumferences that students used in Lesson 4. At the start of the lesson, display the frequency table, and ask the following:

- What does the 15 in the frequency column represent, and how many caps need to be ordered?
  - *The* 15 *in the frequency column represents the number of people who had head circumferences in the interval of* 550 *to* 570 mm, *not including* 570. *Therefore,* 15 *size medium (M) caps would need to be ordered.*

©2015 Great Minds eureka-math.org
G6-M6-TE-B3-1.3.1-01.2016

This next question leads into the vocabulary of relative frequency as the frequency for an interval divided by the total number of data values.

- How could we determine what fraction of the total order is medium-sized (M) caps?
  - *We could determine the fraction by dividing the number of medium caps needed by the total number of caps ordered.*

Explain the concept of *relative frequency* by working through the calculation of the first two relative frequency rows in the table. Relative frequencies are often interpreted as percentages, so also explain that a relative frequency expressed as a decimal can be multiplied by 100 to obtain the percentage of the data values that fall in a particular interval. In Grade 6, students are expected to be able to change a decimal to a percent (**6.NP.A.3c**), so this is a good place to revisit working with percentages.

- There are 2 people in the XS cap size interval (head circumferences from 510 to 529 mm). The relative frequency for this interval is 2 divided by the total number 40, or $\frac{2}{40}$, which is 0.05, or 5%.

- In the interval from 530 to 549 mm, the frequency is 8. The relative frequency for this interval is $\frac{8}{40}$, which is 0.2, or 20%.

- How do you find the total number of data values?
  - *In order to find the total number of data values, you add all the frequencies together.*

- What will the sum of the relative frequency column equal?
  - *The sum of the relative frequency column will equal* 1.00.

- What is the difference between a frequency table and a relative frequency table?
  - *The frequency table shows the actual number of caps that need to be ordered in each size. The relative frequency table shows the relative frequency for each size that needs to be ordered.*

- How are the two types of tables similar?
  - *Answers will vary. For example, both types of tables list intervals of possible data values and describe how the data values were distributed into these intervals.*

Students should write the relative frequency as a decimal. Converting the decimal to a percentage helps to interpret the value. When writing the relative frequency, students write their answers to two or three decimal places. Some exercises may require rounding to the nearest thousandth.

Exercises 1–4 (10 minutes)

This exercise asks students to complete the relative frequency table and begin to interpret the values in the table. Let students work in pairs, and confirm answers as a class.

Exercises 1–4

1. Complete the relative frequency column in the table below.

Cap Sizes	Interval of Head Circumferences (millimeters)	Tally	Frequency	Relative Frequency
XS	$510-< 530$	||	2	$\frac{2}{40} = 0.050$
S	$530-< 550$	ⅢⅡ |||	8	$\frac{8}{40} = 0.200$
M	$550-< 570$	ⅢⅡ ⅢⅡ ⅢⅡ	15	0.375
L	$570-< 590$	ⅢⅡ ||||	9	0.225
XL	$590-< 610$	||||	4	0.100
XXL	$610-< 630$	||	2	0.050
			Total: 40	1.000 *or* 100%

2. What is the total of the relative frequency column?

    The total of the relative frequency column is 1.000, or 100%.

3. Which interval has the greatest relative frequency? What is the value?

    The interval with the greatest relative frequency is the medium-sized caps, 550–569, which has a relative frequency of 0.375, or 37.5%.

4. What percentage of the head circumferences are between 530 and 589 mm? Show how you determined the answer.

    $0.200 + 0.375 + 0.225 = 0.800$, *or* 80%

Example 2 (5 minutes): Relative Frequency Histogram

MP.1 In this example, students consider the connection between the relative frequency table and the relative frequency histogram. Display the frequency histogram of head circumferences from Lesson 4. Remind students of the importance of the intervals being the same width.

Alongside this frequency histogram, demonstrate how to construct a relative frequency histogram. The labeling of the horizontal axis is the same as for the frequency histogram. The vertical axis scale changes to represent the relative frequency. Students may struggle with the scaling along this vertical axis since they are counting by a decimal rather than by a whole number.

> **Example 2: Relative Frequency Histogram**
>
> The players decided to construct a histogram using the relative frequencies instead of the frequencies.
>
> They noticed that the relative frequencies in the table ranged from close to 0 to about 0.40. They drew a number line and marked off the intervals on that line. Then, they drew the vertical line and labeled it Relative Frequency. They added a scale to this line by starting at 0 and counting by 0.05 until they reached 0.40.

©2015 Great Minds eureka-math.org
G6-M6-TE-B3-1.3.1-01.2016

They completed the histogram by drawing the bars so the height of each bar matched the relative frequency for that interval. Here is the completed relative frequency histogram:

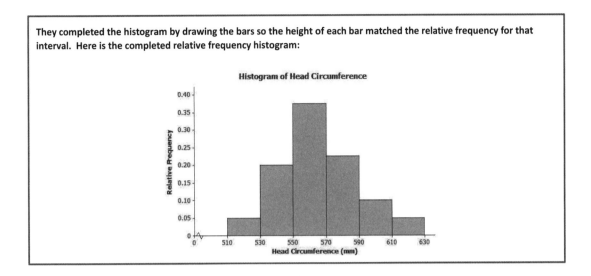

After drawing the relative frequency histogram, ask students to compare the two histograms. They should notice that the center and shape are the same.

- What do you notice about the shape and center of the frequency histogram and the relative frequency histogram?

  □ *They are the same.*

- What is the greatest number that could be on the vertical axis in a relative frequency histogram?

  □ *1.00*

- What is the relative frequency for the large cap sizes? What does this number mean?

  □ *About 0.23; approximately 23% of the people measured would wear a size large cap.*

Exercises 5–6 (18 minutes)

Exercise 5 asks students to compare the two types of histograms: a frequency histogram and a relative frequency histogram. Exercise 6 asks students to calculate relative frequencies and to construct a relative frequency histogram. Let students work in small groups. Allow for calculator usage.

Anticipate that some students may struggle with part (c) of Exercise 6. If they have difficulty setting up the relative frequency axis in order to make the relative frequency histogram, ask them what the largest relative frequency is (0.207). Then, suggest that they start the axis at 0 (relative frequency histograms always have a vertical axis that starts at 0) and go up to 0.25 (something greater than the largest relative frequency that they need to represent). Then, ask how they might divide up the range from 0 to 0.25 in a convenient way, which should lead them to marking off intervals of 0.05.

Exercises 5–6

5.

    a.   Describe the shape of the relative frequency histogram of head circumferences from Example 2.

           The shape of the relative frequency is slightly skewed to the right.

©2015 Great Minds eureka-math.org
G6-M6-TE-B3-1.3.1-01.2016

    b.   How does the shape of this relative frequency histogram compare with the frequency histogram you drew in Exercise 5 of Lesson 4?

The shape is the same in both histograms.

    c.   Isabel said that most of the caps that needed to be ordered were small (S), medium (M), and large (L). Was she right? What percentage of the caps to be ordered are small, medium, or large?

She was right. The total percentage of small, medium, and large caps was 80% (20% small, 37.5% medium, and 22.5% large, for a total of 80%).

6.   Here is the frequency table of the seating capacity of arenas for the NBA basketball teams.

Number of Seats	Tally	Frequency	Relative Frequency
$17,000-<17,500$	‖	2	0.069
$17,500-<18,000$		1	0.034
$18,000-<18,500$	⊞	6	0.207
$18,500-<19,000$	⊞	5	0.172
$19,000-<19,500$	⊞	5	0.172
$19,500-<20,000$	⊞	5	0.172
$20,000-<20,500$	‖	2	0.069
$20,500-<21,000$	‖	2	0.069
$21,000-<21,500$		0	0.000
$21,500-<22,000$		0	0.000
$22,000-<22,500$		1	0.034

    a.   What is the total number of NBA arenas?

There are 29 NBA arenas in total.

    b.   Complete the relative frequency column. Round the relative frequencies to the nearest thousandth.

See the table above.

    c.   Construct a relative frequency histogram.

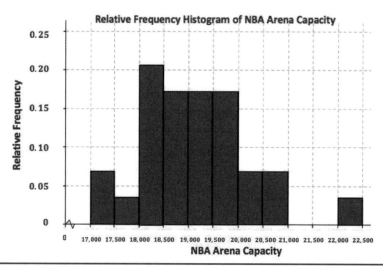

©2015 Great Minds eureka-math.org
G6-M6-TE-B3-1.3.1-01.2016

d. Describe the shape of the relative frequency histogram.

The shape is slightly skewed to the right.

e. What percentage of the arenas have a seating capacity between $18,500$ and $19,999$ seats?

Approximately 0.516, or 51.6%, of the arenas have a seating capacity between $18,500$ and $19,999$ seats.

f. How does this relative frequency histogram compare to the frequency histogram that you drew in Problem 2 of the Problem Set in Lesson 4?

Both histograms have the same shape.

Closing (2 minutes)

- What is the difference between a frequency histogram and a relative frequency histogram?

    □ *The only difference between the two histograms is the vertical axis. A frequency histogram has frequency along the vertical axis, but the relative frequency histogram has relative frequency along the vertical axis.*

- If Sarah created an accurate frequency histogram and Robert created an accurate relative frequency histogram of the same data, would the two histograms have the same shape?

    □ *The shapes of the histograms are the same as long as the intervals used are the same.*

Lesson Summary

A <u>relative frequency</u> is the frequency for an interval divided by the total number of data values. For example, if the first interval contains 8 out of a total of 32 data values, the relative frequency of the first interval is $\dfrac{8}{32} = \dfrac{1}{4} = 0.25$, or 25%.

A <u>relative frequency histogram</u> is a histogram that is constructed using relative frequencies instead of frequencies.

Exit Ticket (5 minutes)

©2015 Great Minds eureka-math.org
G6-M6-TE-B3-1.3.1-01.2016

Name _____   Date _____

Lesson 5: Describing a Distribution Displayed in a Histogram

Exit Ticket

Calculators are allowed for completing your problems.

Hector's mom had a rummage sale, and after she sold an item, she tallied the amount of money she received for the item. The following is the frequency table Hector's mom created.

Amount of Money Received for the Item	Tally	Frequency	Relative Frequency
$0−< $5	||	2	
$5−< $10	|	1	
$10−< $15	||||	4	
$15−< $20	HHH HHH	10	
$20−< $25	HHH	5	
$25−< $30	|||	3	
$30−< $35	||	2	

a. What was the total number of items sold at the rummage sale?

b. Complete the relative frequency column. Round the relative frequencies to the nearest thousandth.

c. What percentage of the items Hector's mom sold were sold for $15 or more but less than $20?

©2015 Great Minds eureka-math.org
G6-M6-TE-B3-1.3.1-01.2016

Exit Ticket Sample Solutions

Calculators are allowed for completing your problems.

Hector's mom had a rummage sale, and after she sold an item, she tallied the amount of money she received for the item. The following is the frequency table Hector's mom created:

Amount of Money Received for the Item	Tally	Frequency	Relative Frequency
$0–< $5	||	2	0.074
$5–< $10	|	1	0.037
$10–< $15	||||	4	0.148
$15–< $20	₩₩ ₩₩	10	0.370
$20–< $25	₩₩	5	0.185
$25–< $30	|||	3	0.111
$30–< $35	||	2	0.074

a. What was the total number of items sold at the rummage sale?

The total number of items sold is 27 items.

b. Complete the relative frequency column. Round the relative frequencies to the nearest thousandth.

See the table above.

c. What percentage of the items Hector's mom sold were sold for $15 or more but less than $20?

37% of the items Hector's mom sold were sold for $15 or more but less than $20.

Problem Set Sample Solutions

1. Below is a relative frequency histogram of the maximum drop (in feet) of a selected group of roller coasters.

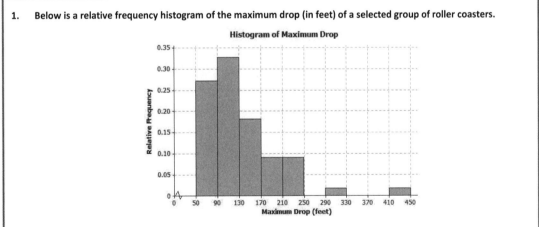

a. Describe the shape of the relative frequency histogram.

The shape is skewed to the right.

©2015 Great Minds eureka-math.org
G6-M6-TE-B3-1.3.1-01.2016

b. What does the shape tell you about the maximum drop (in feet) of roller coasters?

The shape tells us most of the roller coasters have a maximum drop that is between 50 and 170 feet but that some roller coasters have a maximum drop that is quite a bit larger than the others.

c. Jerome said that more than half of the data values are in the interval from 50 to 130 feet. Do you agree with Jerome? Why or why not?

I agree with Jerome because that interval contains 60% of the data.

2. The frequency table below shows the length of selected movies shown in a local theater over the past 6 months.

Length of Movie (minutes)	Tally	Frequency	Relative Frequency
80−< 90	|	1	0.036
90−< 100	||||	4	0.143
100−< 110	ﬀﬁ ||	7	0.250
110−< 120	ﬀﬁ	5	0.179
120−< 130	ﬀﬁ ||	7	0.250
130−< 140	|||	3	0.107
140−< 150	|	1	0.036

a. Complete the relative frequency column. Round the relative frequencies to the nearest thousandth.

See the table above.

b. What percentage of the movie lengths are greater than or equal to 130 minutes?

$0.107 + 0.036 = 0.143$, *or* 14.3% *of the movie lengths are greater than or equal to 130 minutes.*

c. Draw a relative frequency histogram. (Hint: Label the relative frequency scale starting at 0 and going up to 0.30, marking off intervals of 0.05.)

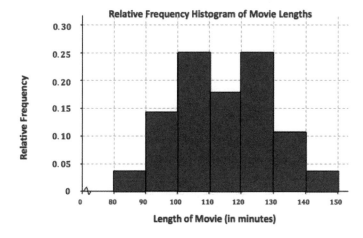

d. Describe the shape of the relative frequency histogram.

The histogram is mound shaped and approximately symmetric.

©2015 Great Minds eureka-math.org
G6-M6-TE-B3-1.3.1-01.2016

e. What does the shape tell you about the length of movie times?

The shape tells us the length of most movies is between 100 *and* 130 *minutes.*

3. The table below shows the highway miles per gallon of different compact cars.

Mileage	Tally	Frequency	Relative Frequency
28−< 31	|||	3	0.188
31−< 34	||||	4	0.250
34−< 37	⊬⊬	5	0.313
37−< 40	||	2	0.125
40−< 43	|	1	0.063
43−< 46		0	0.000
46−< 49		0	0.000
49−< 52	|	1	0.063

a. What is the total number of compact cars?

The total number of compact cars is 16.

b. Complete the relative frequency column. Round the relative frequencies to the nearest thousandth.

See the table above.

c. What percentage of the cars get between 31 and up to but not including 37 miles per gallon on the highway?

$0.250 + 0.313 = 0.563$, *or* 56.3% *of the cars get between* 31 *and up to* 37 *miles per gallon on the highway.*

d. Juan drew the relative frequency histogram of the highway miles per gallon for the compact cars, shown on the right. Did Juan draw the histogram correctly? Explain your answer.

Juan did not draw the histogram correctly because he did not leave spaces for intervals 43−< 46 *and* 46−< 49. *These spaces are needed to represent the relative frequency of zero. He also forgot to draw a bar for the final interval,* 49−< 52.

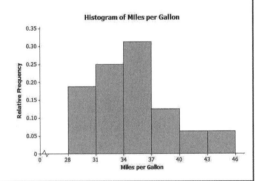

Histogram of Miles per Gallon

©2015 Great Minds eureka-math.org
G6-M6-TE-B3-1.3.1-01.2016

EUREKA
MATH™

Mathematics Curriculum

Topic B

Summarizing a Distribution That Is Approximately Symmetric Using the Mean and Mean Absolute Deviation

6.SP.A.2, 6.SP.A.3, 6.SP.B.4, 6.SP.B.5

Focus Standards:	6.SP.A.2	Understand that a set of data collected to answer a statistical question has a distribution, which can be described by its center, spread, and overall shape.
	6.SP.A.3	Recognize that a measure of center for a numerical data set summarizes all of its values with a single number, while a measure of variation describes how its values vary with a single number.
	6.SP.B.4	Display numerical data in plots on a number line, including dot plots, histograms, and box plots.
	6.SP.B.5	Summarize numerical data sets in relation to their context, such as by:
		a. Reporting the number of observations.
		b. Describing the nature of the attribute under investigation, including how it was measured and its units of measurement.
		c. Giving quantitative measures of center (median and/or mean) and variability (interquartile range and/or mean absolute deviation), as well as describing any overall pattern and any striking deviations from the overall pattern with reference to the context in which the data were gathered.
		d. Relating the choice of measures of center and variability to the shape of the data distribution and the context in which the data were gathered.

©2015 Great Minds eureka-math.org
G6-M6-TE-B3-1.3.1-01.2016

Instructional Days:	6	
Lesson 6:	Describing the Center of a Distribution Using the Mean (P)[1]	
Lesson 7:	The Mean as a Balance Point (P)	
Lesson 8:	Variability in a Data Distribution (P)	
Lesson 9:	The Mean Absolute Deviation (MAD) (P)	
Lessons 10–11:	Describing Distributions Using the Mean and MAD (P, P)	

In Topic B, students begin to summarize data distributions numerically. In Topic A, students have represented data distributions graphically and have described distributions informally in terms of shape, center, and variability. In this topic, students are introduced to a measure of center (the mean) and variability (the mean absolute deviation, MAD) appropriate for describing approximately symmetric data distributions. In Lesson 6, students learn to calculate the mean and to understand the "fair share" interpretation of the mean. In Lesson 7, students develop an understanding of the mean as a balance point of a data distribution—the point where the sum of distances of points to the right of the mean and the sum of distances of points to the left of the mean are equal. This understanding provides a foundation for considering distances from the mean, which are used in calculating the MAD (a measure of variability around the mean). Lessons 8 and 9 introduce the MAD as a measure of variability, and students calculate and interpret the value of the MAD. Lessons 10 and 11 give students the opportunity to use both graphical and numerical summaries to describe data distributions, to compare distributions, and to answer questions in context using information provided by a data distribution.

---

[1]Lesson Structure Key: **P**-Problem Set Lesson, **M**-Modeling Cycle Lesson, **E**-Exploration Lesson, **S**-Socratic Lesson

Lesson 6: Describing the Center of a Distribution Using the Mean

Student Outcomes

- Students describe the center of a data distribution using a *fair share* value called the *mean*.
- Students connect the *fair share* concept with the mathematical formula for finding the mean.

Lesson Notes

In earlier grades, students may have heard the term *average* (or *mean*) to describe a measure of center although it is not part of Common Core Grades K–5. If they have heard the term, typically their understanding of it is the "add up and divide" formula. The goal of Lesson 6 is to guide students to a comprehensive understanding of the term mean, not just how to find it.

For example, if students hear that their class had a mean score of 74 on a test, they need to immediately understand that 74 is the score each student in the class would have received if every student got the same score! That is the *fair share* interpretation of mean. So, when the term *mean* is mentioned, students should think initially of its *fair share* meaning and not of its mathematical formula although they do go hand in hand.

Some students have difficulty understanding what "characterizing a data distribution" means. The idea expressed in this lesson is that single numbers are sought to describe some feature of the data distribution (such as the center) and that there may be several different ways to characterize a given specific feature. If students suggest the *mode* and *median* as measures of center, that is great, although they are not going to be pursued in this lesson. The term *mode* is not discussed much at all in the Common Core, and *median* is covered in a later lesson.

Teachers should be prepared to distribute some type of manipulative, like Unifix cubes, for group work in Exercise 3. Students use cubes to represent data values and manipulate them to develop an interpretation of a measure of center, namely, the "fair share" interpretation of the mean. Each group needs to have 90 units of the manipulative, so teachers should plan accordingly.

Classwork

Example 1 (7 minutes)

Read the introductory paragraph to the class. Choose a student to read Robert's thought process out loud.

> **Example 1**
>
> Recall that in Lesson 3, Robert, a sixth grader at Roosevelt Middle School, investigated the number of hours of sleep sixth-grade students get on school nights. Today, he is to make a short report to the class on his investigation. Here is his report.

EUREKA MATH

©2015 Great Minds eureka-math.org
G6-M6-TE-B3-1.3.1-01.2016

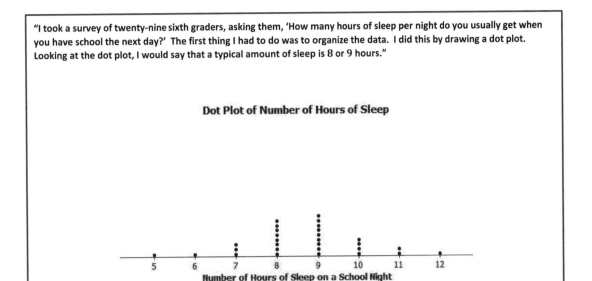

"I took a survey of twenty-nine sixth graders, asking them, 'How many hours of sleep per night do you usually get when you have school the next day?' The first thing I had to do was to organize the data. I did this by drawing a dot plot. Looking at the dot plot, I would say that a typical amount of sleep is 8 or 9 hours."

Dot Plot of Number of Hours of Sleep

Number of Hours of Sleep on a School Night

- Part of our lessons last week was to think about the center, spread, and shape of a data distribution.

- Looking at the dot plot, what would you say is the typical number of hours of sleep sixth-grade students get when they have school the next day?
  □ *The typical amount of sleep is around 8 or 9 hours because that is what most students said, and these values are kind of in the middle.*

- How are the data points spread out compared to the center?
  □ *The data points are spread out from the center by about three or four hours in each direction.*

- What is the shape of the distribution?
  □ *The shape of the distribution is mound shaped and approximately symmetric.*

- How is Robert thinking about the center?
  □ *When characterizing a typical value to describe the center of the hours of sleep data as represented in a dot plot, Robert is drawn to the data point that occurs most often (the mode) or to the middle values in the data set.*

Read through the last two sentences of the example.

Michelle is Robert's classmate. She liked his report but has a really different thought about determining the center of the number of hours of sleep. Her idea is to even out the data in order to determine a typical or center value.

- What do you think Michelle means by evening out the data to determine a typical or center value?
  □ *Answers will vary. Michelle wants to get students thinking a bit more deeply about determining a center. The bottom line is that her view of center is an equal sharing of the total number of hours of sleep (i.e., a* fair share *in which the* fair share *process terminates when all students have the same number of hours of sleep).*

Note: To understand what Michelle is proposing, it is easier to start with a data set that does not have too many values, so start with a data set that is smaller than Robert's data set.

Exercises 1–6 (13 minutes)

Work through Exercises 1 and 2 as a class. Briefly summarize Michelle's fair share method from the text. Then, split students up into groups to work on Exercises 3–6, with each group getting 90 cubes.

Exercises 1–6

Suppose that Michelle asks ten of her classmates for the number of hours they usually sleep when there is school the next day.

Suppose they responded (in hours): 8 10 8 8 11 11 9 8 10 7.

1. How do you think Robert would organize this new data? What do you think Robert would say is the center of these ten data points? Why?

    Robert would use a dot plot to organize his data and would say the center is around 8 hours because it is the most common value.

2. Do you think his value is a good measure to use for the center of Michelle's data set? Why or why not?

    Answers will vary. For example, students might say it is a good measure, as most of the values are around 8 hours, or they might say it is not a good measure because half of the values are greater than 8 hours.

The measure of center that Michelle is proposing is called the *mean*. She finds the total number of hours of sleep for the ten students. That is 90 hours. She has 90 Unifix cubes (Snap cubes). She gives each of the ten students the number of cubes that equals the number of hours of sleep each had reported. She then asks each of the ten students to connect their cubes in a stack and put their stacks on a table to compare them. She then has them share their cubes with each other until they all have the same number of cubes in their stacks when they are done sharing.

3. Make ten stacks of cubes representing the number of hours of sleep for each of the ten students. Using Michelle's method, how many cubes are in each of the ten stacks when they are done sharing?

    There are 9 cubes in each of the 10 stacks.

4. Noting that each cube represents one hour of sleep, interpret your answer to Exercise 3 in terms of number of hours of sleep. What does this number of cubes in each stack represent? What is this value called?

    If all ten students slept the same number of hours, it would be 9 hours. The 9 cubes for each stack represent the 9 hours of sleep for each student if this was a fair share. This value is called the mean.

5. Suppose that the student who told Michelle he slept 7 hours changes his data value to 8 hours. What does Michelle's procedure now produce for her center of the new set of data? What did you have to do with that extra cube to make Michelle's procedure work?

    The extra cube must be split into 10 equal parts. The mean is now $9\frac{1}{10}$.

6. Interpret Michelle's fair share procedure by developing a mathematical formula that results in finding the fair share value without actually using cubes. Be sure that you can explain clearly how the fair share procedure and the mathematical formula relate to each other.

    Answers may vary. The fair share procedure is the same as adding all of the data values and dividing by the total number of data values.

Lesson 6:   Describing the Center of a Distribution Using the Mean

©2015 Great Minds eureka-math.org
G6-M6-TE-B3-1.3.1-01.2016

Example 2 (5 minutes)

This example gets students to distinguish between the representations of a data set using cubes versus a dot plot. It also reinforces the concept of *sharing*—one student gives a pet to another that needs one.

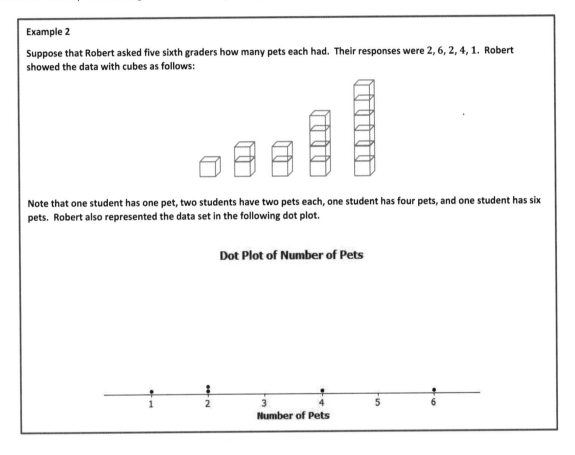

Example 2

Suppose that Robert asked five sixth graders how many pets each had. Their responses were 2, 6, 2, 4, 1. Robert showed the data with cubes as follows:

Note that one student has one pet, two students have two pets each, one student has four pets, and one student has six pets. Robert also represented the data set in the following dot plot.

Dot Plot of Number of Pets

Number of Pets

- Do the original stacks of cubes match the dot plot representation? Explain.
  - *Yes. The number of cubes in each stack corresponds to a dot on the dot plot.*

Read through the next part of the example with students, pointing out where one student *shares* a pet with another. Demonstrate this step, and display the numerical representation next to the dot plot.

Robert wants to illustrate Michelle's fair share method by using dot plots. He drew the following dot plot and said that it represents the result of the student with six pets sharing one of her pets with the student who has one pet.

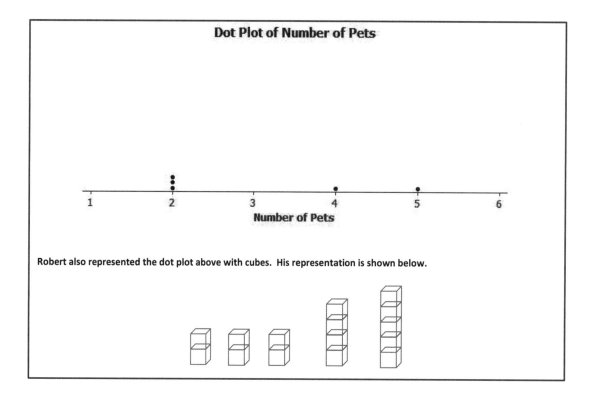

Robert also represented the dot plot above with cubes. His representation is shown below.

Visual to show on the board:

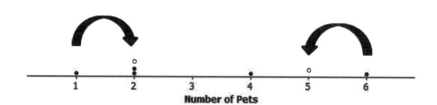

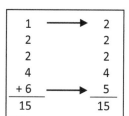

- Is Robert's new dot plot correct?
    □ *Robert's dot plot is correct.*
- How did the dot plot change from Robert's original dot plot?
    □ *The student who had six pets now has five (new dot), and the student who had one pet now has two (new dot)—the dots are moving toward each other.*
- Are the stacks of cubes correct?
    □ *The stacks of cubes are correct.*
- Do the dot plot and stacks represent a fair share yet?
    □ *No. Not all students have the same number of pets yet.*

EUREKA
MATH™

©2015 Great Minds eureka-math.org
G6-M6-TE-B3-1.3.1-01.2016

Exercises 7–10 (13 minutes)

Students work in pairs to complete Exercises 7–10.

Exercises 7–10

Now, continue distributing the pets based on the following steps.

7. Robert does a fair share step by having the student with five pets share one of her pets with one of the students with two pets.

   a. Draw the cubes representation that shows the result of this fair share step.

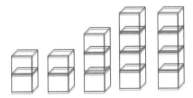

   b. Draw the dot plot that shows the result of this fair share step.

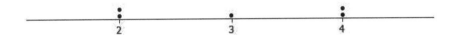

8. Robert does another fair share step by having one of the students who has four pets share one pet with one of the students who has two pets.

   a. Draw the cubes representation that shows the result of this fair share step.

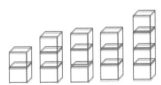

   b. Draw the dot plot that shows the result of this fair share step.

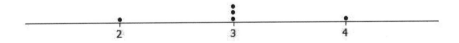

---

9. Robert does a final fair share step by having the student who has four pets share one pet with the student who has two pets.

    a. Draw the cubes representation that shows the result of this final fair share step.

    b. Draw the dot plot representation that shows the result of this final fair share step.

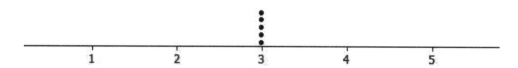

10. Explain in your own words why the final representations using cubes and a dot plot show that the mean number of pets owned by the five students is 3 pets.

    The sharing method produces 3 pets for each of the five students. The cubes representation shows that after sharing, each student has a fair share of three pets. The dot plot representation should have all of the data points at the same point on the number line, the mean. In this problem, the mean number of pets is 3 for these five students, so there should be five dots above 3 on the horizontal scale.

Closing (2 minutes)

- Describe the fair share method.

    - *Students were to have the same data value; this common value is the mean of the data.*

    - *Mathematically, the fair share mean comes from finding the total of all the data values and dividing the total by the number of data points. The arithmetic operation of division divides a total into equal parts.*

Exit Ticket (5 minutes)

©2015 Great Minds eureka-math.org
G6-M6-TE-B3-1.3.1-01.2016

Name _____   Date _____

Lesson 6: Describing the Center of a Distribution Using the Mean

Exit Ticket

1. If a class of 27 students had a mean of 72 on a test, interpret the mean of 72 in the sense of a fair share measure of the center of the test scores.

2. Suppose that your school's soccer team has scored a mean of 2 goals in each of 5 games.

    a. Draw a representation using cubes that displays that your school's soccer team has scored a mean of 2 goals in each of 5 games. Let 1 cube stand for 1 goal.

    b. Draw a dot plot that displays that your school's soccer team has scored a mean of 2 goals in each of 5 games.

Exit Ticket Sample Solutions

1. If a class of 27 students had a mean of 72 on a test, interpret the mean of 72 in the sense of a fair share measure of the center of the test scores.

    Answers will vary. 72 would be the test score that all 27 students would have if all 27 students had the same score.

2. Suppose that your school's soccer team has scored a mean of 2 goals in each of 5 games.

    a. Draw a representation using cubes that displays that your school's soccer team has scored a mean of 2 goals in each of 5 games. Let 1 cube stand for 1 goal.

    Answers will vary. There should be 10 total cubes that are placed in no more than 5 different stacks. One possibility is the one shown here, where each of the 5 stacks contain 2 cubes. However, any set of stacks where 10 cubes are divided into 5 or fewer (assuming that a "missing stack" represents a game in which 0 goals were scored) stacks would have a fair share (mean) of 2 and would be an acceptable representation.

    b. Draw a dot plot that displays that your school's soccer team has scored a mean of 2 goals in each of 5 games.

    Answers will vary. One possibility is the one shown here where all five dots are at 2. However, any dot plot that has exactly 5 dots and for which the sum of the values represented by the dot is 10 would be an acceptable representation of a data set that has a mean of 2.

Problem Set Sample Solutions

1. A game was played where ten tennis balls are tossed into a basket from a certain distance. The numbers of successful tosses for six students were 4, 1, 3, 2, 1, 7.

    a. Draw a representation of the data using cubes where one cube represents one successful toss of a tennis ball into the basket.

    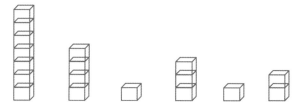

©2015 Great Minds eureka-math.org
G6-M6-TE-B3-1.3.1-01.2016

b. Represent the original data set using a dot plot.

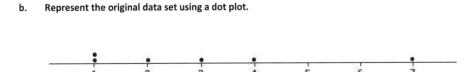

Number of Successful Tosses

2. Find the mean number of successful tosses for this data set using the fair share method. For each step, show the cubes representation and the corresponding dot plot. Explain each step in words in the context of the problem. You may move more than one successful toss in a step, but be sure that your explanation is clear. You must show two or more steps.

Clearly, there are several ways of getting to the final fair share cubes representation where each of the six stacks contains three cubes. Ideally, students move one cube at a time since, for many students, the leveling is seen more easily in that way. If a student shortcuts the process by moving several cubes at once, that is okay, as long as the graphic representations are correctly done and the explanation is clear. The table below provides one possible representation.

Step Described in Words	Fair Share Cubes Representation	Dot Plot
Share two of the cubes in the 7-cube stack with one of the 1-cube stacks. The result would be 5, 4, 3, 3, 1, 2. The 7-cube stack went from 7 successful tosses to 5 successful tosses, and one of the 1-cube stacks went from 1 successful toss to 3 successful tosses.		
Suppose that the student who has 5 successful tosses shares 2 tosses with the student who had 1 successful toss. The student with 5 successful tosses went down 2 tosses to 3 successful tosses, and the student with 1 successful toss went up 2 tosses to 3 successful tosses.		
Finally, the student with 4 successful tosses shares one of them with the student who has 2 successful tosses. The final step of the fair share method shows an even number of tosses for each of the six students. So, the mean number of successful tosses for these six students is 3 tosses.		

3. The numbers of pockets in the clothes worn by four students to school today are 4, 1, 3, and 6. Paige produces the following cubes representation as she does the fair share process. Help her decide how to finish the process now that she has stacks of 3, 3, 3, and 5 cubes.

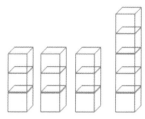

It should be clear to students that there are two extra cubes in the stack of five cubes. Those two extra cubes need to be distributed among the four students. That requires that each of the extra cubes needs to be split in half to produce four halves. Each of the four students gets half of a pocket to have a fair share mean of three and one-half pockets.

4. Suppose that the mean number of chocolate chips in 30 cookies is 14 chocolate chips.

    a. Interpret the mean number of chocolate chips in terms of fair share.

        Answers will vary. If each of the 30 cookies were to have the same number of chocolate chips, each would have 14 chocolate chips.

    b. Describe the dot plot representation of the fair share mean of 14 chocolate chips in 30 cookies.

        Answers will vary. There should be 30 different dots on the dot plot, all of them stacked up at 14.

5. Suppose that the following are lengths (in millimeters) of radish seedlings grown in identical conditions for three days: 12 11 12 14 13 9 13 11 13 10 10 14 16 13 11

    a. Find the mean length for these 15 radish seedlings.

        The mean length is $12\frac{2}{15}$ mm.

    b. Interpret the value from part (a) in terms of the fair share mean length.

        If each of the 15 radish seedlings were to have the same length, each would have a length of $12\frac{2}{15}$ mm.

        Note: Students should realize what the cubes representation for these data would look like but also realize that it may be a little cumbersome to move cubes around in the fair share process. Ideally, they would set up the initial cubes representation and then use the mathematical approach of summing the lengths to be 182 mm, which by division (distributed evenly to 15 plant) would yield $12\frac{2}{15}$ mm as the fair share mean length.

EUREKA
MATH™

©2015 Great Minds eureka-math.org
G6-M6-TE-B3-1.3.1-01.2016

Lesson 7: The Mean as a Balance Point

Student Outcomes

- Students describe the center of a distribution by its mean and interpret it as a balance point.
- Students understand that the mean is a balance point by calculating the distances of the data points from the mean and calling these distances *deviations*.
- Students understand that the balance point is where the sum of the distances above the mean is equal to the sum of the distances below the mean.

Lesson Notes

Consider introducing this lesson by recalling Lessons 3 and 6. In Lesson 3, Robert gathered data from sixth-grade students regarding the amount of sleep they get on school nights. He drew a dot plot of the data and decided informally on a value to describe the *center* of the distribution. In Lesson 6, Michelle proposed describing *center* using the number of hours that all students in the sample would have slept if they all had slept the same number of hours, called the *mean*.

In this lesson, students interpret the mean as a balance point by using a ruler and pennies to represent data. The objective of this lesson is for students to discover that if they were to draw a dot plot of the original data set, it would balance at the mean. They also see that in the process of moving data, if the total movement of points to the left equals the total movement of points to the right, then the balance point does not change.

A word of caution before beginning this lesson: Many rulers have holes in them. When data are not symmetric around the 6-inch mark of a 12-inch ruler, the holes affect the balancing at the correct value for the mean. Balancing pennies can be problematic. Students probably have to tape pennies (or whatever object is used) onto the rulers. Also, if balancing on the eraser end of a pencil proves too difficult, try using a paper towel tube cut in half lengthwise (as suggested in Connected Mathematics Project (CMP), *Data Distributions,* Pearson).

In physics, the underlying principle that pertains to the balance interpretation of mean is called *Archimedes' law of the lever.* Archimedes' law of the lever states that the sum of the products of weights and their distances to the left of the balance point equals the sum of the products of weights and their distances to the right of the balance point. The use of this law is a special case since all of the weights (data points) are considered to be equal. Therefore, the sum of the distances from the balance point to points left of the balance point equals the sum of the distances from the balance point to points right of the balance point. Moreover, the mean of the data is the balance point. Further, note that Archimedes' lever has to be weightless. Clearly, a ruler is not weightless, so when students try to balance various data distributions on a ruler, the balance point may not be exactly at the value of the mean.

Notice that deviations are actually signed distances, but calculations involving signed numbers is not covered until Grade 7. Here students can rely on knowledge from Grade 6 Modules 3, 4, and 5, and they work with the unsigned distances above and below the mean. In Grade 6 Module 3, students identified zero as a balance point between opposites on a number line. In this module, students understand that the mean balances total distances to the left of the mean and to the right of the mean on the number line.

©2015 Great Minds eureka-math.org
G6-M6-TE-B3-1.3.1-01.2016

Classwork

Students read the introduction to the lesson.

> In Lesson 3, Robert gave us an informal interpretation of the center of a data set. In Lesson 6, Michelle developed a more
> formal interpretation of center as a fair share mean, a value that every person in the data set would have if they all had
> the same value. In this lesson, Sabina will show us how to interpret the mean as a balance point.

Example 1 (7 minutes): The Mean as a Balance Point

Recall the scenarios from Lessons 3 and 6 (i.e., Robert's informal interpretation of the center value and Michelle's fair share mean). Now Sabina describes the mean as a balance point. This example introduces the very important concept of deviation of a data point as its distance from the mean. Explain that a deviation is calculated by determining the distance from the mean to the data point, and the total distances on either side of the mean should be equal. Students need to recall from Module 3 that distances are always positive.

Read through the first paragraph as a class.

Example 1: The Mean as a Balance Point

Sabina wants to know how long it takes students to get to school. She asks two students how long it takes them to get to school. It takes one student 1 minute and the other student 11 minutes. Sabina represents these data values on a ruler, putting a penny at 1 inch and another at 11 inches. Sabina thinks that there might be a connection between the mean of two data points and where they balance on a ruler. She thinks the mean may be the balancing point. What do you think? Sabina shows her data using a dot plot.

Dot Plot of Number of Minutes

Number of Minutes

- Will Sabina's ruler balance at 6 inches?
  - *Answers may vary. Sabina's ruler will balance at 6 inches. (Now, show the ruler balancing on a pencil. It should balance at 6 inches or very close to 6 inches, depending on how the two pennies are placed on the ruler.)*
- Is 6 the mean of 1 and 11?
  - *Yes, the mean of 1 and 11 is 6.*

Read through the second paragraph as a class. As the scenario is being read, tell students to mark the new positions of the pennies on the dot plot provided in the example.

Lesson 7:   The Mean as a Balance Point

©2015 Great Minds eureka-math.org
G6-M6-TE-B3-1.3.1-01.2016

> Sabina decides to move the penny at 1 inch to 4 inches and the other penny from 11 inches to 8 inches on the ruler, noting that the movement for the two pennies is the same distance but in opposite directions. Sabina thinks that if two data points move the same distance but in opposite directions, the balance point on the ruler does not change. Do you agree with Sabina?

- Do you think the balance point will remain at 6 inches?
    - *Yes. (Now, show the ruler balancing on a pencil.)*
- What is the mean for two students who live 4 and 8 minutes away from school?
    - *The mean is still 6 minutes.*

Read through the last paragraph as a class. Note that Sabina is moving the first penny from 4 inches to 6 inches.

> Sabina continues by moving the penny at 4 inches to 6 inches. To keep the ruler balanced at 6 inches, how far should Sabina move the penny from 8 inches, and in what direction?
>
> *Since the penny at 4 inches moved two to the right, to maintain the balance, the penny at 8 inches needs to move two inches to the left. Both pennies are now at 6 inches, and the ruler clearly balances there. Note that the mean of these two values (6 minutes and 6 minutes) is still 6 minutes.*

- How far is she moving the penny?
    - *She is moving the penny 2 inches.*
- How far should she move the other penny to keep the ruler in balance?
    - *She should move the penny 2 inches in the opposite direction.*
- If she is moving the penny from 8 inches, where should it be placed?
    - *The penny should be placed at 6 inches. (If students say 10 inches, again remind them they need to move the pennies in opposite directions.)*

Exercises 1–2 (7 minutes)

Let students work in pairs on Exercises 1–2. Each pair will need a ruler, pennies, and tape.

Exercises 1–2

Now it is your turn to try balancing two pennies on a ruler.

1. Tape one penny at 2.5 inches on your ruler.

    a. Where should a second penny be taped so that the ruler will balance at 6 inches?

    The penny should be at 9.5 inches.

    b. How far is the penny at 2.5 inches from 6 inches? How far is the other penny from 6 inches?

    Each penny is 3.5 inches away from 6 inches.

    c. Is 6 inches the mean of the two locations of the pennies? Explain how you know this.

    Yes, the mean of the two locations of the pennies is 6 inches. The distance of the penny that is below 6 inches is equal to the distance to the penny that is above 6 inches.

---

2.   Move the penny that is at 2.5 inches to the right two inches.

    a.   Where will the penny be placed?

        The penny will be placed at 4.5 inches.

    b.   What do you have to do with the other data point (the other penny) to keep the balance point at 6 inches?

        I will have to move it 2 inches to the left.

    c.   What is the mean of the two new data points? Is it the same value as the balance point of the ruler?

        The mean is 6. It is the same value as the balance point of the ruler. (Remember that the ruler might not balance at exactly 6, depending on the accuracy of the placement of the two pennies on the ruler.)

Example 2 (5 minutes): Balancing More Than Two Points

This example extends the data set from one containing two data points to one that contains three data points. The main idea is that it does not matter how many data points there are. Whether the data points are represented as pennies on a ruler or as dots on a dot plot, the mean balances the total of the distances of the points to the left of the mean and the total of the distances of the points to the right of the mean.

Read through the example as a class, and study the diagram.

Example 2: Balancing More Than Two Points

Sabina wants to know what happens if there are more than two data points. Suppose there are three students. One student lives 2 minutes from school, and another student lives 9 minutes from school. If the mean time for all three students is 6 minutes, she wonders how long it takes the third student to get to school. Using what you know about distances from the mean, where should the third penny be placed in order for the mean to be 6 inches? Label the diagram, and explain your reasoning.

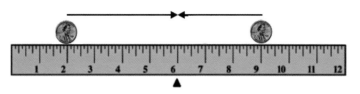

- What is the distance to 6 for each penny in the diagram?
    □   *The distance for the penny at 2 inches is 4 inches, and the distance for the penny at 9 inches is 3 inches.*
- Note that the mean for these two points (or pennies) is not 6 because the distance from 6 inches for the point that is below 6 inches is not equal to the distance from 6 inches for the point that is above 6 inches. We have to determine a point on the ruler where we can place the third penny so the mean is 6 inches. Where can the third penny be placed on the ruler so the mean, or the balance point, is 6 inches? Explain your reasoning.

Allow students time to collaborate with a partner to determine where the penny should be placed. Remind students they cannot move either of the pennies already on the ruler, as they are already established points. They need to find a place to put the third penny so the mean is 6 inches.

©2015 Great Minds eureka-math.org
G6-M6-TE-B3-1.3.1-01.2016

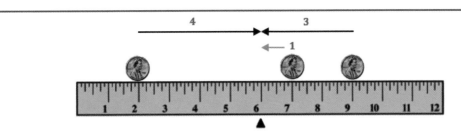

The third penny should be placed at 7 inches. The 7 is 1 inch from 6 inches, and the 9 is 3 inches from 6 inches. Combined, the total distance for these two pennies is 4 inches. Since the distance of the point on the left of 6 inches is also 4 inches, the mean is now 6 inches.

Exercises 3–6 (7 minutes)

Students continue working in pairs. If time is running short, choose just one problem for students to attempt.

Exercises 3–6

Imagine you are balancing pennies on a ruler.

3. Suppose you place one penny each at 3 inches, 7 inches, and 8 inches on your ruler.

    a. Sketch a picture of the ruler. At what value do you think the ruler will balance? Mark the balance point with the symbol Δ.

    Students should represent the pennies at 3 inches, 7 inches, and 8 inches on the ruler with a balancing point at 6 inches.

    b. What is the mean of 3 inches, 7 inches, and 8 inches? Does your ruler balance at the mean?

    The mean is 6 inches. Yes, it balances at the mean.

    c. Show the information from part (a) on a dot plot. Mark the balance point with the symbol Δ.

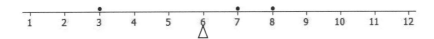

    d. What are the distances on each side of the balance point? How does this prove the mean is 6?

    The distance to the left of the mean (the distance between 3 and 6): 3

    One of the distances to the right of the mean (the distance between 7 and 6): 1

    One of the distances to the right of the mean (the distance between 8 and 6): 2

    The total of the distances to the right of the mean: $2 + 1 = 3$

    The mean is 6 because the total of the distances on either side of 6 is 3.

Lesson 7:   The Mean as a Balance Point

81

©2015 Great Minds eureka-math.org
G6-M6-TE-B3-1.3.1-01.2016

4. Now, suppose you place a penny each at 7 inches and 9 inches on your ruler.

    a. Draw a dot plot representing these two pennies.

        See below.

    b. Estimate where to place a third penny on your ruler so that the ruler balances at 6 inches, and mark the point on the dot plot above. Mark the balance point with the symbol Δ.

        The third penny should be placed at 2 inches.

    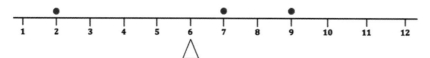

    c. Explain why your answer in part (b) is true by calculating the distances of the points from 6. Are the totals of the distances on either side of the mean equal?

        The distance to the left of the mean (the distance between 2 and 6): 4

        One of the distances to the right of the mean (the distance between 7 and 6): 1

        One of the distances to the right of the mean (the distance between 9 and 6): 3

        The total of the distances to the right of the mean: $3 + 1 = 4$

        The mean is 6 because the total of the distances on either side of 6 is 4.

5. Is the concept of the mean as the balance point true if you put multiple pennies on a single location on the ruler?

    Yes. The balancing process is applicable to stacking pennies or having more than one data point at the same location on a dot plot. (If students have difficulty seeing this, remind them of the fair share interpretation of the mean using a dot plot, where all of the dots were stacked up at the mean.)

6. Suppose you place two pennies at 7 inches and one penny at 9 inches on your ruler.

    a. Draw a dot plot representing these three pennies.

        See below.

    b. Estimate where to place a fourth penny on your ruler so that the ruler balances at 6 inches, and mark the point on the dot plot above. Mark the balance point with the symbol Δ.

        The fourth penny should be placed at 1 inch.

    c. Explain why your answer in part (b) is true by calculating the distances of the points from 6. Are the totals of the distances on either side of the mean equal?

        The total of the distances to the left of the mean is 5. The total of the distances to the right of the mean can be found by calculating the distance between 7 and 6 twice, since there are two data points at 7, and then adding it to the distance between 9 and 6. Therefore, the total of the distances to the right of the mean is 5 because $1 + 1 + 3 = 5$, which is equal to the total of the distances to the left of the mean.

©2015 Great Minds eureka-math.org
G6-M6-TE-B3-1.3.1-01.2016

EUREKA
MATH™

Example 3 (5 minutes): Finding the Mean

This example looks at a data set whose mean is not 6. Read through the example with students. Students work independently or with partners to determine the mean and then discuss their findings.

Example 3: Finding the Mean

What if the data on a dot plot were 1, 3, and 8? Will the data balance at 6? If not, what is the balance point, and why?

The data do not balance at 6. The balance point must be 4 in order for the total of the distances on either side of the mean to be equal.

- Is 6 the balancing point?
  - □ *The data will not balance at 6.*
- Why not?
  - □ *The total of the distances to the left of 6 is 8, and the total of the distances to the right of 6 is 2. Because they are not equal, the mean cannot be 6.*
- What must the balance point be?
  - □ *The balance point must be 4.*
- How did you determine your answer?
  - □ *Answers may vary. Student responses should include that the total of the distances on either side of 4 are equal.*

Exercise 7 (7 minutes)

Students work in pairs on Exercise 7.

Exercise 7

Use what you have learned about the mean to answer the following questions.

7. Recall from Lesson 6 that Michelle asked ten of her classmates for the number of hours they usually sleep when there is school the next day. Their responses (in hours) were 8, 10, 8, 8, 11, 11, 9, 8, 10, 7.

   a. It's hard to balance ten pennies. Instead of actually using pennies and a ruler, draw a dot plot that represents the data set.

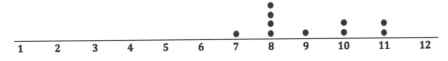

   b. Use your dot plot to find the balance point.

   A balance point of 9 would mean the total of the distances to the left of 9 is 6 because $2 + 1 + 1 + 1 + 1 = 6$, and the total of the distances to the right of 9 is 6 because $1 + 1 + 2 + 2 = 6$. Since the totals of the distances on each side of the mean are equal, 9 is the balance point. The data point that is directly on 9 has a distance of zero, which does not change the total of the distances to the right or the left of the mean.

Closing (2 minutes)

- What does the mean represent on a dot plot or on a ruler balancing pennies?
  - *The mean represents the balance point of the data set.*
  - *The mean is the point that balances the total of the distances to the left of the mean with the total of the distances to the right of the mean.*

Exit Ticket (5 minutes)

©2015 Great Minds eureka-math.org
G6-M6-TE-B3-1.3.1-01.2016

Name _____   Date _____

Lesson 7: The Mean as a Balance Point

Exit Ticket

The dot plot below shows the number of goals scored by a school's soccer team in 7 games so far this season.

Use the balancing process to explain why the mean number of goals scored is 3.

Exit Ticket Sample Solutions

The dot plot below shows the number of goals scored by a school's soccer team in 7 games so far this season.

Use the balancing process to explain why the mean number of goals scored is 3.

The total of the distances to the left of 3 is 4 because $1 + 3 = 4$. The total of the distances to the right of 3 is also 4 because $2 + 2 = 4$. Since the totals of the distances on either side of the mean are equal, then 3 must be the mean.

Problem Set Sample Solutions

1. The number of pockets in the clothes worn by four students to school today is 4, 1, 3, 4.

   a. Perform the fair share process to find the mean number of pockets for these four students. Sketch the cubes representations for each step of the process.

   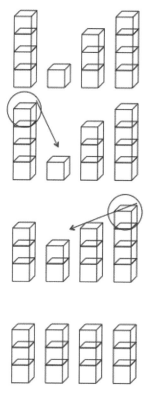

   Each of the 4's gives up a pocket to the person with one pocket, yielding four stacks of three pockets each. The mean is 3 pockets.

EUREKA
MATH™

©2015 Great Minds eureka-math.org
G6-M6-TE-B3-1.3.1-01.2016

b.   Find the total of the distances on each side of the mean to show the mean found in part (a) is correct.

The mean is correct because the total of the distances to the left of 3 is 2, and the total of the distances to the right of 3 is 2 because 1 + 1 = 2.

2.   The times (rounded to the nearest minute) it took each of six classmates to run a mile are 7, 9, 10, 11, 11, and 12 minutes.

   a.   Draw a dot plot representation for the mile times.

Times the Mile Was Run (rounded to the nearest minute)

   b.   Suppose that Sabina thinks the mean is 11 minutes. Is she correct? Explain your answer.

Sabina is incorrect. The total of the distances to the left of 11 is 7, and the total of the distances to the right of 11 is 1. The totals of the distances are not equal; therefore, the mean cannot be 11 minutes.

   c.   What is the mean?

For the total of the distances to be equal on either side of the mean, the mean must be 10 because on the left of 10 the total of the distances is 4 because 1 + 3 = 4, and the total of the distances to the right of 10 is 4 because 1 + 1 + 2 = 4.

3.   The prices per gallon of gasoline (in cents) at five stations across town on one day are shown in the following dot plot. The price for a sixth station is missing, but the mean price for all six stations was reported to be 380 cents per gallon. Use the balancing process to determine the price of a gallon of gasoline at the sixth station.

Dot Plot of Price (cents per gallon)

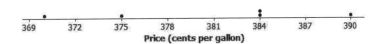

Price (cents per gallon)

To find the price per gallon of gasoline at the sixth station, we need to assess the distances from 380 of the five current data points and then place the sixth data point to ensure that the total of the distances to the left of the mean equals the total of the distances to the right of the mean. Currently, the total of the distances to the left of 380 is 15 because 5 + 10 = 15, and the total of the distances to the right of 380 is 18 because 4 + 4 + 10 = 18. For the mean of all six prices to be 380, the total of the distances to the left of 380 needs to be 18. This means we need to place a dot three cents to the left of the mean. 380 − 3 = 377. The sixth price is 377 cents per gallon.

4. The number of phones (landline and cell) owned by the members of each of nine families is 3, 5, 6, 6, 6, 6, 7, 7, 8.

a. Use the mathematical formula for the mean (determine the sum of the data points, and divide by the number of data points) to find the mean number of phones owned for these nine families.

$\frac{54}{9} = 6$. *The mean is 6 phones.*

b. Draw a dot plot of the data, and verify your answer in part (a) by using the balancing process.

Number of Phones Owned

The total of the distances to the left of 6 is 4 because $3 + 1 = 4$. The total of the distances to the right of 6 is 4 because $1 + 1 + 2 = 4$. Since both totals are equal, 6 is the correct mean.

Lesson 7:   The Mean as a Balance Point

©2015 Great Minds eureka-math.org
G6-M6-TE-B3-1.3.1-01.2016

Lesson 8: Variability in a Data Distribution

Student Outcomes

- Students interpret the mean of a data set as a typical value.

- Students compare and contrast two small data sets that have the same mean but differ in variability.

- Students see that a data distribution is not characterized only by its center. Students also consider variability (spread) when describing a data distribution.

- Students informally evaluate how precise the mean is as an indicator of a typical value for a distribution, based on the variability in the data.

- Students use dot plots to order data distributions according to the variability around the mean of the data distribution.

Classwork

Example 1 (5 minutes): Comparing Two Data Distributions

Read through the introductory paragraph as a class, and then give students time to examine the table.

Example 1: Comparing Two Data Distributions

Robert's family is planning to move to either New York City or San Francisco. Robert has a cousin in San Francisco and asked her how she likes living in a climate as warm as San Francisco. She replied that it doesn't get very warm in San Francisco. He was surprised by her answer. Because temperature was one of the criteria he was going to use to form his opinion about where to move, he decided to investigate the temperature distributions for New York City and San Francisco. The table below gives average temperatures (in degrees Fahrenheit) for each month for the two cities.

City	Jan.	Feb.	Mar.	Apr.	May	June	July	Aug.	Sep.	Oct.	Nov.	Dec.
New York City	39	42	50	61	71	81	85	84	76	65	55	47
San Francisco	57	60	62	63	64	67	67	68	70	69	63	58

Data Source as of 2013: http://www.usclimatedata.com/climate/san-francisco/california/united-states/usca0987

Data Source as of 2013: http://www.usclimatedata.com/climate/new-york/united-states/3202

- What do you notice about the temperatures in New York City?

  □ *The average monthly temperatures vary quite a bit through the year.*

- What do you notice about the temperatures in San Francisco?

  □ *The average monthly temperatures do not change much from month to month.*

Lesson 8:   Variability in a Data Distribution

©2015 Great Minds eureka-math.org
G6-M6-TE-B3-1.3.1-01.2016

Exercises 1–2 (5 minutes)

Students work independently and confirm their answers with a neighbor. Encourage calculator use when working with larger data sets.

Exercises 1–2

Use the data in the table provided in Example 1 to answer the following:

1. Calculate the mean of the monthly average temperatures for each city.

   The mean of the monthly temperatures for New York City is 63 degrees.

   The mean of the monthly temperatures for San Francisco is 64 degrees.

2. Recall that Robert is trying to decide where he wants to move. What is your advice to him based on comparing the means of the monthly temperatures of the two cities?

   Since the means are almost the same, it looks like Robert could move to either city. Even though the question asks students to focus on the means, they might make a recommendation that takes variability into account. For example, they might note that even though the means for the two cities are about the same, there are some much lower and much higher monthly temperatures for New York City and use this as a basis to suggest that Robert move to San Francisco.

Example 2 (5 minutes): Understanding Variability

Read through the first paragraph as a class. Since the means are about the same, it would be helpful if Robert had more information as the basis for a decision. One possibility is that he can take the information about month-to-month variability in the temperatures into consideration.

- In Exercise 2, you found that the mean of the monthly temperatures in both the New York City distribution and the San Francisco distribution was about the same. That didn't help Robert very much in making a decision between the two cities.

- Since the mean monthly temperatures are about the same, should Robert just toss a coin to make his decision? Is there anything else Robert could look at in comparing the two distributions?
   - *Answers will vary. Students may comment on the month-to-month variability in the temperatures or on the extremes (high and low temperatures) for each city.*

- Variability was introduced in an earlier lesson. Variability in a distribution is often described by looking at how spread out the data values are from some measure of center (such as the mean). How could Robert consider the variability of the two sets of data?
   - *Answers will vary. Students might suggest looking at distances from the mean as they did in Lesson 7.*

Example 2: Understanding Variability

Maybe Robert should look at how spread out the New York City monthly temperature data are from the mean of the New York City monthly temperatures and how spread out the San Francisco monthly temperature data are from the mean of the San Francisco monthly temperatures. To compare the variability of monthly temperatures between the two cities, it may be helpful to look at dot plots. The dot plots of the monthly temperature distributions for New York City and San Francisco follow.

©2015 Great Minds eureka-math.org
G6-M6-TE-B3-1.3.1-01.2016

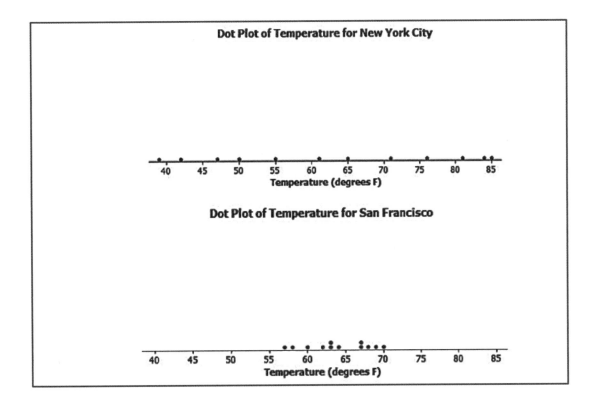

- How are the two dot plots different?
    - *The temperatures for New York City are spread out, while the temperatures for San Francisco are clustered together.*

Exercises 3–7 (6 minutes)

Let students work independently and compare answers with a neighbor.

Exercises 3–7

Use the dot plots above to answer the following:

3. Mark the location of the mean on each distribution with the balancing Δ symbol. How do the two distributions compare based on their means?

    Place Δ at 63 for New York City and at 64 for San Francisco. The means are about the same.

4. Describe the variability of the New York City monthly temperatures from the New York City mean.

    The temperatures are spread out around the mean. The temperatures range from a low of around 39 °F to a high of 85 °F.

5. Describe the variability of the San Francisco monthly temperatures from the San Francisco mean.

    The temperatures are clustered around the mean. The temperatures range from a low of 57 °F to a high of 70 °F.

©2015 Great Minds eureka-math.org
G6-M6-TE-B3-1.3.1-01.2016

6.   Compare the variability in the two distributions. Is the variability about the same, or is it different? If different, which monthly temperature distribution has more variability? Explain.

The variability is different. The variability in New York City is much greater than the variability in San Francisco.

7.   If Robert prefers to choose the city where the temperatures vary the least from month to month, which city should he choose? Explain.

He should choose San Francisco because the temperatures vary the least, from a low of 57 °F to a high of 70 °F. New York City has temperatures with more variability, from a low of 39 °F to a high of 85 °F.

Example 3 (6 minutes): Considering the Mean and Variability in a Data Distribution

The concept in this example may be challenging for some students. When Robert talks about the precision of the mean, Sabina asks him to explain what he means by a mean being precise.

Although the means are about the same for the two distributions, Robert is suggesting that the mean of 64 degrees for San Francisco is a better indicator of the city's typical monthly temperature than the mean of 63 degrees is as an indicator of a typical monthly temperature in New York City. He bases this on the variability of the monthly temperatures in each city. He says that a mean is only a precise indicator of monthly temperatures if the variability in the data is small. The greater the variability, the less precise the mean is as an indicator of a typical monthly temperature.

Example 3: Considering the Mean and Variability in a Data Distribution

The mean is used to describe a typical value for the entire data distribution. Sabina asks Robert which city he thinks has the better climate. How do you think Robert responds?

He responds that they both have about the same mean but that the mean is a better measure or a more precise measure of a typical monthly temperature for San Francisco than it is for New York City.

Sabina is confused and asks him to explain what he means by this statement. How could Robert explain what he means?

The temperatures in New York City in the winter months are in the 40's and in the summer months are in the 80's. The mean of 63 isn't very close to those temperatures. Therefore, the mean is not a good indicator of a typical monthly temperature. The mean is a much better indicator of a typical monthly temperature in San Francisco because the variability of the temperatures there is much smaller.

If there is still confusion, draw two dot plots similar to Example 2 on the board, and ask the following:

- Which dot plot has greater variability?
    - *The dot plot representing New York City has a greater variability.*
- If data points have a lot of variability, is the mean a good indicator of a typical value in the data set?
    - *If there is a lot of variability, the mean is not a good indicator of a typical value in the data set.*
- If the data points are tightly clustered around the mean, is the mean a good indicator of a typical value in the data set?
    - *If the data points are tightly clustered around the mean, the mean is a good indicator of a typical value in the data set.*

©2015 Great Minds eureka-math.org
G6-M6-TE-B3-1.3.1-01.2016

Exercises 8–11 (5 minutes)

Students work independently and confirm their answers with a neighbor.

Exercises 8–14

Consider the following two distributions of times it takes six students to get to school in the morning and to go home from school in the afternoon.

	Time (minutes)					
Morning	11	12	14	14	16	17
Afternoon	6	10	13	18	18	19

8. To visualize the means and variability, draw a dot plot for each of the two distributions.

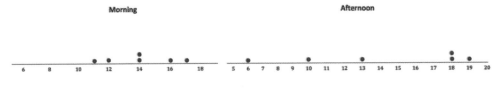

9. What is the mean time to get from home to school in the morning for these six students?

   The mean is 14 minutes.

10. What is the mean time to get from school to home in the afternoon for these six students?

    The mean is 14 minutes.

11. For which distribution does the mean give a more accurate indicator of a typical time? Explain your answer.

    The morning mean is a more accurate indicator. The spread in the afternoon data is far greater than the spread in the morning data.

Exercises 12–14 (6 minutes)

Students work in pairs or small groups. If time allows, discuss Exercise 13 as a class.

Distributions can be ordered according to how much the data values vary around their means.

Consider the following data on the number of green jelly beans in seven bags of jelly beans from each of five different candy manufacturers (AllGood, Best, Delight, Sweet, and Yum). The mean in each distribution is 42 green jelly beans.

	Bag 1	Bag 2	Bag 3	Bag 4	Bag 5	Bag 6	Bag 7
AllGood	40	40	41	42	42	43	46
Best	22	31	36	42	48	53	62
Delight	26	36	40	43	47	50	52
Sweet	36	39	42	42	42	44	49
Yum	33	36	42	42	45	48	48

---

12. Draw a dot plot of the distribution of the number of green jelly beans for each of the five candy makers. Mark the location of the mean on each distribution with the balancing Δ symbol.

The dot plots should each have a balancing Δ symbol located at 42.

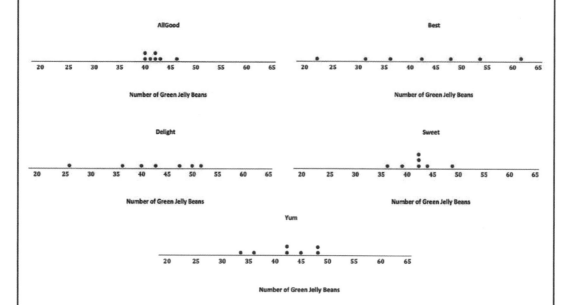

13. Order the candy manufacturers from the one you think has the least variability to the one with the most variability. Explain your reasoning for choosing the order.

Note: Do not be critical; answers and explanations may vary. One possible answer:

In order from least to greatest: AllGood, Sweet, Yum, Delight, Best. The data points are all close to the mean for AllGood, which indicates it has the least variability, followed by Sweet and Yum. The data points are spread farther from the mean for Delight and Best, which indicates they have the greatest variability.

14. For which company would the mean be considered a better indicator of a typical value (based on least variability)?

The mean for AllGood would be the best indicator of a typical value for the distribution.

Closing (2 minutes)

■ How does variability help determine if the mean is an accurate indication of a typical value for a data distribution?

□ *The mean of a distribution with small variability (not a lot of spread) is considered to be a better indication of a typical value than the mean of a distribution with greater variability (wide spread).*

Lesson Summary

We can compare distributions based on their means, but variability must also be considered. The mean of a distribution with small variability (not a lot of spread) is considered to be a better indication of a typical value than the mean of a distribution with greater variability (or wide spread).

Exit Ticket (5 minutes)

EUREKA
MATH™

©2015 Great Minds eureka-math.org
G6-M6-TE-B3-1.3.1-01.2016

Name _____   Date _____

Lesson 8: Variability in a Data Distribution

Exit Ticket

1. Consider the following statement: Two sets of data with the same mean will also have the same variability. Do you agree or disagree with this statement? Explain.

2. Suppose the dot plot on the left shows the number of goals a boys' soccer team has scored in 6 games so far this season and the dot plot on the right shows the number of goals a girls' soccer team has scored in 6 games so far this season.

Goals Scored by Boy's Team   Goals Scored by Girl's Team

a. Compute the mean number of goals for each distribution.

b. For which distribution, if either, would the mean be considered a better indicator of a typical value? Explain your answer.

Exit Ticket Sample Solutions

1. Consider the following statement: Two sets of data with the same mean will also have the same variability. Do you agree or disagree with this statement? Explain.

    Answers will vary, but students should disagree with this statement. There are many examples in this lesson that could be used as the basis for an explanation.

2. Suppose the dot plot on the left shows the number of goals a boys' soccer team has scored in 6 games so far this season and the dot plot on the right shows the number of goals a girls' soccer team has scored in 6 games so far this season.

    a. Compute the mean number of goals for each distribution.

        The mean for each is 3 goals.

    b. For which distribution, if either, would the mean be considered a better indicator of a typical value? Explain your answer.

        Variability in the distribution for girls is less than in the distribution for boys, so the mean of 3 goals for the girls is a better indicator of a typical value.

Problem Set Sample Solutions

1. The number of pockets in the clothes worn by seven students to school yesterday was 4, 1, 3, 4, 2, 2, 5. Today, those seven students each had three pockets in their clothes.

    a. Draw one dot plot of the number of pockets data for what students wore yesterday and another dot plot for what students wore today. Be sure to use the same scale.

        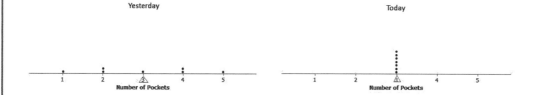

    b. For each distribution, find the mean number of pockets worn by the seven students. Show the means on the dot plots by using the balancing Δ symbol.

        The mean of both dot plots is 3.

    c. For which distribution is the mean number of pockets a better indicator of what is typical? Explain.

        There is certainly variability in the data for yesterday's distribution, whereas today's distribution has none. The mean of 3 pockets is a better indicator (more precise) for today's distribution.

EUREKA
MATH™

©2015 Great Minds eureka-math.org
G6-M6-TE-B3-1.3.1-01.2016

2. The number of minutes (rounded to the nearest minute) it took to run a certain route was recorded for each of five students. The resulting data were 9, 10, 11, 14, and 16 minutes. The number of minutes (rounded to the nearest minute) it took the five students to run a different route was also recorded, resulting in the following data: 6, 8, 12, 15, and 19 minutes.

    a. Draw dot plots for the distributions of the times for the two routes. Be sure to use the same scale on both dot plots.

First Route

Time (minutes)

Second Route

Time (minutes)

    b. Do the distributions have the same mean? What is the mean of each dot plot?

    Yes, both distributions have the same mean, 12 *minutes.*

    c. In which distribution is the mean a better indicator of the typical amount of time taken to run the route? Explain.

    Looking at the dot plots, the times for the second route are more varied than those for the first route. So, the mean for the first route is a better indicator (more precise) of a typical value.

3. The following table shows the prices per gallon of gasoline (in cents) at five stations across town as recorded on Monday, Wednesday, and Friday of a certain week.

Day	R&C	Al's	PB	Sam's	Ann's
Monday	359	358	362	359	362
Wednesday	357	365	364	354	360
Friday	350	350	360	370	370

    a. The mean price per day for the five stations is the same for each of the three days. Without doing any calculations and simply looking at Friday's prices, what must the mean price be?

    Friday's prices are centered at 360 *cents. The sum of the distances from* 360 *for values above* 360 *is equal to the sum of the distances from* 360 *for values below* 360, *so the mean is* 360 *cents.*

    b. For which daily distribution is the mean a better indicator of the typical price per gallon for the five stations? Explain.

    From the dot plots, the mean for Monday is the best indicator of a typical price because there is the least variability in the Monday prices.

Lesson 9: The Mean Absolute Deviation (MAD)

Student Outcomes

- Students calculate the mean absolute deviation (MAD) for a given data set.
- Students interpret the MAD of a data set as the average distance of the data values from the mean.

Lesson Notes

Variability was discussed informally in Lesson 8. This lesson focuses on developing a more formal measure of variability in a data distribution called the *mean absolute deviation*, denoted by MAD. The concept of distance from the mean should be clear to students by now since previous lessons used distances to the right (above) and distances to the left (below) of the mean to develop the idea of the mean as a balance point. This lesson introduces the idea of a deviation as a distance and direction (to the right or to the left) from the mean and challenges students to think about why deviations provide information about variability in a data set.

Mean absolute deviation is the measure of variability used in the middle school curriculum. At the high school level, students see other measures of variability called the *variance* and the *standard deviation* that are also based on deviations from the mean.

Classwork

Example 1 (5 minutes): Variability

> **Example 1: Variability**
>
> In Lesson 8, Robert wanted to decide where he would rather move (New York City or San Francisco). He planned to make his decision by comparing the average monthly temperatures for the two cities. Since the mean of the average monthly temperatures for New York City and the mean for San Francisco turned out to be about the same, he decided instead to compare the cities based on the variability in their monthly average temperatures. He looked at the two distributions and decided that the New York City temperatures were more spread out from their mean than were the San Francisco temperatures from their mean.

Read through Example 1 as a class, and recall the main idea of Lesson 8.

- What is variability?
  - *Variability is when not all the values in a data set are the same. When the values in a data set are all very similar, there isn't much variability, but if the values differ a lot, there is more variability.*
- What does a distribution that has no variability look like?
  - *All of the data values are the same.*
- What does a distribution that has a lot of variability look like?
  - *The data points are spread far apart.*

> *Scaffolding:*
>
> Show students different dot plots, and have them discuss which one has no variability, little variability, and a lot of variability.

Lesson 9: The Mean Absolute Deviation (MAD)

©2015 Great Minds eureka-math.org
G6-M6-TE-B3-1.3.1-01.2016

Remind students that variability is another word for "spread" and that whether there is a lot or a little variability can be seen visually in a dot plot of a data set. Suggest that students can visually order data sets, based on the spread in the dot plots. Consider showing several dot plots of data and asking students to order them from least variability to most variability.

Exercises 1–3 (8 minutes)

Students work in small groups on these exercises. Then, confirm answers as a class. The discussion of Exercise 3 leads into Example 2.

Students are asked to order the seven data sets from least variability to most variability. Students will no doubt suggest different orderings. Several orderings are reasonable—focus on students' explanations for ordering the distributions. What is important is not their suggested orderings but rather their arguments to support their orderings. Also, the goal for these exercises is for students to realize that they need to have a more formal way of determining the best ordering. Sabina suggests that a formula is needed to measure variability, and she proceeds in this lesson to develop one.

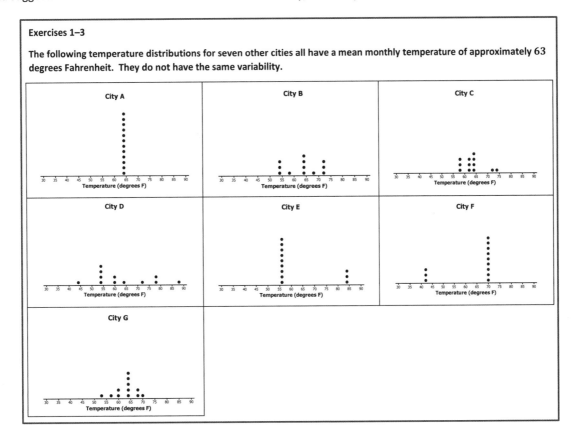

Exercises 1–3

The following temperature distributions for seven other cities all have a mean monthly temperature of approximately 63 degrees Fahrenheit. They do not have the same variability.

1.   **Which distribution has the smallest variability? Explain your answer.**

     City A has the smallest variability because all the data points are the same.

2.   **Which distribution or distributions seem to have the most variability? Explain your answer.**

     One or more of the following is acceptable: Cities D, E, and F. They appear to have data points that are the most spread out.

3.   **Order the seven distributions from least variability to most variability. Explain why you listed the distributions in the order that you chose.**

     Several orderings are reasonable. Focus on students' explanations for choosing the order, making sure that the ordering is consistent with an understanding of spread. There are some that will be hard for students to order, and if students have trouble, use this opportunity to point out that it would be useful to have a more formal way to measure variability in a data set. Such a measure is developed in Example 2.

Example 2 (5 minutes): Measuring Variability

Example 2: Measuring Variability

Based on just looking at the distributions, there are different orderings of variability that seem to make some sense. Sabina is interested in developing a formula that will produce a number that measures the variability in a data distribution. She would then use the formula to measure the variability in each data set and use these values to order the distributions from smallest variability to largest variability. She proposes beginning by looking at how far the values in a data set are from the mean of the data set.

No doubt students had different orderings of variability for the seven cities in Exercise 2. Sabina suggests that, in this example, a formula is needed to measure variability and that this could be used to establish an order. She proposes looking at distances from the mean to develop a formula for a measure of variability.

- ▪   Do you think using distances from the mean is a good basis for a formula to measure variability?
    - ▫   *Yes. If there is not much variability in a data set, the values will all be close together, so the distances from the mean will be small. If there is a lot of variability in a data set, the data values will be spread out, and some points will be far away from the mean.*

Introduce the term *deviation* at this point. In Grade 6, a *deviation* is defined as a distance and a direction (to the left or to the right of the mean). In later grades, after students have more experience with signed numbers, a deviation is defined as a signed distance from the mean and is calculated by subtracting the mean from a data value. If the data value is to the left of (below) the mean, the deviation is negative. If the data value is to the right of (above) the mean, the deviation is positive. Here, just focus on distance, and then attach a direction to the distance, as is done in Exercise 4.

The name *mean absolute deviation* comes from the fact that this measure of variability is calculated as the mean of the unsigned distances from the mean (the absolute values of the deviations).

Exercises 4–5 (5 minutes)

Guide students to work in pairs during the following exercises.

In these exercises, students use City G to calculate deviations and verify that the total of the distances from the mean on either side are equal.

©2015 Great Minds eureka-math.org
G6-M6-TE-B3-1.3.1-01.2016

Exercises 4–5

The dot plot for the monthly temperatures in City G is shown below. Use the dot plot and the mean monthly temperature of 63 degrees Fahrenheit to answer the following questions.

City G

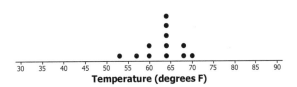

Temperature (degrees F)

4. Fill in the following table for City G's temperature deviations.

Temperature (in degrees Fahrenheit)	Distance (in degrees Fahrenheit) from the Mean of 63°F	Deviation from the Mean (distance and direction)
53	10	10 to the left
57	6	6 to the left
60	3	3 to the left
60	3	3 to the left
64	1	1 to the right
64	1	1 to the right
64	1	1 to the right
64	1	1 to the right
64	1	1 to the right
68	5	5 to the right
68	5	5 to the right
70	7	7 to the right

5. What is the sum of the distances to the left of the mean? What is the sum of the distances to the right of the mean?

    The sum of the distances to the left of the mean is $10 + 6 + 3 + 3 = 22$. The sum of the distances to the right of the mean is $1 + 1 + 1 + 1 + 1 + 5 + 5 + 7 = 22$.

Example 3 (6 minutes): Finding the Mean Absolute Deviation (MAD)

Example 3: Finding the Mean Absolute Deviation (MAD)

Sabina notices that when there is not much variability in a data set, the distances from the mean are small and that when there is a lot of variability in a data set, the data values are spread out and at least some of the distances from the mean are large. She wonders how she can use the distances from the mean to help her develop a formula to measure variability.

©2015 Great Minds eureka-math.org
G6-M6-TE-B3-1.3.1-01.2016

One way to measure variability in a data set is to look at the mean (average) distance of data values from the mean of the data set. To help students understand the name *mean absolute deviation,* define the term **absolute deviation** as distance from the mean. In later grades, students see deviations as signed numbers, and then absolute deviation is just the absolute value of the deviation. Because this is equivalent to distance, in Grade 6, it is appropriate to just define *absolute deviation* as the distance, ignoring the direction.

Introduce the MAD as the mean of the absolute deviations, meaning the mean of the distances. Consider showing a dot plot with little variability, and ask students if the distances from the mean would be large or small and if the average distance would be large or small. Then, show a dot plot with more variability, and ask students if the average distance of data values from the mean would be smaller than or greater than the average for the first dot plot. This helps students understand how average distance from the mean works as a measure of variability.

Exercises 6–7 (9 minutes)

Students continue to work in pairs or small groups. If students have trouble getting started, consider working through Exercise 6 parts (a)–(c) as a class.

Exercises 6–7

6. Use the data on monthly temperatures for City G given in Exercise 4 to answer the following questions.

    a.   Fill in the following table.

Temperature (in degrees Fahrenheit)	Distance from the Mean (absolute deviation)
53	10
57	6
60	3
60	3
64	1
64	1
64	1
64	1
64	1
68	5
68	5
70	7

    b.   The absolute deviation for a data value is its distance from the mean of the data set. For example, for the first temperature value for City G (53 degrees), the absolute deviation is 10. What is the sum of the absolute deviations?

        The sum of the absolute deviations is $10 + 6 + 3 + 3 + 1 + 1 + 1 + 1 + 1 + 5 + 5 + 7 = 44$.

    c.   Sabina suggests that the mean of the absolute deviations (the mean of the distances) could be a measure of the variability in a data set. Its value is the average distance of the data values from the mean of the monthly temperatures. It is called the m*ean absolute deviation* and is denoted by the letters MAD. Find the MAD for this data set of City G's temperatures. Round to the nearest tenth.

        The MAD (mean absolute deviation) is $\frac{44}{12}$, or 3.7 degrees to the nearest tenth of a degree.

©2015 Great Minds eureka-math.org
G6-M6-TE-B3-1.3.1-01.2016

d. Find the MAD values in degrees Fahrenheit for each of the seven city temperature distributions, and use the values to order the distributions from least variability to most variability. Recall that the mean for each data set is 63 degrees Fahrenheit. Looking only at the distributions, does the list that you made in Exercise 2 match the list made by ordering MAD values?

If time is a factor in completing this lesson, assign cities to individual students. After each student has calculated the mean deviation, organize the results for the whole class. Direct students to calculate the MAD to the nearest tenth of a degree.

> MAD values (in °F):
>
> *City A* = 0   *City E* = 10.5   *The order from least to greatest is*
> *City B* = 5.3   *City F* = 10.5   *A, C, G, B, and*
> *City C* = 3.2   *City G* = 3.7   *D, E, and F (all tied).*
> *City D* = 10.5

e. Which of the following is a correct interpretation of the MAD?

 i.   The monthly temperatures in City G are all within 3.7 degrees from the approximate mean of 63 degrees.

 ii. The monthly temperatures in City G are, on average, 3.7 degrees from the approximate mean temperature of 63 degrees.

 iii. All of the monthly temperatures in City G differ from the approximate mean temperature of 63 degrees by 3.7 degrees.

 The answer is (ii). Remind students that the MAD is an average of the distances from the mean, so some distances may be smaller and some larger than the value of the MAD. Point out that the distances from the mean for City G were not all equal to 3.7 and that some were smaller (for example, the distances of 1 and 3) and that some were larger (for example, the distances of 5 and 10).

7. The dot plot for City A's temperatures follows.

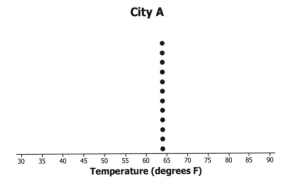

City A

Temperature (degrees F)

a. How much variability is there in City A's temperatures? Why?

There is no variability in City A's temperatures. The absolute deviations (distances from the mean) are all 0.

b. Does the MAD agree with your answer in part (a)?

The MAD does agree with my answer from part (a). The value of the MAD is 0.

Closing (2 minutes)

- How do you calculate the mean absolute deviation (MAD)?
    - *The MAD is computed by finding the sum of the absolute deviations and then dividing the sum by the number of data values.*

Lesson Summary

In this lesson, a formula was developed that measures the amount of variability in a data distribution.

- The absolute deviation of a data point is the distance that data point is from the mean.
- The mean absolute deviation (MAD) is computed by finding the mean of the absolute deviations (distances from the mean) for the data set.
- The value of MAD is the average distance that the data values are from the mean.
- A small MAD indicates that the data distribution has very little variability.
- A large MAD indicates that the data points are spread out and that at least some are far away from the mean.

Exit Ticket (5 minutes)

©2015 Great Minds eureka-math.org
G6-M6-TE-B3-1.3.1-01.2016

Name _____   Date _____

Lesson 9: The Mean Absolute Deviation (MAD)

Exit Ticket

1. The mean absolute deviation (MAD) is a measure of variability for a data set. What does a data distribution look like if its MAD equals zero? Explain.

2. Is it possible to have a negative value for the MAD of a data set?

3. Suppose that seven students have the following numbers of pets: 1, 1, 1, 2, 4, 4, 8.

    a. The mean number of pets for these seven students is 3 pets. Use the following table to find the MAD for this distribution of number of pets.

Student	Number of Pets	Deviation from the Mean (distance and direction)	Absolute Deviation (distance from the mean)
1	1		
2	1		
3	1		
4	2		
5	4		
6	4		
7	8		
Sum			

    b. Explain in words what the MAD means for this data set.

©2015 Great Minds eureka-math.org
G6-M6-TE-B3-1.3.1-01.2016

Exit Ticket Sample Solutions

1. The mean absolute deviation (MAD) is a measure of variability for a data set. What does a data distribution look like if its MAD equals zero? Explain.

   If the MAD is zero, then all of the absolute deviations are zero. The MAD measures the average distance from the mean, and distance is never negative. The only way the MAD could average to zero is if all the absolute deviations are zero. For example, City A had a dot plot where all of the temperatures were the same. Because all of the temperatures were the same, all of the absolute deviations were zero, which indicates that there was no variability in the temperatures.

2. Is it possible to have a negative value for the MAD of a data set?

   Because a MAD is the average of distances, which can never be negative, the MAD is always zero or a positive number.

3. Suppose that seven students have the following numbers of pets: 1, 1, 1, 2, 4, 4, 8.

   a. The mean number of pets for these seven students is 3 pets. Use the following table to find the MAD for this distribution of number of pets.

   $$\frac{14}{7} = 2$$

   The MAD number of pets is 2.

Student	Number of Pets	Deviation from the Mean (distance and direction)	Absolute Deviation (distance from the mean)
1	1	2 to the left	2
2	1	2 to the left	2
3	1	2 to the left	2
4	2	1 to the left	1
5	4	1 to the right	1
6	4	1 to the right	1
7	8	5 to the right	5
Sum			14

   b. Explain in words what the MAD means for this data set.

   On average, the number of pets for these students differs by 2 from the mean of 3 pets.

EUREKA
MATH

©2015 Great Minds eureka-math.org
G6-M6-TE-B3-1.3.1-01.2016

Problem Set Sample Solutions

1. Suppose the dot plot on the left shows the number of goals a boys' soccer team has scored in six games so far this season and the dot plot on the right shows the number of goals a girls' soccer team has scored in six games so far this season. The mean for both of these teams is 3.

    Dot Plot of Number of Goals Scored by Boys' Team   Dot Plot of Number of Goals Scored by Girls' Team

    a. Before doing any calculations, which dot plot has the larger MAD? Explain how you know.

        The graph of the boys' team has a larger MAD because the data are more spread out and have the larger distances from the mean.

    b. Use the following tables to find the MAD for each distribution. Round your calculations to the nearest hundredth.

Boys' Team	
Number of Goals	Absolute Deviation
0	3
0	3
3	0
3	0
5	2
7	4
Sum	12

Girls' Team	
Number of Goals	Absolute Deviation
2	1
2	1
3	0
3	0
3	0
5	2
Sum	4

    The MAD for the boys' team is 2 goals because $\frac{12}{6} = 2$. The MAD for the girls' team is 0.67 goal because $\frac{4}{6} \approx 0.67$.

    c. Based on the computed MAD values, for which distribution is the mean a better indication of a typical value? Explain your answer.

        The mean is a better indicator of a typical value for the girls' team because the measure of variability given by the MAD is lower (0.67 goal) than the boys' MAD (2 goals).

2. Recall Robert's problem of deciding whether to move to New York City or to San Francisco. A table of temperatures (in degrees Fahrenheit) and absolute deviations for New York City follows:

Average Temperature in New York City												
Month	Jan.	Feb.	Mar.	Apr.	May	June	July	Aug.	Sep.	Oct.	Nov.	Dec.
Temperature	39	42	50	61	71	81	85	84	76	65	55	47
Absolute Deviation	24	21	13	2	8	18	22	21	13	2	8	16

a. The absolute deviations for the monthly temperatures are shown in the above table. Use this information to calculate the MAD. Explain what the MAD means in words.

The sum of the absolute deviations is 168. *The MAD is the average of the absolute deviations. The MAD is* 14 *degrees because* $\frac{168}{12} = 14$. *On average, the monthly temperatures in New York City differ from the mean of* 63 *degrees Fahrenheit by* 14 *degrees.*

b. Complete the following table, and then use the values to calculate the MAD for the San Francisco data distribution.

The sum of the absolute deviations is 42. *The MAD is the mean of the absolute deviations. The MAD is* 3.5 *degrees because* $\frac{42}{12} = 3.5$.

Average Temperature in San Francisco												
Month	Jan.	Feb.	Mar.	Apr.	May	June	July	Aug.	Sep.	Oct.	Nov.	Dec.
Temperature	57	60	62	63	64	67	67	68	70	69	63	58
Absolute Deviation	7	4	2	1	0	3	3	4	6	5	1	6

c. Comparing the MAD values for New York City and San Francisco, which city would Robert choose to move to if he is interested in having a lot of variability in monthly temperatures? Explain using the MAD.

New York City has a MAD of 14 *degrees, as compared to* 3.5 *degrees in San Francisco. Robert should choose New York City if he wants to have more variability in monthly temperatures.*

3. Consider the following data of the number of green jelly beans in seven bags sampled from each of five different candy manufacturers (Awesome, Delight, Finest, Sweeties, YumYum). Note that the mean of each distribution is 42 green jelly beans.

	Bag 1	Bag 2	Bag 3	Bag 4	Bag 5	Bag 6	Bag 7
Awesome	40	40	41	42	42	43	46
Delight	22	31	36	42	48	53	62
Finest	26	36	40	43	47	50	52
Sweeties	36	39	42	42	42	44	49
YumYum	33	36	42	42	45	48	48

a. Complete the following table of the absolute deviations for the seven bags for each candy manufacturer.

Absolute Deviations							
	Bag 1	Bag 2	Bag 3	Bag 4	Bag 5	Bag 6	Bag 7
Awesome	2	2	1	0	0	1	4
Delight	20	11	6	0	6	11	20
Finest	16	6	2	1	5	8	10
Sweeties	6	3	0	0	0	2	7
YumYum	9	6	0	0	3	6	6

Lesson 9:   The Mean Absolute Deviation (MAD)

©2015 Great Minds eureka-math.org
G6-M6-TE-B3-1.3.1-01.2016

b. Based on what you learned about MAD, which manufacturer do you think will have the lowest MAD? Calculate the MAD for the manufacturer you selected.

Use the MAD for each manufacturer to evaluate students' responses.

	Bag 1	Bag 2	Bag 3	Bag 4	Bag 5	Bag 6	Bag 7	SUM	MAD
Awesome	2	2	1	0	0	1	4	10	1.4
Delight	20	11	6	0	6	11	20	74	10.6
Finest	16	6	2	1	5	8	10	48	6.9
Sweeties	6	3	0	0	0	2	7	18	2.6
YumYum	9	6	0	0	3	6	6	30	4.3

©2015 Great Minds eureka-math.org
G6-M6-TE-B3-1.3.1-01.2016

Lesson 10: Describing Distributions Using the Mean and MAD

Student Outcomes

- Students calculate the mean and MAD for a data distribution.
- Students use the mean and MAD to describe a data distribution in terms of center and variability.

Lesson Notes

This is the first of two lessons that help students apply what they have learned about the mean and the MAD in order to describe a data distribution. In this lesson, students calculate and then interpret the mean as a measure of center, the MAD as a measure of spread or variability, and use a dot plot to learn about the shape of a data distribution. The next lesson, Lesson 11, is also entitled Describing Distributions Using the Mean and MAD. Lesson 11 challenges students to interpret and compare two data distributions with respect to center, shape, and spread.

Classwork

Example 1 (8 minutes): Describing Distributions

Example 1: Describing Distributions

In Lesson 9, Sabina developed the mean absolute deviation (MAD) as a number that measures variability in a data distribution. Using the mean and MAD along with a dot plot allows you to describe the center, spread, and shape of a data distribution. For example, suppose that data on the number of pets for ten students are shown in the dot plot below.

There are several ways to describe the data distribution. The mean number of pets for these students is 3, which is a measure of center. There is variability in the number of pets the students have, and data values differ from the mean by about 2.2 pets on average (the MAD). The shape of the distribution is heavy on the left, and then it thins out to the right.

Introduce the data set, and explain that distributions can be described by their center, spread, and shape. Note that the mean is 3 pets, and the MAD is 2.2 pets. The shape is described as well.

In the discussion, students need to begin to conceptualize the measures of center and spread. Have them draw a triangle under the 3 on the number line and see that the distribution is balanced at the mean.

©2015 Great Minds eureka-math.org
G6-M6-TE-B3-1.3.1-01.2016

Remind students of the method used to determine the MAD of 2.2 pets.

Find the mean for the data set. For this data set, the mean is 3 pets.

Use the mean to calculate the absolute deviations (the distances from the mean).

Find the mean of the absolute deviations. This value is the MAD. For this data set, the sum of the absolute deviations is 22, and the value of the MAD is 2.2 pets because $\frac{22}{10} = 2.2$.

Exercises 1–4 (10 minutes)

Students work with a partner. Then, discuss and confirm answers to Exercises 1–4.

Exercises 1–4

1. Suppose that the weights of seven middle school students' backpacks are given below.

   a. Fill in the following table.

Student	Alan	Beth	Char	Damon	Elisha	Fred	Georgia
Weight (pounds)	18	18	18	18	18	18	18
Deviation	0	0	0	0	0	0	0
Absolute Deviation	0	0	0	0	0	0	0

   b. Draw a dot plot for these data, and calculate the mean and MAD.

   Weight of Students' Backpacks

   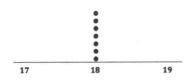

   Weight (in pounds)

   The mean is 18 pounds.

   The MAD is 0 pounds.

   c. Describe this distribution of weights of backpacks by discussing the center, spread, and shape.

   The mean is 18 pounds. There is no variability.

   All of the data values are equal.

2. Suppose that the weight of Elisha's backpack is 17 pounds rather than 18 pounds.

   a. Draw a dot plot for the new distribution.

   Weight of Students' Backpacks

   Weight (in pounds)

©2015 Great Minds eureka-math.org
G6-M6-TE-B3-1.3.1-01.2016

   b.   Without doing any calculations, how is the mean affected by the lighter weight? Would the new mean be the same, smaller, or larger?

   The mean will be smaller because the new weight is smaller than the other weights.

   c.   Without doing any calculations, how is the MAD affected by the lighter weight? Would the new MAD be the same, smaller, or larger?

   The MAD would be larger because now there is variability, so the MAD is greater than zero.

3.   Suppose that in addition to Elisha's backpack weight having changed from 18 to 17 pounds, Fred's backpack weight is changed from 18 to 19 pounds.

   a.   Draw a dot plot for the new distribution.

Weight of Students' Backpacks

Weight (in pounds)

   b.   Without doing any calculations, how would the new mean compare to the original mean?

   The new mean is 18 lb., which was also the original mean.

   c.   Without doing any calculations, would the MAD for the new distribution be the same as, smaller than, or larger than the original MAD?

   Since there is more variability, the MAD is larger than the original MAD.

   d.   Without doing any calculations, how would the MAD for the new distribution compare to the one in Exercise 2?

   There is more variability, so the MAD is greater than the MAD in Exercise 2.

4.   Suppose that seven second graders' backpack weights were as follows:

Student	Alice	Bob	Carol	Damon	Ed	Felipe	Gale
Weight (pounds)	5	5	5	5	5	5	5

   a.   How is the distribution of backpack weights for the second graders similar to the original distribution for the middle school students given in Exercise 1?

   Both have no variability, so the MAD is 0 pounds in both cases. The shapes of the distributions on the dot plots are the same.

   b.   How are the distributions different?

   The means are different. One mean is 18 pounds, and the other is 5 pounds.

©2015 Great Minds eureka-math.org
G6-M6-TE-B3-1.3.1-01.2016

Example 2 (5 minutes): Using the MAD

Read through the example as a class. Note that although the mean provides useful information, it does not give a picture of the *spread* of monthly temperatures for New York City. It is important to consider the center, spread, and shape of distributions when making decisions.

Example 2: Using the MAD

Using data to make decisions often involves comparing distributions. Recall that Robert is trying to decide whether to move to New York City or to San Francisco based on temperature. Comparing the center, spread, and shape for the two temperature distributions could help him decide.

Dot Plot of Temperature for New York City

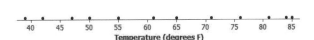

Temperature (degrees F)

Dot Plot of Temperature for San Francisco

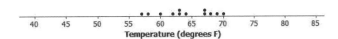

Temperature (degrees F)

From the dot plots, Robert saw that monthly temperatures in New York City were spread fairly evenly from around 40 degrees to around 85 degrees, but in San Francisco, the monthly temperatures did not vary as much. He was surprised that the mean temperature was about the same for both cities. The MAD of 14 degrees for New York City told him that, on average, a month's temperature was 14 degrees away from the mean of 63 degrees. That is a lot of variability, which is consistent with the dot plot. On the other hand, the MAD for San Francisco told him that San Francisco's monthly temperatures differ, on average, only 3.5 degrees from the mean of 64 degrees. So, the mean doesn't help Robert very much in making a decision, but the MAD and dot plot are helpful.

Which city should he choose if he loves warm weather and really dislikes cold weather?

He should choose San Francisco because there is little variability, and it does not get as cold as New York City.

- What measure of the data would justify your decision? Why did you choose that measure?
    - *The mean absolute deviation (MAD) justifies the choice of San Francisco, as it provides a measure of the variability. On average, the monthly temperatures for San Francisco do not vary as much from the mean monthly temperature as the temperatures for New York City.*

Exercises 5–7 (15 minutes)

Students work independently but confirm answers with a neighbor as needed. If time allows, discuss answers as a class. Allow students to use calculators for this exercise. Try to allow time to discuss Exercise 7 because it is the first time students see distributions where both the MADs and the means are the same for all of the distributions. This gets students to consider what the shape of the distribution tells them.

Exercises 5–7

5. Robert wants to compare temperatures for Cities B and C.

	Jan.	Feb.	Mar.	Apr.	May	June	July	Aug.	Sept.	Oct.	Nov.	Dec.
City B	54	54	58	63	63	68	72	72	72	63	63	54
City C	54	44	54	61	63	72	78	85	78	59	54	54

a. Draw a dot plot of the monthly temperatures for each of the cities.

City B

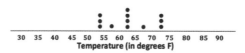

City C

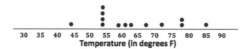

b. Verify that the mean monthly temperature for each distribution is 63 degrees.

The data are nearly symmetrical around 63 degrees for City B. The sum of the distances to the left of the mean is equal to the sum of the distances to the right of the mean. Each of these sums is equal to 32 degrees.

For City C, the sum of the distances to the left of the mean is equal to the sum of the distances to the right of the mean. Each sum is equal to 61.

c. Find the MAD for each of the cities. Interpret the two MADs in words, and compare their values. Round your answers to the nearest tenth of a degree.

The MAD is 5.3 degrees for City B, which means that, on average, the monthly temperatures differ by 5.3 degrees from the mean of 63 degrees.

The MAD is 10.2 degrees for City C, which means that, on average, the monthly temperatures differ by 10.2 degrees from the mean of 63 degrees.

6. How would you describe the differences in the shapes of the monthly temperature distributions of the two cities?

The temperatures are nearly symmetric around the mean in City B. The temperatures are compact to the left of the mean for City C and then spread out to the right (skewed right).

©2015 Great Minds eureka-math.org
G6-M6-TE-B3-1.3.1-01.2016

7. Suppose that Robert had to decide between Cities D, E, and F.

	Jan.	Feb.	Mar.	Apr.	May	June	July	Aug.	Sept.	Oct.	Nov.	Dec.	Mean	MAD
City D	54	44	54	59	63	72	78	87	78	59	54	54	63	10.5
City E	56	56	56	56	56	84	84	84	56	56	56	56	63	10.5
City F	42	42	70	70	70	70	70	70	70	70	70	42	63	10.5

a. Draw a dot plot for each distribution.

City D

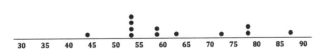

Temperature (in degrees F)

City E

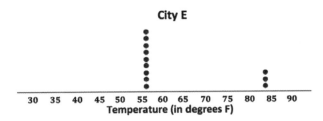

Temperature (in degrees F)

City F

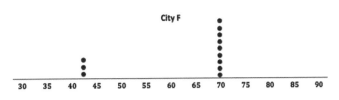

Temperature (in degrees F)

b. Interpret the MAD for the distributions. What does this mean about variability?

The MADs are all the same, so the monthly temperatures differ, on average, 10.5 degrees from the mean of 63 degrees. This means that all of the distributions have the same amount of variability.

c. How will Robert decide to which city he should move? List possible reasons Robert might have for choosing each city.

Robert needs to look more at the shapes of the distributions to help him make a decision.

City D—Appears to have four seasons with widespread temperatures.

City E—Has mainly cold weather and is only hot for 3 months.

City F—Has mainly moderate weather and only a few cold months.

Closing (2 minutes)

- How are the mean and the mean absolute deviation (MAD) related?
    - *The MAD represents the average distance each data value is away from the mean.*

Lesson Summary

A data distribution can be described in terms of its center, spread, and shape.

- The center can be measured by the mean.
- The spread can be measured by the mean absolute deviation (MAD).
- A dot plot shows the shape of the distribution.

Exit Ticket (5 minutes)

©2015 Great Minds eureka-math.org
G6-M6-TE-B3-1.3.1-01.2016

Name _____   Date _____

Lesson 10: Describing Distributions Using the Mean and MAD

Exit Ticket

1. A dot plot of times that five students studied for a test is displayed below.

Studying for a Test

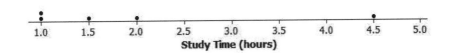

Study Time (hours)

a. Calculate the mean number of hours that these five students studied. Then, use the mean to calculate the absolute deviations, and complete the table.

Student	Aria	Ben	Chloe	Dellan	Emma
Number of Study Hours	1	1	1.5	2	4.5
Absolute Deviation					

b. Find and interpret the MAD for this data set.

2. The same five students are preparing to take a second test. Suppose that the numbers of study hours were the same except that Ben studied 2.5 hours for the second test (1.5 hours more), and Emma studied only 3 hours for the second test (1.5 hours less).

a. Without doing any calculations, is the mean for the second test the same as, greater than, or less than the mean for the first test? Explain your reasoning.

b. Without doing any calculations, is the MAD for the second test the same as, greater than, or less than the MAD for the first test? Explain your reasoning.

©2015 Great Minds eureka-math.org
G6-M6-TE-B3-1.3.1-01.2016

Exit Ticket Sample Solutions

1. A dot plot of times that five students studied for a test is displayed below.

    Studying for a Test

    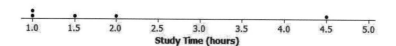

    Study Time (hours)

    a. Calculate the mean number of hours that these five students studied. Then, use the mean to calculate the absolute deviations, and complete the table.

    The mean is 2 hours since the sums of the distances on either side of 2 hours are equal.

Student	Aria	Ben	Chloe	Dellan	Emma
Number of Study Hours	1	1	1.5	2	4.5
Absolute Deviation	1	1	0.5	0	2.5

    b. Find and interpret the MAD for this data set.

    $$\frac{5}{5} = 1.$$

    The MAD is 1 hour. This means that, on average, the study times differed by 1 hour from the group mean of 2 hours.

2. The same five students are preparing to take a second test. Suppose that the numbers of study hours were the same except that Ben studied 2.5 hours for the second test (1.5 hours more), and Emma studied only 3 hours for the second test (1.5 hours less).

    a. Without doing any calculations, is the mean for the second test the same as, greater than, or less than the mean for the first test? Explain your reasoning.

    The mean would be the same since the distance that one data value moved to the right was matched by the distance another data value moved to the left. The distribution is still balanced at the same place.

    b. Without doing any calculations, is the MAD for the second test the same as, greater than, or less than the MAD for the first test? Explain your reasoning.

    The MAD would be smaller since the data values are clustered closer to the mean.

©2015 Great Minds eureka-math.org
G6-M6-TE-B3-1.3.1-01.2016

Problem Set Sample Solutions

1. Draw a dot plot of the times that five students studied for a test if the mean time they studied was 2 hours and the MAD was 0 hours.

    Since the MAD is 0 hours, all data values are all the same, and they would be equal to the mean value.

    Studying For a Test

    Time (in hours)

2. Suppose the times that five students studied for a test are as follows:

Student	Aria	Ben	Chloe	Dellan	Emma
Time (hours)	1.5	2	2	2.5	2

    Michelle said that the MAD for this data set is 0 hours because the dot plot is balanced around 2. Without doing any calculations, do you agree with Michelle? Why or why not?

    No. Michelle is wrong. There is variability within the data set, so the MAD is greater than 0 hours.

    Note: If students agree with Michelle, then they have not yet mastered an understanding that the MAD is measuring variability. They need to understand that if data values differ in a distribution, whether the distribution is symmetric or not, then there is variability. Therefore, the MAD cannot be 0 hours.

3. Suppose that the number of text messages eight students receive on a typical day is as follows:

Student	1	2	3	4	5	6	7	8
Number of Text Messages	42	56	35	70	56	50	65	50

    a. Draw a dot plot for the number of text messages received on a typical day for these eight students.

    Text Messages on a Typical Day

    Number of Text Messages

    b. Find the mean number of text messages these eight students receive on a typical day.

    Since the distribution appears to be somewhat symmetrical around a value in the 50's, students could guess a value for the mean, such as 52 or 53, and then check the sum of the distances on either side of their predictions. Using the formula, the mean is 53 text messages because $\frac{424}{8} = 53$.

EUREKA MATH™

©2015 Great Minds eureka-math.org
G6-M6-TE-B3-1.3.1-01.2016

c. Find the MAD for the number of text messages, and explain its meaning using the words of this problem.

The sum of the absolute deviations is 70. *So,* $\frac{70}{8}$ *yields a MAD of* 8.75 *text messages.*

This means that, on average, the number of text messages these eight students receive on a typical day differs by 8.75 *text messages from the group mean of* 53 *text messages.*

d. Describe the shape of this data distribution.

The shape of this distribution is fairly symmetrical (balanced) around the mean of 53 *messages.*

e. Suppose that in the original data set, Student 3 receives an additional five text messages per day and Student 4 receives five fewer text messages per day.

i. Without doing any calculations, does the mean for the new data set stay the same, increase, or decrease as compared to the original mean? Explain your reasoning.

The mean would remain at 53 *messages because one data value moved the same number of units to the right as another data value moved to the left. So, the balance point of the distribution does not change.*

ii. Without doing any calculations, does the MAD for the new data set stay the same, increase, or decrease as compared to the original MAD? Explain your reasoning.

Since the lowest data point moved closer to the mean and the highest data point moved closer to the mean, the resulting distribution would be more compact than the original distribution. Therefore, the MAD would decrease.

EUREKA MATH

©2015 Great Minds eureka-math.org
G6-M6-TE-B3-1.3.1-01.2016

Lesson 11: Describing Distributions Using the Mean and MAD

Student Outcomes

- Students use the mean and MAD to describe a data distribution in terms of center and variability.
- Students use the mean and MAD to describe similarities and differences between two distributions.

Lesson Notes

This lesson is similar to Lesson 10 and focuses on describing distributions in terms of center and variability using the mean and the MAD. Students compare two data distributions and comment on similarities and differences in shape, center, and variability.

Classwork

Example 1 (5 minutes): Comparing Distributions with the Same Mean

Example 1: Comparing Distributions with the Same Mean

In Lesson 10, a data distribution was characterized mainly by its center (mean) and variability (MAD). How these measures help us make a decision often depends on the context of the situation. For example, suppose that two classes of students took the same test, and their grades (based on 100 points) are shown in the following dot plots. The mean score for each distribution is 79 points. Would you rather be in Class A or Class B if you had a score of 79?

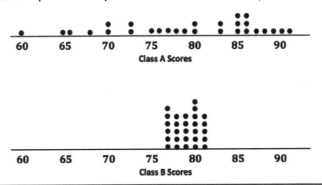

MP.6

In Lesson 10, a data distribution was characterized mainly by its center (mean) and variability (MAD). How these measures help students make a decision often depends on the context of the situation. This example shows two distributions of test scores with the same mean, 79, but clearly very different variability. Students need to be able to explain their reasoning in making decisions in a way that considers both center and variability.

- In which class would you rather be if you scored a 79? Explain your reasoning.
  - *Answers may vary.*
  - *I would rather be in Class A because 79 is in the middle of the distribution, and there are some students who scored a lot lower than 79.*
  - *I would rather be in Class B because every student in the class has a score close to 79, and no one scored much higher than 79.*
- How would you describe the variability of the data?
  - *Class A has a lot of variability, but Class B doesn't have much variability because the scores are all clustered around the mean.*

Exercises 1–3 (5 minutes)

Students work independently. Then, discuss and confirm answers as a class.

Exercises 1–6

1. Looking at the dot plots, which class has the greater MAD? Explain without actually calculating the MAD.

   Class A. The data for Class A have a much wider spread. Thus, it has greater variability and a larger MAD.

2. If Liz had one of the highest scores in her class, in which class would she rather be? Explain your reasoning.

   She would rather be in Class A. This class had higher scores in the 90's, whereas Class B had a high score of only 81.

3. If Logan scored below average, in which class would he rather be? Explain your reasoning.

   Logan would rather be in Class B. The low scores in Class B were in the 70's, whereas Class A had low scores in the 60's.

Exercises 4–6 (11 minutes)

Students work in pairs. Discuss answers to Exercises 5–6 as a class.

Your little brother asks you to replace the battery in his favorite remote control car. The car is constructed so that it is difficult to replace its battery. Your research of the lifetimes (in hours) of two different battery brands (A and B) shows the following lifetimes for 20 batteries from each brand:

A	12	14	14	15	16	17	17	18	19	20	21	21	23	23	24	24	24	25	26	27
B	18	18	19	19	19	19	19	19	20	20	20	20	20	21	21	21	21	22	22	22

---

4. To help you decide which battery to purchase, start by drawing a dot plot of the lifetimes for each brand.

Batteries

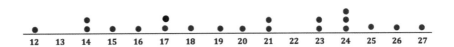

Brand A Time (in hours)

Batteries

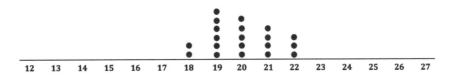

Brand B Time (in hours)

5. Find the mean battery lifetime for each brand, and compare them.

   The mean of Brand A is 20 hours.

   The mean of Brand B is 20 hours.

   Both Brand A and Brand B have the same mean lifetime.

6. Looking at the variability in the dot plot for each data set, give one reason you might choose Brand A. What is one reason you might choose Brand B? Explain your reasoning.

   Answers will vary.

   If I choose Brand A, I might get a battery that lasts a lot longer than 20 hours, or I might get a battery that has a much shorter lifetime. If I choose Brand B, I would always get a battery that lasts approximately 20 hours.

Example 2 (6 minutes): Comparing Distributions with Different Means

Remind students of the pairs of distributions from Example 1 and Exercises 1–6 that had the same means and how variability played a role in making decisions.

Then, answer the question posed in the text.

Example 2: Comparing Distributions with Different Means

You have been comparing distributions that have the same mean but different variability. As you have seen, deciding whether large variability or small variability is best depends on the context and on what is being asked. If two data distributions have different means, do you think that variability will still play a part in making decisions?

Yes, because considering variability in addition to center provides us with more information about the distributions and allows us to make more informed decisions.

It is especially important for students to use the same scale when they are making graphical displays in order to compare two data distributions. If two dot plots are drawn using very different scales, it is difficult to compare variability, and what may appear to be differing amounts of spread may not be that different at all. When comparing distributions, encourage students to draw dot plots using a scale that covers the span of both distributions whenever possible.

Exercises 7–9 (11 minutes)

Students continue to work in pairs to complete Exercises 7–9. Then, confirm answers to Exercises 8 and 9 as a class. Calculators are needed for this exercise.

Exercises 7–9

Suppose that you wanted to answer the following question: Are field crickets better predictors of air temperature than katydids? Both species of insect make chirping sounds by rubbing their front wings together.

The following data are the number of chirps (per minute) for 10 insects of each type. All the data were taken on the same evening at the same time.

Insect	1	2	3	4	5	6	7	8	9	10
Crickets	35	32	35	37	34	34	38	35	36	34
Katydids	66	62	61	64	63	62	68	64	66	64

7. Draw dot plots for these two data distributions using the same scale, going from 30 to 70. Visually, what conclusions can you draw from the dot plots?

Crickets

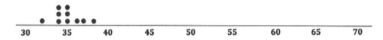

Number of Chirps

Katydids

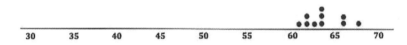

Number of Chirps

Visually, you can see that the value for the mean number of chirps is higher for the katydids. The variability looks to be similar.

Lesson 11:   Describing Distributions Using the Mean and MAD

©2015 Great Minds eureka-math.org
G6-M6-TE-B3-1.3.1-01.2016

8. Calculate the mean and MAD for each distribution.

Crickets: The mean is 35 chirps per minute.

The sum of all the distances from the mean is 12 because $0 + 3 + 0 + 2 + 1 + 1 + 3 + 0 + 1 + 1 = 12$. Therefore, the MAD is 1.2 chirps per minute because $\frac{12}{10} = 1.2$.

Katydids: The mean is 64 chirps per minute.

The sum of all the distances from the mean is 16 because $2 + 2 + 3 + 0 + 1 + 2 + 4 + 0 + 2 + 0 = 16$. Therefore, the MAD is 1.6 chirps per minute because $\frac{16}{10} = 1.6$.

9. The outside temperature T, in degrees Fahrenheit, can be predicted by using two different formulas. The formulas include the mean number of chirps per minute made by crickets or katydids.

    a. For crickets, T is predicted by adding 40 to the mean number of chirps per minute. What value of T is being predicted by the crickets?

    The predicted temperature is $35 + 40$, or 75 degrees.

    b. For katydids, T is predicted by adding 161 to the mean number of chirps per minute and then dividing the sum by 3. What value of T is being predicted by the katydids?

    The predicted temperature is $\frac{(64+161)}{3}$, or 75 degrees.

    c. The temperature was 75 degrees Fahrenheit when these data were recorded, so using the mean from each data set gave an accurate prediction of temperature. If you were going to use the number of chirps from a single cricket or a single katydid to predict the temperature, would you use a cricket or a katydid? Explain how variability in the distributions of number of chirps played a role in your decision.

    The crickets had a smaller MAD. This indicates that an individual cricket is more likely to have a number of chirps that is close to the mean.

Closing (2 minutes)

- How are the means and mean absolute deviations (MADs) helpful when comparing data distributions?

  □ *The means and MADs are helpful when comparing data distributions because they describe the centers and the variability in the distributions.*

Exit Ticket (5 minutes)

©2015 Great Minds eureka-math.org
G6-M6-TE-B3-1.3.1-01.2016

Name _____   Date _____

Lesson 11: Describing Distributions Using the Mean and MAD

Exit Ticket

You need to decide which of two brands of chocolate chip cookies to buy. You really love chocolate chip cookies. The numbers of chocolate chips in each of five cookies from each brand are as follows:

Cookie	1	2	3	4	5
ChocFull	17	19	18	18	18
AllChoc	22	15	14	21	18

a. Draw a dot plot for each set of data that shows the distribution of the number of chips for that brand. Use the same scale for both of your dot plots (one that covers the span of both distributions).

b. Find the mean number of chocolate chips for each of the two brands. Compare the means.

c. Looking at your dot plots and considering variability, which brand do you prefer? Explain your reasoning.

EUREKA MATH

©2015 Great Minds eureka-math.org
G6-M6-TE-B3-1.3.1-01.2016

Exit Ticket Sample Solutions

You need to decide which of two brands of chocolate chip cookies to buy. You really love chocolate chip cookies. The numbers of chocolate chips in each of five cookies from each brand are as follows:

Cookie	1	2	3	4	5
ChocFull	17	19	18	18	18
AllChoc	22	15	14	21	18

a. Draw a dot plot for each set of data that shows the distribution of the number of chips for that brand. Use the same scale for both of your dot plots (one that covers the span of both distributions).

ChocFull

Number of Chips

AllChoc

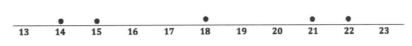

Number of Chips

b. Find the mean number of chocolate chips for each of the two brands. Compare the means.

Mean for ChocFull: 18 chocolate chips

Mean for AllChoc: 18 chocolate chips

The means for the two different brands are the same.

c. Looking at your dot plots and considering variability, which brand do you prefer? Explain your reasoning.

Students could argue either way:

- *Students who prefer ChocFull may argue that they are assured of getting 18 chips most of the time, with no fewer than 17 chips, and a bonus once in a while of 19 chips. With AllChoc, they may sometimes get more than 20 chips but would sometimes get only 14 or 15 chips.*

- *Students who prefer AllChoc are the risk takers who are willing to tolerate the chance of getting only 14 or 15 chips for the chance of getting 21 or 22 chips.*

©2015 Great Minds eureka-math.org
G6-M6-TE-B3-1.3.1-01.2016

Problem Set Sample Solutions

1. Two classes took the same mathematics test. Summary measures for the two classes are as follows:

	Mean	MAD
Class A	78	2
Class B	78	10

a. Suppose that you received the highest score in your class. Would your score have been higher if you were in Class A or Class B? Explain your reasoning.

My score would have been higher if I had been in Class B because the means are the same, and the variability, as measured by the MAD, is higher in that class than it is in Class A.

b. Suppose that your score was below the mean score. In which class would you prefer to have been? Explain your reasoning.

I would prefer to have been in Class A because the variability, as measured by the MAD, indicates a more compact distribution around the mean. In contrast, a score below the mean in Class B could be far lower than in Class A.

2. Eight of each of two varieties of tomato plants, LoveEm and Wonderful, are grown under the same conditions. The numbers of tomatoes produced from each plant of each variety are shown:

Plant	1	2	3	4	5	6	7	8
LoveEm	27	29	27	28	31	27	28	27
Wonderful	31	20	25	50	32	25	22	51

a. Draw dot plots to help you decide which variety is more productive.

LoveEm

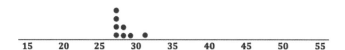

Number of Tomatoes

Wonderful

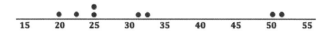

Number of Tomatoes

EUREKA MATH™

©2015 Great Minds eureka-math.org
G6-M6-TE-B3-1.3.1-01.2016

b. Calculate the mean number of tomatoes produced for each variety. Which one produces more tomatoes on average?

The mean number of LoveEm tomatoes is 28, and the mean number of Wonderful tomatoes is 32. Wonderful produces more tomatoes on average.

c. If you want to be able to accurately predict the number of tomatoes a plant is going to produce, which variety should you choose—the one with the smaller MAD or the one with the larger MAD? Explain your reasoning.

LoveEm produces fewer tomatoes on average but is far more consistent. Looking at the dot plots, its variability is far less than that of Wonderful tomatoes. Based on these data sets, choosing LoveEm should yield numbers in the high 20's consistently, but the number from Wonderful could vary wildly from lower yields in the low 20's to huge yields around 50.

d. Calculate the MAD of each plant variety.

The sum of the distances from the mean for LoveEm is 8 because $1 + 1 + 1 + 0 + 3 + 1 + 0 + 1 = 8$. Therefore, the MAD for LoveEm is 1 tomato because $\frac{8}{8} = 1$.

The sum of the distances from the mean for Wonderful is 74 because $1 + 12 + 7 + 18 + 0 + 7 + 10 + 19 = 74$. Therefore, the MAD for Wonderful is 9.25 tomatoes because $\frac{74}{8} = 9.25$.

©2015 Great Minds eureka-math.org
G6-M6-TE-B3-1.3.1-01.2016

Name _____   Date _____

1. For each of the following, identify whether or not it would be a valid *statistical question* you could ask about people at your school. Explain for each why it is, or is not, a statistical question.

   a. What are a typical number of hours of television watched by students at your school last night?

   b. What is the school principal's favorite television program?

   c. Do most students at your school tend to watch at least one hour of television on the weekend?

   d. What is the recommended amount of television specified by the American Pediatric Association?

©2015 Great Minds eureka-math.org
G6-M6-TE-B3-1.3.1-01.2016

2. In 2013, there were nine judges serving on the Supreme Court of the United States. The following table lists how long (the number of years) each judge had served on the court as of 2013.

Judge	Length of Service
Antonin Scalia	27
Anthony Kennedy	25
Clarence Thomas	22
Ruth Bader Ginsburg	20
Stephen Breyer	19
John Roberts	8
Samuel Alito	7
Sonia Sotomayor	4
Elena Kagan	3

a. Calculate the mean length of service for these nine judges. Show your work.

b. Calculate the mean absolute deviation (MAD) of the lengths of service for these nine judges. Show your work.

c. Explain why the mean may not be the best way to summarize a typical length of service for these nine judges.

©2015 Great Minds eureka-math.org
G6-M6-TE-B3-1.3.1-01.2016

3. The following table displays data on calories for several Chinese foods (from Center for Science in the Public Interest, tabulated by the *Philadelphia Inquirer*).

Dish	Dish Size	Calories	Dish	Dish Size	Calories
Egg Roll	1 roll	190	House Lo Mein	5 cups	1,059
Moo Shu Pork	4 pancakes	1,228	House Fried Rice	4 cups	1,484
Kung Pao Chicken	5 cups	1,620	Chicken Chow Mein	5 cups	1,005
Sweet and Sour Pork	4 cups	1,613	Hunan Tofu	4 cups	907
Beef with Broccoli	4 cups	1,175	Shrimp in Garlic Sauce	3 cups	945
General Tso's Chicken	5 cups	1,597	Stir-Fried Vegetables	4 cups	746
Orange (crispy) Beef	4 cups	1,766	Szechuan Shrimp	4 cups	927
Hot and Sour Soup	1 cup	112			

a. Round the Calories values to the nearest 100 calories, and use these rounded values to produce a dot plot of the distribution of the calories in these dishes.

b. Describe the distribution of the calories in these dishes.

c. Suppose you wanted to report data on calories per cup for different Chinese foods. What would be the calories per cup for Kung Pao chicken?

Module 6:   Statistics

EUREKA MATH

©2015 Great Minds eureka-math.org
G6-M6-TE-B3-1.3.1-01.2016

d. Could you calculate calories per cup for all of the foods listed in the table? Explain why or why not.

e. If you wanted to compare the healthiness of these foods in terms of calories, would you compare the calorie amounts or the calories per cup? Explain your choice.

4. A father wanted some pieces of wood that were 10 inches long for a building project with his son. He asked the hardware store to cut some longer pieces of wood into 10-inch pieces. However, he noticed that not all of the pieces given to him were the same length. He then took the cut pieces of wood home and measured the length (in inches) of each piece. The table below summarizes the lengths that he found.

Length (inches)	8.50– < 8.75	8.75– < 9.00	9.00– < 9.25	9.25– < 9.50	9.50– < 9.75	9.75– < 10.00	10.00– < 10.25	10.25– < 10.50	10.50– < 10.75	12.00– < 12.25
Frequency	1	2	2	4	3	2	5	6	1	1

a. Create a histogram for these data.

b. Describe the shape of the histogram you created.

©2015 Great Minds eureka-math.org
G6-M6-TE-B3-1.3.1-01.2016

c. The father wanted to know whether the mean length was equal to 10 inches or if the wood cutter cut pieces that tended to be too long or tended to be too short. Without calculating the mean length, explain based on the histogram whether the mean board length should be equal to 10 inches, greater than 10 inches, or less than 10 inches. Explain what strategy you used to determine this.

d. Based on the histogram, should the mean absolute deviation (MAD) be larger than 0.25 inch or smaller than 0.25 inch? Explain how you made this decision.

e. Suppose this project was repeated at two different stores and the following two dot plots of board lengths were found. Would you have a preference for one store over the other store? If so, which store would you prefer, and why? Justify your answer based on the displayed distributions.

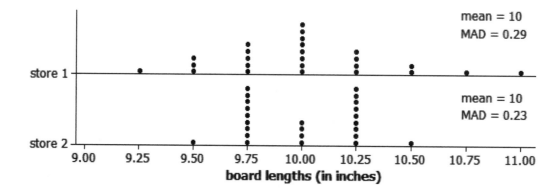

EUREKA
MATH™

©2015 Great Minds eureka-math.org
G6-M6-TE-B3-1.3.1-01.2016

5. Suppose you are timing how long it takes a car to race down a wood track placed at a forty-five degree angle. The times for five races are recorded. The mean time for the five races is 2.75 seconds.

   a. What is the total time for the five races (the times of the five races summed together)?

   b. Suppose you learn that the timer malfunctioned on one of the five races. The result of the race had been reported to be 3.6 seconds. If you remove that time from the list and recompute the mean for the remaining four times, what do you get for the mean? Show your work.

©2015 Great Minds eureka-math.org
G6-M6-TE-B3-1.3.1-01.2016

A Progression Toward Mastery					
Assessment Task Item		STEP 1 Missing or incorrect answer and little evidence of reasoning or application of mathematics to solve the problem.	STEP 2 Missing or incorrect answer but evidence of some reasoning or application of mathematics to solve the problem.	STEP 3 A correct answer with some evidence of reasoning or application of mathematics to solve the problem, OR an incorrect answer with substantial evidence of solid reasoning or application of mathematics to solve the problem.	STEP 4 A correct answer supported by substantial evidence of solid reasoning or application of mathematics to solve the problem.
1	a 6.SP.A.1	Student simply provides a numerical response to the question.	Student incorrectly identifies this as an invalid question. OR Student identifies this as a valid question but with an incorrect justification.	Student identifies this as a valid question but does not give a complete justification that distinguishes it from other questions (e.g., "We can record this.").	Student identifies this as a valid question and justifies the choice based on the variability in the answers (amount watched last night) among students at the school.
	b 6.SP.A.1	Student only provides a guess for the answer to the question.	Student incorrectly identifies this as a valid question. OR Student identifies this as an invalid question with an incorrect justification.	Student identifies this as an invalid question but fails to give a clear explanation (e.g., "There is just one answer.").	Student identifies this as an invalid question and justifies the choice by the lack of variation in the responses for students at the school.
	c 6.SP.A.1	Student simply provides a yes/no response to the question.	Student identifies this as an invalid question with an incorrect justification.	Student identifies this as a valid question but fails to give a clear explanation. OR Student identifies this as an invalid question assuming that every student at the school would have the same answer.	Student identifies this as a valid question and justifies the choice based on the variability in the answers (whether or not students watch at least one hour on the weekend) among students at the school.

Module 6:   Statistics

©2015 Great Minds eureka-math.org
G6-M6-TE-B3-1.3.1-01.2016

	d **6.SP.A.1**	Student simply provides a numerical response to the question.	Student identifies this as a valid question with an incorrect justification.	Student identifies this as an invalid question but fails to give a clear explanation. OR Student identifies this as a valid question assuming that every student at the school would respond with different guesses.	Student identifies this as an invalid question and justifies the choice based on the lack of ability to gather data from the students to address the question.
2	**a** **6.SP.B.5c**	Student does not provide a sensible answer (e.g., outside 3–27).	Student makes a major calculation error such as reporting the median.	Student correctly calculates the mean but does not show work or has a minor, but traceable, calculation error.	Student calculates 15 years.
	b **6.SP.B.5c**	Student does not provide a sensible answer (e.g., greater than 12).	Student demonstrates understanding of measuring spread but not of deviation.	Student calculates deviations from the mean but does not combine them correctly.	Student calculates 8.44 years.
	c **6.SP.B.5d**	Student response confirms the mean as a measure of the center of a distribution.	Student discusses the disadvantages of mean in general but does not relate to context (e.g., not best with skewed data).	Student discusses the possibility of the mean being thrown off by outliers but does not address the bimodal shape of this distribution.	Student comments that there are two clusters of data, one below 15 and one above 15, but that there are no judges with length of service right around 15.
3	**a** **6.SP.B.4**	Student fails to create a graph displaying the distribution of calories.	Student produces a graph other than a dot plot for the calories data.	Student produces a graph that is poorly labeled or poorly scaled, or student makes major errors in rounding.	Student correctly rounds the values to the nearest 100 (or makes a minor error) and constructs, scales, and labels a dot plot.
	b **6.SP.B.5**	Student does not provide a reasonable description of the graph constructed.	Student only addresses one aspect (e.g., center) of describing the distribution.	Student comments on numerous features of the distribution but does not describe the distribution as a whole in terms of tendency and variability.	Student comments on the shape, center, and variability of the distribution. The distribution is not very symmetric, the center is around 1,000 calories, and the dishes range from about 200 to 1,766 calories.

©2015 Great Minds eureka-math.org
G6-M6-TE-B3-1.3.1-01.2016

	c **6.SP.B.5b**	Student fails to correctly perform the calculation.	Student reports the cup/calorie value.	Student gives the value but has a minor calculation error or does not show the work.	Student reports 324 calories/cup.
	d **6.SP.B.5b**	Student does not attempt the question.	Student says yes without considering all the dishes.	Student recognizes the need to have a common scale among the dishes but does not notice the two dishes without cup sizes.	Student recognizes that we do not have "per cup" results for every food item. (The egg roll and moo shu pork are not clearly single servings as the other food items are.)
	e **6.SP.B.5b**	Student does not understand the goal of comparing the calorie amounts across these different dishes.	Student relates comments to the context but relies on external information rather than the information presented in the table.	Student recognizes that the comparisons should be made on an equivalent scale but does not specifically answer the question.	Student selects the calories per cup as a more reasonable way to compare across the different-sized dishes. Student could select calories with an assumption that the original values corresponded to equivalent serving sizes.
4	**a** **6.SP.B.4**	Student fails to use the provided information to construct a histogram.	Student produces a type of dot plot or box plot from the data.	Student produces a histogram but does not scale the x-axis appropriately (e.g., does not leave a gap between 10.75 and 12).	Student produces a complete and correctly labeled (i.e., lengths) histogram using all 10 frequencies.
	b **6.SP.A.2**	Student does not address the shape of the distribution.	Student provides a description of the shape that is not consistent with the graph.	Student describes the distribution in detail but does not use accepted language to efficiently describe the shape.	Student provides a description of the shape that is consistent with the constructed graph. This may or may not include separate comments on outliers.
	c **6.SP.B.5c**	Student provides a response that does not relate to the center of the distribution.	Student only attempts to calculate the mean and ignores the tallies.	Student only attempts to calculate the mean using tallied information but does not arrive at a reasonable answer. OR Student provides an explanation that only applies to determining the location of the median.	Student uses the tallied information and/or histogram and the idea of balancing to conclude that the mean is less than 10 inches.

EUREKA
MATH

©2015 Great Minds eureka-math.org
G6-M6-TE-B3-1.3.1-01.2016

	d **6.SP.B.5c**	Student provides a response that does not relate to the spread of the distribution.	Student only attempts to calculate the MAD and ignores the tallies. OR Student confuses the MAD with the bin widths of the histogram.	Student only attempts to calculate the MAD using the tallied information but does not arrive at a reasonable answer. OR Student provides an explanation that only applies to determining the value of the MAD.	Student uses the tallied information and/or histogram and the idea of balancing deviations to draw a consistent conclusion about the value of the MAD (for the mean identified in part (c)). Student may notice that 0.25 is too small, as it would only encompass about 5 of the 27 values; some values are much farther out.
	e **6.SP.A.3**	Student does not use information from the graph to address the question.	Student only justifies the choice based on Store 1 having more values at 10.00.	Student provides an explanation that is not consistent with the choice but attempts to make use of the dot plot, mean, and MAD information.	Student provides justification that relates to the dot plots and the mean and MAD values. Student may prefer the store with a smaller MAD or the store with all but two values between 9.75 and 10.25.
5	**a** **6.SP.B.5c**	Student does not use the information provided to address the question.	Student does not recognize the relationship between the mean and total time.	Student makes a minor calculation error.	Student provides the total time of 13.75 seconds.
	b **6.SP.B.5c**	Student is unable to begin the problem.	Student makes a calculation error and arrives at a nonsensical answer.	Student makes a minor calculation error, but the answer is still reasonable (between 2.5 seconds and 2.7 seconds).	Student provides the correct mean as 2.54 seconds.

©2015 Great Minds eureka-math.org
G6-M6-TE-B3-1.3.1-01.2016

Name _____   Date _____

1. For each of the following, identify whether or not it would be a valid *statistical question* you could ask about people at your school. Explain for each why it is, or is not, a statistical question.

    a. What are a typical number of hours of television watched by students at your school last night?

    > This is a statistical question because
    > the number of TV hours will vary from
    > student to student.

    b. What is the school principal's favorite television program?

    > This is not a statistical question because
    > there is just one principal at the school and
    > the answer each student would get is the same.

    c. Do most students at your school tend to watch at least one hour of television on the weekend?

    > This is a statistical question because
    > some students will have watched at least
    > one hour and some will not.
    > (Answers will vary).

    d. What is the recommended amount of television specified by the American Pediatric Association?

    > This is not a statistical question because
    > we would not ask different students at
    > the school this question. There is only
    > one answer.

©2015 Great Minds eureka-math.org
G6-M6-TE-B3-1.3.1-01.2016

EUREKA
MATH™

2. In 2013, there were nine judges serving on the Supreme Court of the United States. The following table lists how long (the number of years) each judge had served on the court as of 2013.

Judge	Length of Service
Antonin Scalia	27
Anthony Kennedy	25
Clarence Thomas	22
Ruth Bader Ginsburg	20
Stephen Breyer	19
John Roberts	8
Samuel Alito	7
Sonia Sotomayor	4
Elena Kagan	3

a. Calculate the mean length of service for these nine judges. Show your work.

$$27 + 25 + 22 + 20 + 19 + 8 + 7 + 4 + 3 = 135$$

$$\frac{135}{9} = 15 \quad \text{The mean length of service is 15 years.}$$

b. Calculate the mean absolute deviation (MAD) of the lengths of service for these nine judges. Show your work.

$$27 - 15 = 12 \qquad 20 - 15 = 5 \qquad 15 - 7 = 8$$
$$25 - 15 = 10 \qquad 19 - 15 = 4 \qquad 15 - 4 = 11$$
$$22 - 15 = 7 \qquad 15 - 8 = 7 \qquad 15 - 3 = 12$$

$$12 + 10 + 7 + 5 + 4 + 7 + 8 + 11 + 12 = 76$$

$$\frac{76}{9} \approx 8.44 \quad \text{The MAD of the lengths of service is 8.44 inches.}$$

c. Explain why the mean may not be the best way to summarize a typical length of service for these nine judges.

There are no judges around 15 years. In fact, we have two clumps of judges. One clump is 3-8 years and the other is 19-27 years. Giving one center is not useful here.

©2015 Great Minds eureka-math.org
G6-M6-TE-B3-1.3.1-01.2016

3. The following table displays data on calories for several Chinese foods (from Center for Science in the Public Interest, tabulated by the *Philadelphia Inquirer*).

Dish	Dish Size	Calories	Dish	Dish Size	Calories
Egg Roll	1 roll	190 *200*	House Lo Mein	5 cups	1,059 *1,100*
Moo Shu Pork	4 pancakes	1228 *1,200*	House Fried Rice	4 cups	1484 *1,500*
Kung Pao Chicken	5 cups	1,620 *1,600*	Chicken Chow Mein	5 cups	1,005 *1,000*
Sweet and Sour Pork	4 cups	1,613 *1,600*	Hunan Tofu	4 cups	907 *900*
Beef with Broccoli	4 cups	1,175 *1,200*	Shrimp in Garlic Sauce	3 cups	945 *900*
General Tso's Chicken	5 cups	1,597 *1,600*	Stir-fried Vegetables	4 cups	746 *700*
Orange (crispy) Beef	4 cups	1,766 *1,800*	Szechuan Shrimp	4 cups	927 *900*
Hot and Sour Soup	1 cup	112 *100*			

a. Round the Calories values to the nearest 100 calories, and use these rounded values to produce a dot plot of the distribution of the calories in these dishes.

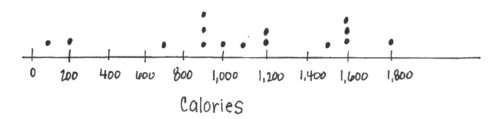

b. Describe the distribution of the calories in these dishes.

A typical number of calories is around 900 calories with several dishes around 1,600 calories, as well. There is a lot of variability in the number of calories from 112 to 1,766. Two dishes have a lot fewer calories than the rest.

c. Suppose you wanted to report data on calories per cup for different Chinese foods. What would be the calories per cup for Kung Pao chicken?

$$\frac{1,620}{5}\ \frac{\text{calories}}{\text{cup}} = 324\ \frac{\text{calories}}{\text{cup}}$$

©2015 Great Minds eureka-math.org
G6-M6-TE-B3-1.3.1-01.2016

EUREKA MATH

d. Could you calculate calories per cup for all of the foods listed in the table? Explain why or why not.

No. We do not have "cups" for egg rolls and Mu Shu Pork.

e. If you wanted to compare the healthiness of these foods in terms of calories, would you compare the calorie amounts or the calories per cup? Explain your choice.

Calories per cup seems more fair because the number of cups vary across the dishes.

4. A father wanted some pieces of wood that were 10 inches long for a building project with his son. He asked the hardware store to cut some longer pieces of wood into 10-inch pieces. However, he noticed that not all of the pieces given to him were the same length. He then took the cut pieces of wood home and measured the length (in inches) of each piece. The table below summarizes the lengths that he found.

Length (inches)	8.50– < 8.75	8.75– < 9.00	9.00– < 9.25	9.25– < 9.50	9.50– < 9.75	9.75– < 10.00	10.00– < 10.25	10.25– < 10.50	10.50– < 10.75	12.00– < 12.25
Frequency	1	2	2	4	3	2	5	6	1	1

a. Create a histogram for these data.

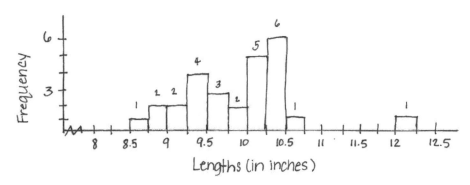

b. Describe the shape of the histogram you created.

The histogram is skewed right.

©2015 Great Minds eureka-math.org
G6-M6-TE-B3-1.3.1-01.2016

c. The father wanted to know whether the mean length was equal to 10 inches or if the wood cutter cut pieces that tended to be too long or tended to be too short. Without calculating the mean length, explain based on the histogram whether the mean board length should be equal to 10 inches, greater than 10 inches, or less than 10 inches. Explain what strategy you used to determine this.

> I think the mean would be less than 10 inches.
> There are more observations below 10 inches (14)
> than above 10 inches (13). Most of the lengths
> below 10 inches are more spread out and less
> than 10 inches.

d. Based on the histogram, should the mean absolute deviation (MAD) be larger than 0.25 inch or smaller than 0.25 inch? Explain how you made this decision.

> Too many data values are more than 0.25
> inches from the mean, so the MAD is
> greater than 0.25 inches.

e. Suppose this project was repeated at two different stores and the following two dot plots of board lengths were found. Would you have a preference for one store over the other store? If so, which store would you prefer, and why? Justify your answer based on the displayed distributions.

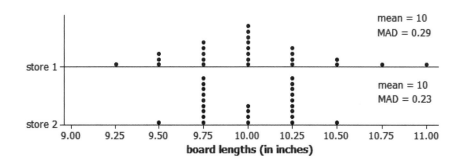

> I prefer the second store. All but 2 boards
> are within 0.25 inches of 10 inches. Some of
> the boards in the top graph are very far from
> 10 inches.

EUREKA MATH™

©2015 Great Minds eureka-math.org
G6-M6-TE-B3-1.3.1-01.2016

5. Suppose you are timing how long it takes a car to race down a wood track placed at a forty-five degree angle. The times for five races are recorded. The mean time for the five races is 2.75 seconds.

    a. What is the total time for the five races (the times of the five races summed together)?

    $$\text{mean} = \frac{\text{total}}{5}, \text{ so the total} = 5 \times \text{mean}$$
    $$= 5 \times 2.75 \text{ seconds}$$
    $$= 13.75 \text{ seconds}$$

    b. Suppose you learn that the timer malfunctioned on one of the five races. The result of the race had been reported to be 3.6 seconds. If you remove that time from the list and recompute the mean for the remaining four times, what do you get for the mean? Show your work.

    $$13.75 \text{ seconds} - 3.6 \text{ seconds} = 10.15 \text{ seconds}$$
    $$10.15 \text{ seconds} \div 4 \approx 2.54 \text{ seconds}$$

©2015 Great Minds eureka-math.org
G6-M6-TE-B3-1.3.1-01.2016

Mathematics Curriculum

6
GRADE

Topic C

Summarizing a Distribution That Is Skewed Using the Median and the Interquartile Range

6.SP.A.2, 6.SP.A.3, 6.SP.B.4, 6.SP.B.5

Focus Standards:	6.SP.A.2	Understand that a set of data collected to answer a statistical question has a distribution, which can be described by its center, spread, and overall shape.
	6.SP.A.3	Recognize that a measure of center for a numerical data set summarizes all of its values with a single number, while a measure of variation describes how its values vary with a single number.
	6.SP.B.4	Display numerical data in plots on a number line, including dot plots, histograms, and box plots.
	6.SP.B.5	Summarize numerical data sets in relation to their context, such as by:
		a. Reporting the number of observations.
		b. Describing the nature of the attribute under investigation, including how it was measured and its units of measurement.
		c. Giving quantitative measures of center (median and/or mean) and variability (interquartile range and/or mean absolute deviation), as well as describing any overall pattern and any striking deviations from the overall pattern with reference to the context in which the data were gathered.
		d. Relating the choice of measures of center and variability to the shape of the data distribution and the context in which the data were gathered.

©2015 Great Minds eureka-math.org
G6-M6-TE-B3-1.3.1-01.2016

Instructional Days:	5
Lesson 12:	Describing the Center of a Distribution Using the Median (P)[1]
Lesson 13:	Describing Variability Using the Interquartile Range (IQR) (P)
Lesson 14:	Summarizing a Distribution Using a Box Plot (P)
Lesson 15:	More Practice with Box Plots (P)
Lesson 16:	Understanding Box Plots (P)

In Topic C, students are introduced to a measure of center (the median) and a measure of variability (the interquartile range, IQR) that are appropriate for describing data distributions that are skewed. Box plots are also introduced in this topic. In Lesson 12, students learn to calculate and interpret the median. Quartiles are introduced in Lesson 13, and the quartiles are then used to calculate the IQR. Students also learn to interpret the IQR as a measure of variability in a data distribution. Lessons 14–16 introduce box plots. Box plots are often difficult for students to interpret because they are not a graph of a data distribution (as are dot plots and histograms); rather, they are a graph of five key summary statistics of a data set (the minimum, lower quartile, median, upper quartile, and the maximum). In Lesson 16, students use box plots to compare groups, setting the stage for future work on comparing groups in Grade 7.

---

[1]Lesson Structure Key: **P**-Problem Set Lesson, **M**-Modeling Cycle Lesson, **E**-Exploration Lesson, **S**-Socratic Lesson

©2015 Great Minds eureka-math.org
G6-M6-TE-B3-1.3.1-01.2016

Lesson 12: Describing the Center of a Distribution Using the Median

Student Outcomes

- Given a data set, students determine the median of the data.

Lesson Notes

The focus of this lesson is on using the median as a summary statistic to describe a data set. Students find the value of the median for data sets with an odd number of observations and for data sets with an even number of observations. Informally, they consider the variability among three different data sets to assess a claim about typical behavior. In preparation for a later lesson on finding quartiles, students calculate the median of the values below the median and the median of the values above the median. This lesson provides the background needed for the development of a box plot.

In this lesson, students construct arguments and critique the reasoning of others. They respond to the reasoning of others in some of the tasks, distinguish correct reasoning from flawed reasoning, and explain why incorrect reasoning is flawed. They also model with mathematics, apply mathematics to problems from everyday life, and interpret results in the context of the situation.

It should be noted that students should have access to calculators throughout this module.

Classwork

Students read the following paragraph silently.

> How do we summarize a data distribution? What provides us with a good description of the data? The following exercises help us to understand how a numerical summary provides an answer to these questions.

Example 1 (5 minutes): The Median—A Typical Number

The activity begins with a set of data represented as a dot plot. The concept of median is then developed by having students consider a sequence of questions. Once the concept has been developed, the median is formally defined. Begin by introducing the data presented in the example.

> **Example 1: The Median—A Typical Number**
>
> Suppose a chain restaurant (Restaurant A) advertises that a typical number of french fries in a large bag is 82. The dot plot shows the number of french fries in a sample of twenty large bags from Restaurant A.
>
>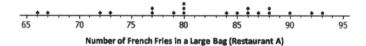
>
> Number of French Fries in a Large Bag (Restaurant A)

©2015 Great Minds eureka-math.org
G6-M6-TE-B3-1.3.1-01.2016

- What could the restaurant mean when they say that the typical number of french fries in a large bag is 82?

  - *Answers will vary, but students may suggest that the mean is about 82.*

- Locate 82 on the dot plot. What do you notice about the number of data values that are above 82 and the number of data values that are below 82?

  - *There are the same number of data values on either side of 82—ten data values are greater than 82, and 10 data values are less than 82.*

- The restaurant used a summary measure called the *median* to describe the typical number of french fries. The median represents the middle value in a data set when the data values are arranged in order from smallest to largest. The same number of values will be above the median as are below the median.

> Sometimes it is useful to know what point separates a data distribution into two equal parts, where one part represents the upper half of the data values and the other part represents the lower half of the data values. This point is called the *median*. When the data are arranged in order from smallest to largest, the same number of values will be above the median point as below the median.

Exercises 1–3 (4 minutes)

Students work independently on the exercises and confirm answers with a neighbor.

> **Exercises 1–3**
>
> 1. You just bought a large bag of fries from the restaurant. Do you think you have exactly 82 french fries? Why or why not?
>
>   *The number of fries in a bag seems to vary greatly from bag to bag. No bag had exactly 82 fries, so mine probably will not. The bags that were in the sample had from 66 to 93 french fries.*
>
> 2. How many bags were in the sample?
>
>   *20 bags were part of the sample.*
>
> 3. Which of the following statement(s) would seem to be true for the given data? Explain your reasoning.
>   a. Half of the bags had more than 82 fries in them.
>   b. Half of the bags had fewer than 82 fries in them.
>   c. More than half of the bags had more than 82 fries in them.
>   d. More than half of the bags had fewer than 82 fries in them.
>   e. If you got a random bag of fries, you could get as many as 93 fries.
>
>   *Statements (a) and (b) are true because there are 10 bags above 82 fries and 10 bags below 82 fries. Also, statement (e) is true because that happened once, so it could probably happen again.*

Examples 2–4 (8 minutes)

As a class, work through the examples one at a time.

Example 2

Examine the dot plot below.

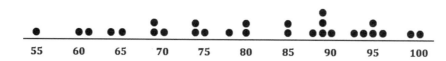

Grades on a Science Test

a. How many data values are represented on the dot plot above?

There are 28 data values on the dot plot.

b. How many data values should be located above the median? How many below the median? Explain.

There should be 14 data values above the median and 14 data values below the median because the median represents the middle value in a sorted data set.

c. For this data set, 14 values are 80 or smaller, and 14 values are 85 or larger, so the median should be between 80 and 85. When the median falls between two values in a data set, we use the average of the two middle values. For this example, the two middle values are 80 and 85. What is the median of the data presented on the dot plot?

The median of the dot plot is 82.5.

Students may need help determining the median when there are an even number of data values. If needed, guide them through the process with the discussion below.

- What is the middle data value?

  □ *The median score must have 14 scores above and 14 scores below. If you start counting from the smallest score, you find that the 14th score is 80, so 14 scores are 80 or less. The next score is 85, and there are 14 scores that are 85 or greater. This means that the median must be between 80 and 85.*

- What would you suggest as a score to represent the median? Explain your answer.

  □ *Answers will vary. Students may select the value that is the middle of the interval from 80 to 85, or they may say that any number in this interval could be the median. Indicate that the usual thing to do when there are an even number of observations is to define the median to be the mean (average) of the middle two values. In this example, the middle two values are 80 and 85:*

$$\frac{80 + 85}{2} = \frac{165}{2} = 82.5$$

©2015 Great Minds eureka-math.org
G6-M6-TE-B3-1.3.1-01.2016

d.   **What does this information tell us about the data?**

The median tells us half of the students in the class scored below an 82.5 on the science test, and the other half of the students scored above an 82.5 on the science test.

Example 3

Use the information from the dot plot in Example 2.

a.   **What percentage of students scored higher than the median? Lower than the median?**

50% of the students scored higher than the median, and 50% of the students scored lower than the median.

b.   **Suppose the teacher made a mistake, and the student who scored a 65 actually scored a 71. Would the median change? Why or why not?**

The median would not change because there would still be 14 scores below 82.5 and 14 scores above 82.5.

c.   **Suppose the student who scored a 65 actually scored an 89. Would the median change? Why or why not?**

The median would change because now there would be 13 scores below 82.5 and 15 scores above 82.5, so 82.5 would not be the median.

Example 4

A grocery store usually has three checkout lines open on Saturday afternoons. One Saturday afternoon, the store manager decided to count how many customers were waiting to check out at 10 different times. She calculated the median of her ten data values to be 8 customers.

a.   **Why might the median be an important number for the store manager to consider?**

Answers will vary. For example, students might point out that this means that half the time there were more than 8 customers waiting to check out. If there are only 3 checkout lines open, there would be a lot of people waiting to check out. She might want to consider having more checkout lines open on Saturday afternoons.

b.   **Give another example of when the median of a data set might provide useful information. Explain your thinking.**

Answers will vary.

Possible responses: When the data are about how much time students spend doing homework, it would be interesting to know the amount of time that more than half of the students spend on homework. If you are looking at the number of points earned in a competition, it would be good to know what number separates the top half of the competitors from the bottom half.

■   How do you find the median if there are an odd number of data points?

▫   *Put the data values in order from smallest to largest, or construct a dot plot of the data.*

▫   *Find the middle number in the ordered list or on the dot plot. One way to do this is to divide the number of observations by 2 and then round up to get an integer. This identifies the position of the median. For example, if there are 15 observations, dividing by 2 gives us 7.5 , which rounds up to 8. Then, starting with the smallest observation, count up to find the 8th number in the ordered list. This number is the median.*

©2015 Great Minds eureka-math.org
G6-M6-TE-B3-1.3.1-01.2016

- How do you find the median if there are an even number of data points?

  - *Put the data values in order from smallest to largest, or construct a dot plot of the data.*

  - *Find the middle two numbers in the ordered list or on the dot plot. One way to do this is to divide the number of observations by 2. This identifies the position of the first of the two middle numbers. For example, if there are 18 observations, dividing by 2 gives us 9 observations. Then, starting with the smallest observation, count up to find the 9th number in the ordered list. This number and the next number in the list are the two middle values.*

  - *Find the mean of the two middle values. This number is the median.*

Exercises 4–5 (10 minutes): A Skewed Distribution

In this set of exercises, students have to put the data in order from smallest to largest before they find the median. There are 19 values, so the median is the 10th value with 9 data values above and 9 data values below. Another way to determine the median after ordering the data is to cross out the maximum and minimum values, then the next largest and smallest values, and so on until students are left with just one number in the middle if there are an odd number of data values, or two numbers if there are an even number of data values. If this process results in a single number, that number is the median. If this process results in two numbers in the middle, students would then find the mean of the two values to get the value of the median.

MP.3

The questions are designed to help students confront some common misconceptions and errors: not ordering the data before counting to the middle, confusing median and mode (most frequent value), and confusing median and midrange (halfway between the maximum and the minimum). They also compute the mean and compare the median to the mean, noting that the median might be more reflective of a typical value because several bags with low numbers of french fries pulled the mean down.

Consider the following questions as students are completing the exercises:

- Why is it necessary to order the data before you find the median?

  - *In order to find the value that has half of the data values smaller and half of the data values larger, the data values must first be put in order.*

- Is the median connected to the range (maximum − minimum) of the data? Why or why not?

  - *The median is not connected to the range because it is possible for the range to change while the median stays the same.*

- What is the difference in the effect of a few very extreme values on the mean and on the median?

  - *Extreme values will have a big effect on the mean but will not affect the median.*

Exercises 4–5: A Skewed Distribution

4. The owner of the chain decided to check the number of french fries at another restaurant in the chain. Here are the data for Restaurant B: 82, 83, 83, 79, 85, 82, 78, 76, 76, 75, 78, 74, 70, 60, 82, 82, 83, 83, 83

    a. How many bags of fries were counted?

        19 bags of fries were counted.

Lesson 12:   Describing the Center of Distribution Using the Median

©2015 Great Minds eureka-math.org
G6-M6-TE-B3-1.3.1-01.2016

b. Sallee claims the median is 75 because she sees that 75 is the middle number in the data set listed on the previous page. She thinks half of the bags had fewer than 75 fries because there are 9 data values that come before 75 in the list, and there are 9 data values that come after 75 in the list. Do you think she would change her mind if the data were plotted in a dot plot? Why or why not?

Yes. You cannot find the median unless the data are organized from least to greatest. Plotting the number of fries in each bag on a dot plot would order the data correctly. You would probably get a different halfway point because the data above are not ordered from least to greatest.

> **Scaffolding:**
> If students are struggling, allow them to determine the median before answering the questions.

c. Jake said the median was 83. What would you say to Jake?

83 is the most common number of fries in the bags (5 bags had 83 fries), but it is not in the middle of the data.

d. Betse argued that the median was halfway between 60 and 85, or 72.5. Do you think she is right? Why or why not?

She is wrong because the median is not calculated from the distance between the largest and smallest values in the data set. This is not the same as finding a point that separates the ordered data into two parts with the same number of values in each part.

e. Chris thought the median was 82. Do you agree? Why or why not?

Chris is correct because if you order the numbers, the middle number will be the 10th number in the ordered list, with at most 9 bags that have more than 82 fries and at most 9 bags that have fewer than 82 fries.

5. Calculate the mean, and compare it to the median. What do you observe about the two values? If the mean and median are both measures of center, why do you think one of them is smaller than the other?

The mean is 78.6, and the median is 82. The bag with only 60 fries decreased the value of the mean.

Exercises 6–8 (10 minutes): Finding Medians from Frequency Tables

MP.4 In these exercises, students find the median using data summarized in a frequency table. The median falls halfway between the 13th and 14th data value when the data are ordered from smallest to largest. They also find the medians of the top and bottom halves of the data set, the 7th value from the top and from the bottom, as a precursor to finding quartiles and the interquartile range in a later lesson. Consider having students write out the individual counts in a long ordered list. For example, the first 13 counts would be as follows:

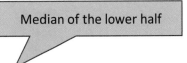

75 75 76 77 77 78 **78** 78 79 79 79 79 79 ...

©2015 Great Minds eureka-math.org
G6-M6-TE-B3-1.3.1-01.2016

In these exercises, students need to deal with repeated data values when finding the median. In this case, have students find the median by counting from the top and bottom of the list, noting that values for bags with the same count can fall on both sides of the median. It might help to think about the individual bags: One of the bags with 78 fries is in the first half, one of the bags with 78 fries is in the second half, and one of the bags divides the two halves and marks the median of the data set. At this point, the important idea is that students get a sense of how to find a median: Order the values, and find a middle value in the ordered list of data values.

Exercises 6–8: Finding Medians from Frequency Tables

6. A third restaurant (Restaurant C) tallied the number of fries for a sample of bags of french fries and found the results below.

Number of Fries	Frequency
75	II
76	I
77	II
78	III
79	++++
80	IIII
81	I
82	I
83	
84	III
85	III
86	I

Scaffolding:

If students are struggling, encourage them to list out the values in a numerical list or to create a dot plot from the frequency table.

a. How many bags of fries did they count?

They counted 26 bags of fries.

b. What is the median number of fries for the sample of bags from this restaurant? Describe how you found your answer.

79.5; I took half of 26, which is 13, and then counted 13 tallies from 86 to reach 80. I also counted 13 tallies from 75 to reach 79. The point halfway between 79 and 80 is the median.

7. Robere wanted to look more closely at the data for bags of fries that contained a smaller number of fries and bags that contained a larger number of fries. He decided to divide the data into two parts. He first found the median of the whole data set and then divided the data set into the bottom half (the values in the ordered list that are before the median) and the top half (the values in the ordered list that are after the median).

a. List the 13 values in the bottom half. Find the median of these 13 values.

75   75   76   77   77   78   78   78   79   79   79   79   79

The median of the lower half is 78.

b. List the 13 values of the top half. Find the median of these 13 values.

80   80   80   80   81   82   84   84   84   85   85   85   86

The median of the top half is 84.

©2015 Great Minds eureka-math.org
G6-M6-TE-B3-1.3.1-01.2016

8. Which of the three restaurants seems most likely to really have 82 fries in a typical bag? Explain your thinking.

   Answers will vary. The data sets for Restaurants A and B both have a median of 82. Look for answers that consider how much the data values vary around 82. Restaurant B seems to have the most bags closest to a count of 82. The data set for Restaurant C has a median of 79.5, but the data values are not very spread out, and most are close to 82, so some students might make a case for Restaurant C.

Closing (3 minutes)

- Does the median have to be a value in the data set?

  □ *The median does not have to be a value in the data set.*

- Is calculating the median the same as calculating the middle of the range? Explain.

  □ *The median is not the same as calculating the middle of the range. Finding the point that is halfway between the largest and the smallest data value is not the same as finding a value that will have half of the data values above and half of the data values below. For example, think about the data set consisting of $1, 2, 3, 4, 19$. The median is 3, but halfway between the largest and smallest data values is 10.*

> **Lesson Summary**
>
> The <u>median</u> is the middle value (or the mean of the two middle values) in a data set that has been ordered from smallest to largest. The median separates the data into two parts with the same number of data values below the median as above the median in the ordered list. To find a median, you first have to order the data. For an even number of data values, you find the average of the two middle numbers. For an odd number of data values, you use the middle value.

Exit Ticket (5 minutes)

©2015 Great Minds eureka-math.org
G6-M6-TE-B3-1.3.1-01.2016

Name _____   Date_____

Lesson 12: Describing the Center of a Distribution Using the Median

Exit Ticket

1. What is the median age for the following data set representing the ages of students requesting tickets for a summer band concert? Explain your reasoning.

    13 14 15 15 16 16 17 18 18

2. What is the median number of diseased trees from a data set representing the numbers of diseased trees on each of 12 city blocks? Explain your reasoning.

    11 3 3 4 6 12 9 3 8 8 8 1

3. Describe how you would find the median for a set of data that has 35 values. How would this be different if there were 36 values?

©2015 Great Minds eureka-math.org
G6-M6-TE-B3-1.3.1-01.2016

EUREKA
MATH

Exit Ticket Sample Solutions

1. What is the median age for the following data set representing the ages of students requesting tickets for a summer band concert? Explain your reasoning.

    13 14 15 15 16 16 17 18 18

    The median is the 5th value in the ordered list, or 16 years, as there are 4 values less than 16 and 4 values greater than or equal to 16 (excluding the 5th value).

2. What is the median number of diseased trees from a data set representing the numbers of diseased trees on each of 12 city blocks? Explain your reasoning.

    11 3 3 4 6 12 9 3 8 8 8 1

    To find the median, the values first need to be ordered: 1 3 3 3 4 6 8 8 8 9 11 12.

    Because there are an even number of data values, the median would be the mean of the 6th and 7th values: $\frac{6+8}{2}$, *or 7 diseased trees.*

3. Describe how you would find the median for a set of data that has 35 values. How would this be different if there were 36 values?

    Answers will vary. First, you would order the data from least to greatest. Because there are 35 values, you would look for the 18th value from the top or bottom in the ordered list. This would be the median with 17 values above and 17 values below. If the set had 36 values, you would find the average of the middle two data values, which would be the average of the 18th and the 19th values in the ordered list.

Problem Set Sample Solutions

1. The amount of precipitation in each of the western states in the United States is given in the table as well as the dot plot.

State	Amount of Precipitation (inches)
WA	38.4
OR	27.4
CA	22.2
MT	15.3
ID	18.9
WY	12.9
NV	9.5
UT	12.2
CO	15.9
AZ	13.6
NM	14.6
AK	58.3
HI	63.7

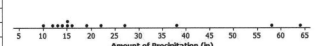

Amount of Precipitation (in)

Source: http://www.currentresults.com/Weather/US/average-annual-state-precipitation.php

   a.   How do the amounts vary across the states?

Answers will vary. The spread is pretty large: 54.2 inches. Nevada has the lowest precipitation at 9.5 inches per year. Hawaii, Alaska, and Washington have more rain than most of the states. Hawaii has the most precipitation with 63.7 inches, followed by Alaska at 58.3 inches.

   b.   Find the median. What does the median tell you about the amount of precipitation?

The median is 15.9 inches. Half of the western states have more than 15.9 inches of precipitation per year, and half have less.

   c.   Do you think the mean or median would be a better description of the typical amount of precipitation? Explain your thinking.

The mean at 24.8 inches reflects the extreme values, while the median seems more typical at 15.9 inches.

2.   Identify the following as true or false. If a statement is false, give an example showing why.

   a.   The median is always equal to one of the values in the data set.

False. If the middle two values in the ordered data set are 1 and 5, the median is 3, and 3 is not in the set.

   b.   The median is halfway between the least and greatest values in the data set.

False. For example, looking at the number of french fries per bag for Restaurant A in Example 1, the median is 82, which is not halfway between 66 and 93 (79.5).

   c.   At most, half of the values in a data set have values less than the median.

True

   d.   In a data set with 25 different values, if you change the two smallest values in the data set to smaller values, the median will not be changed.

True

   e.   If you add 10 to every value in a data set, the median will not change.

False. The median will increase by 10 as well. If the data set is 1, 2, 3, 4 , 5, the median is 3. For the data set 11, 12, 13, 14, 15, the median is 13.

3.   Make up a data set such that the following is true:

   a.   The data set has 11 different values, and the median is 5.

Answers will vary. If the numbers are whole numbers, the set would be 0, 1, 2, 3, 4, 5, 6, 7, 8, 9, 10.

   b.   The data set has 10 values, and the median is 25.

Answers will vary. One answer is to have ten values that are all 25's.

   c.   The data set has 7 values, and the median is the same as the least value.

Answers will vary. One answer is to have 1, 1, 1, 1, 2, 3, 4.

    Lesson 12:   Describing the Center of Distribution Using the Median

©2015 Great Minds eureka-math.org
G6-M6-TE-B3-1.3.1-01.2016

4. The dot plot shows the number of landline phones that a sample of people have in their homes.

Number of Phones

a. How many people were in the sample?

There are 25 people in the sample.

b. Why do you think three people have no landline phones in their homes?

Possible answers: Some people might only have cell phones, or some people may not be able to afford a phone or may not want a phone.

c. Find the median number of phones for the people in the sample.

The median number of phones per home is 2.

5. The salaries of the Los Angeles Lakers for the 2012–2013 basketball season are given below. The salaries in the table are ordered from largest to smallest.

Player	Salary
Kobe Bryant	$27,849,149
Dwight Howard	$19,536,360
Pau Gasol	$19,000,000
Steve Nash	$8,700,000
Metta World Peace	$7,258,960
Steve Blake	$4,000,000
Jordan Hill	$3,563,600
Chris Duhon	$3,500,000
Jodie Meeks	$1,500,000
Earl Clark	$1,240,000
Devin Ebanks	$1,054,389
Darius Morris	$962,195
Antawn Jamison	$854,389
Robert Sacre	$473,604
Darius Johnson-Odom	$203,371

Source: www.basketball-reference.com/contracts/LAL.html

Teacher Note: Students may struggle a bit with Problems 5 and 6 because the numerical values are quite large. If this presents a challenge for students, these two problems could be done as part of a class discussion. The points being made in these two problems (how the mean can be affected by extreme values in a data set and the difference between how the mean and the median are affected by extreme values) are important, so it is worth taking time to make sure students see these problems.

a. Just looking at the data, what do you notice about the salaries?

Possible answer: A few of the salaries for the big stars like Kobe Bryant are really big, while others are very small in comparison.

b. Find the median salary, and explain what it tells you about the salaries.

The median salary is $3,500,000 for Chris Duhon. Half of the players make more than $3,500,000, and half of the players make less than $3,500,000.

c. Find the median of the lower half of the salaries and the median of the upper half of the salaries.

$962,195 *is the median for the bottom half of the salaries.* $8,700,000 *is the median for the top half of the salaries.*

d. Find the width of each of the following intervals. What do you notice about the size of the interval widths, and what does that tell you about the salaries?

i. Minimum salary to the median of the lower half: $758,824

ii. Median of the lower half to the median of the whole data set: $2,537,805

iii. Median of the whole data set to the median of the upper half: $5,200,000

iv. Median of the upper half to the highest salary: $19,149,149

The largest width is from the median of the upper half to the highest salary. The smaller salaries are closer together than the larger ones.

6. Use the salary table from the previous page to answer the following.

a. If you were to find the mean salary, how do you think it would compare to the median? Explain your reasoning.

Possible answer: The mean will be a lot larger than the median because when you add in the really big salaries, the size of the mean will increase a lot.

b. Which measure do you think would give a better picture of a typical salary for the Lakers, the mean or the median? Explain your thinking.

Possible answer: The median seems better, as it is more typical of most of the salaries.

Lesson 13: Describing Variability Using the Interquartile

Range (IQR)

Student Outcomes

- Given a set of data, students describe how the data might have been collected.
- Students describe the unit of measurement for observations in a data set.
- Students calculate the median of the data and describe the variability in the data by calculating the interquartile range.

Lesson Notes

Students develop understanding of statistical variability, in particular recognizing that a measure of center for a numerical data set summarizes all of its values with a single number, while a measure of variation describes how the values in the data set vary.

Students are also expected to summarize numerical data sets in relation to their context. This is done by reporting the number of observations and describing the nature of the attribute under investigation. Students indicate how data were measured and the units of measurement. They provide a quantitative measure of center (median) and of variability (interquartile range), as well as describing any overall pattern and any striking deviations from the overall pattern with reference to the context in which the data were gathered.

In this lesson, students are engaged in making sense of problems and solving them (MP.1). As the contexts change, they are asked to pay attention to the units for each (MP.6). They are also engaged in working in groups, sharing their reasoning and critiquing the reasoning of others as they create contexts that satisfy given constraints (MP.3).

Classwork

Students read the paragraph silently.

> In Lesson 12, the median was used to describe a typical value for a data set. But the values in a data set vary around the median. What is a good way to indicate how the data vary when we use a median as an indication of a typical value? These questions are explored in the following exercises.

Exercises 1–4 (13 minutes): More French Fries

 These exercises return to the data from Lesson 12, raising questions about how the data might have been collected and whether any bias (the formal word is not used) might be inherent in the process. Students examine work from Lesson 12 where they found medians of the lower half and upper half of a data set and use these medians to calculate the interquartile range (IQR).

These exercises build an understanding of quartiles. Quartiles divide a data set into quarters, with 25% of the data falling below the lower quartile, 25% falling between the lower quartile and the median (which is sometimes called the *middle quartile*), 25% falling between the median and the upper quartile, and 25% falling above the upper quartile. The upper quartile is found by finding the median of the top half of the data set, and the lower quartile is found by finding the median of the bottom half of the data set. This is why students began looking at medians of the top and bottom halves in Lesson 12. The upper and lower quartiles are then used to compute the interquartile range (IQR), which is a measure of variability in a data set. Students should be able to approximate the number of elements in each section in terms of $\frac{1}{4}$, or 25%, of the data or by giving an estimate of the actual number of data values as well as knowing that $\frac{1}{2}$, or 50%, of the data values are between the lower and upper quartiles. They should also recognize that the IQR is a measure of spread around the median (it is the length of the interval that captures the middle 50% of the data).

Consider the following question while discussing the exercise questions with students:

- What measures of center and spread have you studied, and how do you think they would compare to the median and IQR?

    □ *We have also examined the mean and MAD. They are similar to the median and IQR because they also describe the center and variability of the data.*

This question provides students an opportunity to discuss what they might recall about the mean as a measure of center and the MAD as a measure of variability.

Data from Lesson 12: Number of french fries

Restaurant A: 80, 72, 77, 80, 90, 85, 93, 79, 84, 73, 87, 67, 80, 86, 92, 88, 86, 88, 66, 77

Restaurant B: 82, 83, 83, 79, 85, 82, 78, 76, 76, 75, 78, 74, 70, 60, 82, 82, 83, 83, 83

Restaurant C: 75, 75, 76, 77, 85, 85, 80, 80, 80, 80, 81, 82, 84, 84, 84, 85, 77, 86, 78, 78, 78, 79, 79, 79, 79, 79

Students work in small groups to complete the following exercises.

Exercises 1–4: More French Fries

1. In Lesson 12, you thought about the claim made by a chain restaurant that the typical number of french fries in a large bag was 82. Then, you looked at data on the number of fries in a bag from three of the restaurants.

    a. How do you think the data were collected, and what problems might have come up in collecting the data?

    Answers will vary. They probably went to the restaurants and ordered a bunch of large bags of french fries. Sometimes the fries are broken, so they might have to figure out what to do with those—either count them as a whole, discard them, or put them together to make whole fries.

    b. What scenario(s) would give counts that might not be representative of typical bags?

    Answers will vary. Different workers might put different amounts in a bag, so if you bought the bags at lunch, you might have different numbers than if you did it in the evening. The restaurants might weigh the bags to see that the weight was constant despite the size of the fries, so you could have the same weight of fries even though you had different counts for the bags.

©2015 Great Minds eureka-math.org
G6-M6-TE-B3-1.3.1-01.2016

2. The medians of the top half and the medians of the bottom half of the data for each of the three restaurants are as follows: Restaurant A—87.5 and 77; Restaurant B—83 and 76; Restaurant C—84 and 78. The difference between the medians of the two halves is called the *interquartile range,* or IQR.

   a. What is the IQR for each of the three restaurants?

   The IQR for Restaurant A is $87.5 - 77 = 10.5$; Restaurant B is $83 - 76 = 7$; Restaurant C is $84 - 78 = 6$.

   b. Which of the restaurants had the smallest IQR, and what does that tell you?

   Restaurant C had the smallest IQR. This indicates that the spread around the median number of fries is smaller than for either of the other two restaurants. About half of the data are within a range of 6 fries and near the median, so the median is a pretty good description of what is typical.

   c. The median of the bottom half of the data is called the *lower quartile* (denoted by Q1), and the median of the top half of the data is called the *upper quartile* (denoted by Q3). About what fraction of the data would be between the lower and upper quartiles? Explain your thinking.

   About $\frac{1}{2}$, or 50%, of the counts would be between the quartiles because about $\frac{1}{4}$ of the counts are between the median and the lower quartile, and $\frac{1}{4}$ of the counts are between the median and the upper quartile.

3. Why do you think that the median of the top half of the data is called the *upper quartile* and the median of the bottom half of the data is called the *lower quartile*?

   Answers will vary. Students might say that quartile is related to quarter, and the lower quartile, the median, and the upper quartile divide the data into four sections with about one fourth, or a quarter, of the data values in each section.

4.
   a. Mark the quartiles for each restaurant on the graphs below.

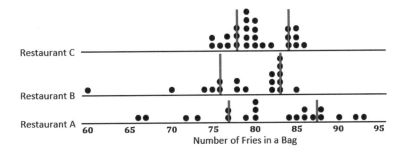

   b. Does the IQR help you decide which of the three restaurants seems most likely to really have 82 fries in a typical large bag? Explain your thinking.

   The IQR does help decide which restaurant is most likely to have 82 fries in a typical large bag because the IQR explains the variability of the data. Because Restaurant C has the smallest IQR, the middle half of the counts of the number of fries in a bag is really close to the median. In addition, Restaurant C also has the smallest range.

Example 1 (5 minutes): Finding the IQR

This example is intended as a reference for students and not to be reproduced during class unless students need more clarity. If that is the case, have students explain the diagram to each other rather than recreating it on the board. Make sure that students understand that the lower quartile is the number marking the median of the lower half.

Example 1: Finding the IQR

Read through the following steps. If something does not make sense to you, make a note, and raise it during class discussion. Consider the data: $1, 1, 3, 4, 6, 6, 7, 8, 10, 11, 11, 12, 15, 15, 17, 17, 17$

Creating an IQR:

    a.   **Put the data in order from smallest to largest.**

          The data are already ordered.

$$1, 1, 3, 4, 6, 6, 7, 8, 10, 11, 11, 12, 15, 15, 17, 17, 17$$

    b.   **Find the minimum and maximum.**

          The minimum data point is 1, and the maximum is 17.

$$①1, 3, 4, 6, 6, 7, 8, 10, 11, 11, 12, 15, 15, 17, 17⑰$$

    c.   **Find the median.**

          There are 17 data points, so the ninth one from the smallest or the largest is the median.

$$1, 1, 3, 4, 6, 6, 7, 8, ⑩ 11, 11, 12, 15, 15, 17, 17, 17$$

                                 median

    d.   **Find the lower quartile and upper quartile.**

          The lower quartile (Q1) is halfway between the 4th and 5th data points (the average of 4 and 6), or 5, and the upper quartile (Q3) is halfway between the 13th and the 14th data points (the average of 15 and 15), or 15.

$$1, 1, 3, ④, ⑥, 6, 7, 8, 10, 11, 11, 12, ⑮, ⑮, 17, 17, 17$$

               Q1 is 5   *Q3 is 15*

    e.   **Calculate the IQR by finding the difference between Q3 and Q1.**

          $IQR = 15 - 5 = 10.$

Exercise 5 (5 minutes): When Should You Use the IQR?

This exercise points out how a skewed distribution might not be adequately summarized by the mean and its corresponding measure of spread, the MAD.

©2015 Great Minds eureka-math.org
G6-M6-TE-B3-1.3.1-01.2016

Exercise 5: When Should You Use the IQR?

5. When should you use the IQR? The data for the 2012 salaries for the Lakers basketball team are given in the two plots below. (See Problem 5 in the Problem Set from Lesson 12.)

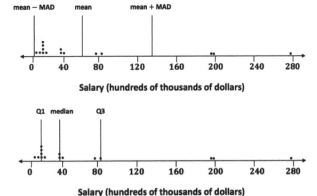

a. The data are given in hundreds of thousands of dollars. What would a salary of 40 hundred thousand dollars be?

The salary would be $4,000,000.

b. The vertical lines on the top plot show the mean and the mean plus and minus the MAD. The bottom plot shows the median and the IQR. Which interval is a better picture of the typical salaries? Explain your thinking.

The median and the IQR seem to represent the typical salaries better than the mean plus or minus the MAD. The mean salary is above all but five of the salaries. Both the mean and the MAD are affected by the three unusually large salaries in the data set.

Exercise 6 (15 minutes): On Your Own with IQRs

Students work together in pairs or groups of three on this exercise. After they develop three examples, encourage them to select one of their examples and explain it by creating a simple poster. If a poster is used for this exercise, indicate to students that they should do the following:

- Explain the context for the example, and describe the data and how they would be collected.
- Explain how to find the median, the upper quartile, and the lower quartile.
- Explain what the IQR would mean in the context of the selected example.

Either discuss student examples or have students present their posters.

Encourage students to use their imaginations and identify contexts for which the IQR might provide useful information. If time permits, have students explain their posters to other students. Display posters as possible examples of problems for future lessons or discussions.

Exercise 6: On Your Own with IQRs

6. Create three different examples where you might collect data and where that data might have an IQR of 20. Define a median in the context of each example. Be specific about how the data might have been collected and the units involved. Be ready to describe what the median and IQR mean in each context.

    It may be difficult for students to get started on the exercise. If students struggle, consider a class discussion of one of the examples that follow. Student answers will vary. Some examples that could be included in this exercise are as follows: number of books read by students during a school year (some students read a lot of books, while other students may not read as many), number of movies viewed at a theater during the last year by students in a class, number of text messages students receive during a specific day (for example, on Monday), number of commercials on TV during a specific time period that are about buying a car, number of different states students have visited, number of healthy trees on certain blocks of a city, and number of students in each classroom of a school during a specific time period. Remind students that the goal is to have them think of data that if collected might have an IQR of approximately 20, meaning that the middle half of the data would spread out over an interval of length 20. These ideas also allow students to start thinking of the process of actually collecting data that are needed later.

Closing (2 minutes)

- What is the interquartile range? How do you find the IQR?
    - *The interquartile range is the length of the interval that includes the middle half of the data. The lower quartile is the median of the bottom half of the data, and the upper quartile is the median of the top half of the data. In order to find the IQR, you calculate the difference between the upper quartile and the lower quartile.*

- What information does the IQR provide about the spread of the data?
    - *A large IQR means there is a large spread because the middle 50% of the data covers a large range of numbers. A small IQR means there is a small spread because the middle 50% of the data covers a small range of numbers.*

Lesson Summary

To find the IQR, you order the data, find the median of the data, and then find the median of the bottom half of the data (the lower quartile) and the median of the top half of the data (the upper quartile). The IQR is the difference between the upper quartile and the lower quartile, which is the length of the interval that includes the middle half of the data.

The median and the two quartiles divide the data into four sections, with about $\frac{1}{4}$ of the data in each section. Two of the sections are between the quartiles, so the interval between the quartiles would contain about 50% of the data.

Exit Ticket (5 minutes)

Lesson 13:   Describing Variability Using the Interquartile Range (IQR)

©2015 Great Minds eureka-math.org
G6-M6-TE-B3-1.3.1-01.2016

Name _____   Date_____

Lesson 13: Describing Variability Using the Interquartile Range (IQR)

Exit Ticket

1. On the dot plot below, insert the following words in approximately the correct position.

Maximum   Minimum   IQR   Median   Lower Quartile (Q1)   Upper Quartile (Q3)

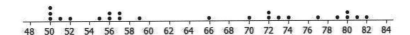

2. Estimate the IQR for the data set shown in the dot plot.

©2015 Great Minds eureka-math.org
G6-M6-TE-B3-1.3.1-01.2016

Exit Ticket Sample Solutions

1. On the dot plot below, insert the following words in approximately the correct position.

   Maximum   Minimum   IQR   Median   Lower Quartile (Q1)   Upper Quartile (Q3)

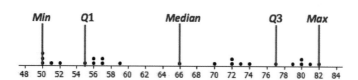

2. Estimate the IQR for the data set shown in the dot plot.

   The IQR is approximately 22.

Problem Set Sample Solutions

1. The average monthly high temperatures (in degrees Fahrenheit) for St. Louis and San Francisco are given in the table below.

	Jan.	Feb.	Mar.	Apr.	May	June	July	Aug.	Sept.	Oct.	Nov.	Dec.
St. Louis	40	45	55	67	77	85	89	88	81	69	56	43
San Francisco	57	60	62	63	64	67	67	68	70	69	63	57

Data Source: http://www.weather.com

a. How do you think the data might have been collected?

Someone at a park or the airport or someplace probably records the temperature every hour of every day and then takes all of the highest daily temperatures and finds the mean.

b. Do you think it would be possible for $\frac{1}{4}$ of the temperatures in the month of July for St. Louis to be 95°F or above? Why or why not?

Yes, it is possible. The mean temperature in St. Louis for July is 89°F. There are 31 days in July, so $\frac{1}{4}$ of the days would be about 8 days. Student answers should have 8 or more temperatures that are above 95 °F, and then the other values could be anything that would result in an overall mean of 89 °F. For example, if the temperature was 95°F for 5 days, 100°F for 3 days, and 86°F for all of the rest of the days, there would be 8 days with temperatures of 95 °F or higher, and the mean for the month would be 89 °F.

c. Make a prediction about how the values of the IQR for the temperatures for each city compare. Explain your thinking.

San Francisco probably has the smaller IQR because those temperatures do not seem to vary as much as the St. Louis temperatures.

©2015 Great Minds eureka-math.org
G6-M6-TE-B3-1.3.1-01.2016

d. Find the IQR for the average monthly high temperature for each city. How do the results compare to what you predicted?

The IQRs for San Francisco and St. Louis are $6.5°F$ and $33°F$, respectively. This result matches my prediction in part (c).

2. The plot below shows the years in which each of 100 pennies were made.

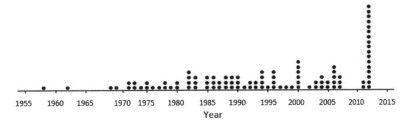

a. What does the stack of 17 dots at 2012 representing 17 pennies tell you about the age of these pennies in 2014?

17 pennies were made in 2012, and they would be 2 years old in 2014.

b. Here is some information about the sample of 100 pennies. The mean year they were made is 1994; the first year any of the pennies were made was 1958; the newest pennies were made in 2012; Q1 is 1984, the median is 1994, and Q3 is 2006; the MAD is 11.5 years. Use the information to indicate the years in which the middle half of the pennies was made.

In this case, the IQR is 22 years, so the middle half of the pennies was made over an interval of 22 years.

3. In each of parts (a)–(c), create a data set with at least 6 values such that it has the following properties:

a. A small IQR and a big range (maximum − minimum)

Answers will vary. One example is $\{0, 100, 50, 50, 50, 50, 50\}$ where the range is 100 and the IQR is 0.

b. An IQR equal to the range

Answers will vary. One example is $\{10, 10, 10, 15, 20, 20, 20\}$.

c. The lower quartile is the same as the median.

Answers will vary. One example is $\{1, 1, 1, 1, 1, 5, 6, 7\}$.

4. Rank the following three data sets by the value of the IQR.

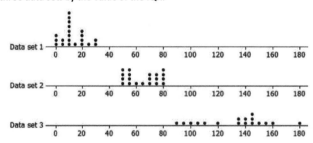

Data set 1 has the smallest IQR at about 14; data set 2 has the next smallest IQR at about 22, and data set 3 has the largest IQR at about 41.

5. Here are the number of fries in each of the bags from Restaurant A:

$$80, 72, 77, 80, 90, 85, 93, 79, 84, 73, 87, 67, 80, 86, 92, 88, 86, 88, 66, 77$$

a. Suppose one bag of fries had been overlooked and that bag had only 50 fries. If that value is added to the data set, would the IQR change? Explain your reasoning.

The IQR would be larger, 12.5, because the median number of fries would be at 80 now instead of 82, which would make the lower quartile at 75 instead of 77.

b. Will adding another data value always change the IQR? Give an example to support your answer.

No. It depends on how many values you have in the data set and what value is added. For example, if the set of data is $\{2, 2, 2, 6, 9, 9, 9\}$, the IQR is $9 - 2 = 7$. If you add another 6, the IQR would stay at 7.

Lesson 13:   Describing Variability Using the Interquartile Range (IQR)

©2015 Great Minds eureka-math.org
G6-M6-TE-B3-1.3.1-01.2016

Lesson 14: Summarizing a Distribution Using a Box Plot

Student Outcome

- Students construct a box plot from a given set of data.

Lesson Notes

In this lesson, students transition from using dot plots to display data to using box plots. The lesson begins with exercises that lay the foundation for the development of a box plot. Students inspect dot plots of several sets of data and think about how to group or section the plots to get a sense of the spread of data values in each of the sections. When individual students determine how to make the sections, the results differ, and the process seems arbitrary and inconsistent. Thus, there is a need for a standard procedure for making a box plot. Using the median and the quartiles introduced in the previous lesson leads to a standard procedure.

The lesson begins and ends with interactive activities. If time allows, students create a "human box plot" of the time it took them to get to school. Supplies are needed for this exercise: one sticky note for every student, one large piece of rope or yarn, and signs with the names of each of the five numbers included in the five-number summary.

Classwork

Students read the paragraph silently.

> A box plot is a graph that is used to summarize a data distribution. What does the box plot tell us about the data distribution? How does the box plot indicate the variability of the data distribution? These questions are explored in this lesson.

Example 1 (5 minutes): Time to Get to School

The questions in this example are designed to help students begin to think about grouping data in order to get a sense of the spread of the data values in various parts of the data set. Let each student write an estimate of the time it took them to get to school on a sticky note. Teachers may want individual students to place their sticky notes on a dot plot that is displayed on the classroom board at the beginning of class, or they can make the dot plot as a class.

> **Example 1: Time to Get to School**
>
> Consider the statistical question, "What is the typical amount of time it takes for a person in your class to get to school?" The amount of time it takes to get to school in the morning varies for the students in your class. Take a minute to answer the following questions. Your class will use this information to create a dot plot.
>
> Write your name and an estimate of the number of minutes it took you to get to school today on a sticky note.
>
> *Answers will vary.*
>
> What were some of the things you had to think about when you made your estimate?
>
> *Answers will vary. Some examples include: Does it count when you have to wait in the car for your sister? I usually walk, but today I got a ride. Does it matter that we had to go a different way because the road was closed? The bus was late.*

©2015 Great Minds eureka-math.org
G6-M6-TE-B3-1.3.1-01.2016

- What does a dot on the dot plot represent?

  □ *Each dot on a dot plot represents one value in a set of data.*

- What is an estimate of the median time to get to school? Does the median do a good job of describing a typical time for students in your class?

  □ *Answers will depend on the class data.*

- What are the minimum and maximum times?

  □ *Answers will depend on the class data.*

Exercises 1–4 (7 minutes)

Students work individually on the exercises and compare their plots with their neighbors' plots. Students should recognize that their divisions of the data are close but not always the same.

If time permits, bring the class together for a discussion of the answers, and stress the idea that it is useful to see how the data values group together in different parts of the distribution.

- Are there a lot of values in the middle or at one end?

  □ *The values in the lower half are closer together than the numbers in the upper half.*

- What was the shortest time a student in Mr. S's class took to get to school? The longest?

  □ *A few students got to school in 5 minutes, which was the shortest. One student took 60 minutes to get to school, which was the longest.*

- Looking at the plot, what is a typical time it takes for students in Mr. S's class to get to school?

  □ *Examining the dot plot, it looks like the typical time is 15 minutes.*

Exercises 1–4

Here is a dot plot of the estimates of the times it took students in Mr. S's class to get to school one morning.

Mr. S's Class

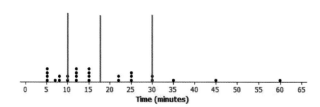

Time (minutes)

1. Put a line on the dot plot that you think separates the times into two groups—one group representing the longer times and the other group representing the shorter times.

   Answers may vary. Some might put the dividing line between 15 and 20.

2. Put another line on the dot plot that separates out the times for students who live really close to the school. Add another line that separates out the times for students who take a very long time to get to school.

   Responses will be different. Some might put a line at 30 and a line at 10.

Lesson 14:   Summarizing a Distribution Using a Box Plot

©2015 Great Minds eureka-math.org
G6-M6-TE-B3-1.3.1-01.2016

3. Your dot plot should now be divided into four sections. Record the number of data values in each of the four sections.

Answers will vary. Depending on the divisions, 7 or 8 in the lower one, 9 in the next, 5 in the next, and 5 in the upper section

4. Share your marked-up dot plot with some of your classmates. Compare how each of you divided the dot plot into four sections.

Different responses; students should recognize that the divisions might be close but that some are different.

Exercises 5–7 (8 minutes): Time to Get to School

Students work individually on the questions. Then, discuss the answers as a class. Reinforce the idea of the *five-number summary* (the *minimum*, *lower quartile* (or *Q1*), *median*, *upper quartile* (or *Q3*), and the *maximum*) and how the five-number summary is used to create a box plot.

- Can you think of a way to divide the data set into four parts so that everyone would divide it up in the same way?
  - *Using the median and quartiles would divide a data set into four parts with about the same number of data values in each part.*

Exercises 5–7: Time to Get to School

The times (in minutes) for the students in Mr. S's class have been put in order from smallest to largest and are shown below.

5 5 5 5 7 8 8 10 10 12 12 12 12 15 15 15 15 22 22 25 25 25 30 30 35 45 60

5. What is the value of the median time to get to school for students in Mr. S's class?

There are 27 times in the data set, so the median is the 14th value in the ordered list. The median is 15.

6. What is the value of the lower quartile? The upper quartile?

The lower quartile is the 7th value in the ordered list, and the upper quartile is the 21st value in the ordered list. The lower quartile is 8, and the upper quartile is 25.

7. The lines on the dot plot below indicate the location of the median, the lower quartile, and the upper quartile. These lines divide the data set into four parts. About what fraction of the data values are in each part?

Mr. S's Class

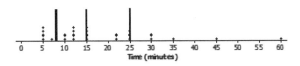

There are about $\frac{3}{4}$ of the data values in each part.

©2015 Great Minds eureka-math.org
G6-M6-TE-B3-1.3.1-01.2016

Example 2 (7 minutes): Making a Box Plot

This example describes the procedure for finding a box plot. Consider having students read through the steps themselves, and then ask them to restate the directions.

Example 2: Making a Box Plot

A box plot is a graph made using the following five numbers: the smallest value in the data set, the lower quartile, the median, the upper quartile, and the largest value in the data set.

To make a box plot:

- Find the median of all of the data.
- Find Q1, the median of the bottom half of the data, and Q3, the median of the top half of the data.
- Draw a number line, and then draw a box that goes from Q1 to Q3.
- Draw a vertical line in the box at the value of the median.
- Draw a line segment connecting the minimum value to the box and a line segment that connects the maximum value to the box.

You will end up with a graph that looks something like this:

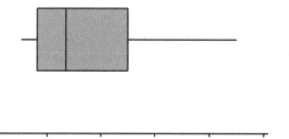

Now, use the given number line to make a box plot of the data below.

20, 21, 25, 31, 35, 38, 40, 42, 44

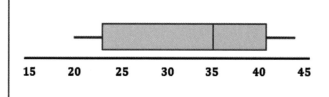

| 15 | 20 | 25 | 30 | 35 | 40 | 45 |

The five-number summary is as follows:

Min = 20
Q1 = 23
Median = 35
Q3 = 41
Max = 44

Ask students the following when the box plot is complete.

- Why is it important to have a standard way to make a box plot?
    - *It is important to have a standard way to make a box plot because it guarantees that everyone will have the same plot when given the same set of data.*

©2015 Great Minds eureka-math.org
G6-M6-TE-B3-1.3.1-01.2016

- What does a box plot tell you about the *story* in the data? What does it not tell you?
  - *A box plot divides the data in four parts, which each contain about 25% of the data values. The "box" part of the box plot shows where the middle 50% of the data values are.*
  - *The box plot does not show us specific data values.*
- What proportion (percent) of the data are in each of the sections of the box plot? How do you know?
  - *Each section of the box plot represents 25% of the data because the median and quartiles divide the data into four sections that have the same number of data values.*

Exercises 8–11 (11 minutes): A Human Box Plot

Depending on the amount of time left in class, this exercise can either be completed on the board as a class or by using selected students to create a human box plot. If possible, try to involve approximately 15 students. This would put 3 students in each quarter of the data set. If time is running short and the problem is completed as a class, use the focus questions listed below.

Preparation for Human Box Plot:

The class data are already ordered from the sticky notes on the dot plot on the classroom board. Call out students' names to have them form an ordered line of data. Find a place in the classroom (or hall) that allows all students to line up and that can accommodate a number line that goes from 0 to as large as 60 minutes. Have some props that can represent a number line, for example, large cards with a scale in 5-minute intervals. Do not start with the number line, however. A ball of yarn or rope can be used to mark off the box part of the box plot.

Once students are in line, have them identify the median and the two quartiles. Give the signs for the five-number summary values to the appropriate students, and ask them to step out with their signs. Ask each of the quartiles to hold one end of the rope marking off the box that extends from Q1 to Q3. Students may not recognize at first that the plot has no scale and thus does not really tell the story. Try to get them to see how important the scale is by asking questions such as the following:

- You all are a human box plot of the times it took you to come to school. Did it take most of you a short time or a longer time?
  - *Answers will vary depending on the data.*
- Did it take anyone a really long time?
  - *Answers will vary depending on the data.*
- Can you tell from our plot?
  - *There is no scale, so it is hard to tell if any student took a really long time to get to school.*

When students realize that it looks like the times were all evenly spaced because of how they are standing, bring out the props for the number line (be sure to make the intervals wide enough to accommodate several students). Then, have students rearrange themselves using the scale and re-create the box plot with the five-number summary values and the rope to represent the box. Then, ask the following:

- How many people are in each of the sections? Which section has the most people? The fewest?
  - *Answers will vary to the first question, but if the recommended 15 students participated, 3 students should be in each section.*
  - *Every section has the same number of people.*

- Were there any sections where the people were all crowded together? How did this show up in the box plot?
  - *It is possible that one section has people grouped close together. The section of the box plot would be small because the values in that section are close together.*

Exercises 8–11: A Human Box Plot

Consider again the sticky note that you used to write down the number of minutes it takes you to get to school. If possible, you and your classmates will form a human box plot of the number of minutes it takes students in your class to get to school.

8. Find the median of the group. Does someone represent the median? If not, who is the closest to the median?

    Answers will vary depending on the data.

9. Find the maximum and minimum of the group. Who are they?

    Answers will vary depending on the data.

10. Find Q1 and Q3 of the group. Does anyone represent Q1 or Q3? If not, who is the closest to Q1? Who is the closest to Q3?

    Answers will vary depending on the data.

11. Sketch the box plot for this data set.

    Answers will vary depending on the data.

Closing (2 minutes)

- What are some things you learned about box plots?
  - $\frac{1}{4}$ *of the data are in each of the sections of the plot.*
  - *The length of the interval for a section does not indicate either how many values are in the interval.*

Lesson Summary

You learned how to make a box plot by doing the following:

- Finding the median of the entire data set.
- Finding Q1, the median of the bottom half of the data, and Q3, the median of the top half of the data.
- Drawing a number line and then drawing a box that goes from Q1 to Q3.
- Drawing a vertical line in the box at the value of the median.
- Drawing a line segment connecting the minimum value to the box and one that connects the maximum value to the box.

Exit Ticket (5 minutes)

©2015 Great Minds eureka-math.org
G6-M6-TE-B3-1.3.1-01.2016

Name _____   Date_____

Lesson 14: Summarizing a Distribution Using a Box Plot

Exit Ticket

Sulee explained how to make a box plot to her sister as follows:

"First, you find the smallest and largest values and put a mark halfway between them, and then put a mark halfway between that mark and each end. So, if 10 is the smallest value and 30 is the largest value, you would put a mark at 20. Then, another mark belongs halfway between 20 and 10, which would be at 15. And then one more mark belongs halfway between 20 and 30, which would be at 25. Now, you put a box around the three middle marks, and draw lines from the box to the smallest and largest values."

Here is her box plot. What would you say to Sulee?

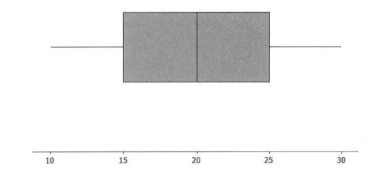

©2015 Great Minds eureka-math.org
G6-M6-TE-B3-1.3.1-01.2016

Exit Ticket Sample Solutions

Sulee explained how to make a box plot to her sister as follows:

"First, you find the smallest and largest values and put a mark halfway between them, and then put a mark halfway between that mark and each end. So, if 10 is the smallest value and 30 is the largest value, you would put a mark at 20. Then, another mark belongs halfway between 20 and 10, which would be at 15. And then one more mark belongs halfway between 20 and 30, which would be at 25. Now, you put a box around the three middle marks, and draw lines from the box to the smallest and largest values."

Here is her box plot. What would you say to Sulee?

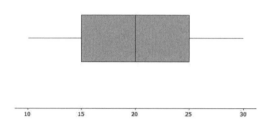

Sulee is wrong. This is not the correct way to create a box plot. Sulee did not find the median or the quartiles using the data values; she just divided up the length between the smallest and largest numbers into four equal sections. For a box plot, the sections will not always have the same length, but there will be the same number of observations in the sections. Teacher note: This Exit Ticket problem addresses a very common student misconception about box plots. Make sure students understand how the median and quartiles are used to create the four sections of the box plot.

Problem Set Sample Solutions

1. Dot plots for the amount of time it took students in Mr. S's and Ms. J's classes to get to school are below.

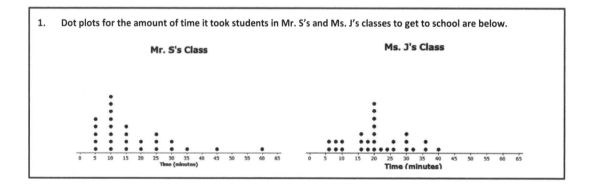

©2015 Great Minds eureka-math.org
G6-M6-TE-B3-1.3.1-01.2016

a. Make a box plot of the times for each class.

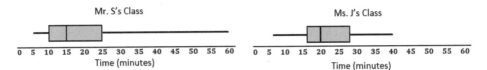

Mr. S's five-number summary: 5, 10, 15, 25, 60

Ms. J's five-number summary: 5, 16, 20, 28, 40

b. What is one thing you can see in the dot plot that you cannot see in the box plot? What is something that is easier to see in the box plot than in the dot plot?

The dot plot shows individual times, which you cannot see in the box plot. The box plot shows the location of the median and of the lower and upper quartiles.

2. The dot plot below shows the vertical jump of some NBA players. A vertical jump is how high a player can jump from a standstill. Draw a box plot of the heights for the vertical jumps of the NBA players above the dot plot.

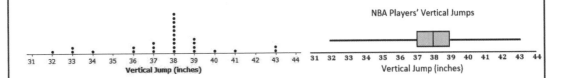

Five-number summary: 32, 37, 38, 39, 43

3. The mean daily temperatures in degrees Fahrenheit for the month of February for a certain city are as follows:

4, 11, 14, 15, 17, 20, 30, 23, 20, 35, 35, 31, 34, 23, 15, 19, 39, 22, 15, 15, 19, 39, 22, 23, 29, 26, 29, 29

a. Make a box plot of the temperatures.

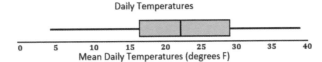

Five-number summary: 4, 16, 22.5, 29.5, 39

b. Make a prediction about the part of the United States you think the city might be located. Explain your reasoning.

Answers will vary. The city was probably somewhere in the northern states, either in the Midwest or Northeast, maybe Montana or Wyoming, because the temperatures are typically pretty cold in those regions.

c. Describe the temperature data distribution. Include a description of center and spread.

The IQR is $29.5°F - 16°F$, or $13.5°F$. Half of the temperatures were near the middle between $16°F$ and $29.5°F$. The median is $22.5°F$. A quarter of the temperatures are less than $16°F$ but greater than or equal to $4°F$. A quarter of the temperatures are greater than $29.5°F$ and less than or equal to $39°F$.

©2015 Great Minds eureka-math.org
G6-M6-TE-B3-1.3.1-01.2016

4. The box plot below summarizes data from a survey of households about the number of dogs they have. Identify each of the following statements as true or false. Explain your reasoning in each case.

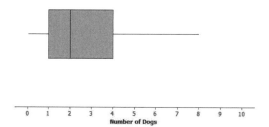

a. The maximum number of dogs per house is 8.

    True, because the line segment at the top goes to 8.

b. At least $\frac{1}{2}$ of the houses have 2 or more dogs.

    True, because 2 is the median.

c. All of the houses have dogs.

    False, because the lower line segment starts at 0, so at least one household does not have a dog as a pet.

d. Half of the houses surveyed have between 2 and 4 dogs.

    False, because only about 25% of the houses would have between 2 and 4 dogs.

e. Most of the houses surveyed have no dogs.

    False, because at least $\frac{3}{4}$ of those surveyed had 1 or more dogs.

EUREKA
MATH™

©2015 Great Minds eureka-math.org
G6-M6-TE-B3-1.3.1-01.2016

Lesson 15: More Practice with Box Plots

Student Outcomes

- Given a box plot, students estimate the values that make up the five-number summary (Minimum, Q1, Median, Q3, Maximum).
- Students describe a data set using the five-number summary and the interquartile range.
- Students construct a box plot from a five-number summary.

Lesson Notes

In this lesson, students summarize and describe data distributions. They consider data displayed in dot plots and box plots and summarize data sets in relation to their context. Students describe center and spread using the five-number summary (Minimum, Q1, Median, Q3, and Maximum) and the interquartile range. The questions in this lesson show students how box plots provide information about center and variability in a data distribution.

Students begin by looking at a box plot, estimating the values in the five-number summary, and using the five-number summary to describe the data. They then consider the variability in two different data sets, the maximum speeds of selected birds and of land animals with very different spreads. They create box plots using the five-number summary for each data set. In the last example, students interpret the IQR for different data sets.

To help students make sense of box plots and to confront typical misconceptions they may have, it would be very valuable to engage students with an interactive dynamic software that allows them to explore the relationship between box plots and dot plots.

Classwork

Students read the paragraph silently.

> You reach into a jar of Tootsie Pops. How many Tootsie Pops do you think you could hold in one hand? Do you think the number you could hold is greater than or less than what other students can hold? Is the number you could hold a typical number of Tootsie Pops? This lesson examines these questions.

Example 1 (3 minutes): Tootsie Pops

Consider actually doing this experiment with students. Have them see how many Tootsie Pops they can grab, and then replace the data in the example with the class data. (The data in the example were not collected from sixth-grade students, so results might be different, as hand sizes might be larger as students get older.) In later grades, data from the size of handspans could be used to see whether any correlation exists between handspan and the number of Tootsie Pops someone can hold.

- As you learned earlier, the five numbers that are needed to make a box plot are the minimum, the lower quartile, the median, the upper quartile, and the maximum. These numbers make up the *five-number summary* of the data.

©2015 Great Minds eureka-math.org
G6-M6-TE-B3-1.3.1-01.2016

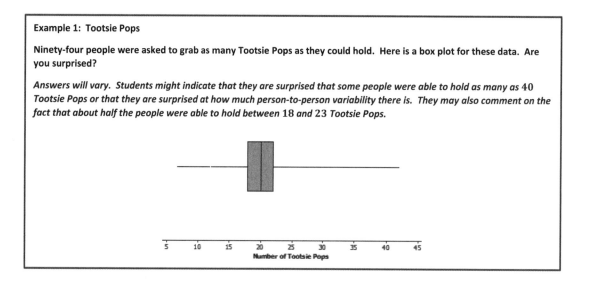

Example 1: Tootsie Pops

Ninety-four people were asked to grab as many Tootsie Pops as they could hold. Here is a box plot for these data. Are you surprised?

Answers will vary. Students might indicate that they are surprised that some people were able to hold as many as 40 Tootsie Pops or that they are surprised at how much person-to-person variability there is. They may also comment on the fact that about half the people were able to hold between 18 and 23 Tootsie Pops.

Exercises 1–5 (8 minutes)

As students work with the exercises, they should recognize that at least one person was able to hold a lot of Tootsie Pops because the upper segment extends to 42. They should also note that the typical number was about 20 because the median line in the box plot is at about 20. The middle 50% of the data values were bunched up close to the median in an interval that spans about four or five numbers.

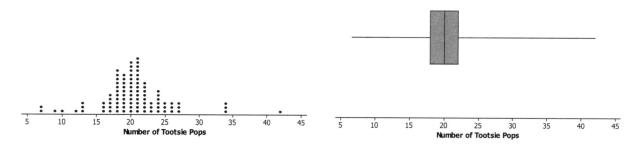

A dot plot of the data can be used to informally introduce the concept of outliers as data values that seem far away from all of the others; consider using the term without giving a formal definition.

Technology can be used to help students visualize the relationship between a dot plot and a box plot. An example of software that provides this visual transition is TI-Nspire™ software. With this software, the dot plot is changed to a box plot as the dots "climb" into their place in the box plot. Going back and forth between plots several times gives students a very visual impression of what a box plot represents. Being able to simultaneously look at the two plots allows teachers to ask questions that probe student understanding, such as "Why is the segment on the right so long?" and "What do you think would happen if the point at 42 were removed or had been at 35?" Interactive dynamic technology allows students to make conjectures and actually test them out by moving points and observing the consequences (see the *Mathematical Education of Teachers, Edition 2,* from the Conference Board of Mathematical Sciences).

©2015 Great Minds eureka-math.org
G6-M6-TE-B3-1.3.1-01.2016

As students work through the exercises in small groups, ask them the following questions:

- How many Tootsie Pops do you think people can hold in one hand? Make a prediction.

Record students' estimates for this question. If possible, demonstrate grabbing a handful of Tootsie Pops.

- How do you find the upper and lower quartiles?
  - *Order the data, find the median of the ordered data, and then find the middle of the top half and the bottom half as the upper and lower quartiles.*
- What is a five-number summary?
  - *The five-number summary includes the following: the minimum data value, the lower quartile (Q1), the median, the upper quartile (Q3), and the maximum data value.*
- About what fraction of the data values should be in each section of the box plot?
  - *Approximately $\frac{1}{4}$ (or 0.25 or 25%) of the data values should be found in each section.*

Exercises 1–5

1. **What might explain the variability in the number of Tootsie Pops that the 94 people were able to hold?**

    Answers will vary. Possible answers include size of people's hands, handspan, and whether a person is flexible in moving his fingers.

2. **Use the box plot to estimate the values in the five-number summary.**

    Min = 7, Q1 = 18, Median = 20, Q3 = 22, Max = 42

3. **Describe how the box plot can help you understand differences in the numbers of Tootsie Pops people could hold.**

    The maximum of about 42 and minimum of about 7 indicate that there is a lot of variability in the number of Tootsie Pops that people can hold, with the numbers covering a range of about 35 Tootsie Pops. The "box" part of the box plot shows that about half of the people can hold within about 2 Tootsie Pops of the median, which was 20 Tootsie Pops.

4. **Here is Jayne's description of what she sees in the box plot. Do you agree or disagree with her description? Explain your reasoning.**

    "One person could hold as many as 42 Tootsie Pops. The number of Tootsie Pops people could hold was really different and spread about equally from 7 to 42. About one-half of the people could hold more than 20 Tootsie Pops."

    You cannot tell that they are evenly spread—the "box" part of the box plot contains about half of the values for the number of Tootsie Pops. However, the box is only four units long. That means half of the people were bunched over those four numbers.

5.   Here is a different box plot of the same data on the number of Tootsie Pops 94 people could hold.

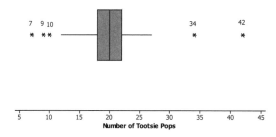

    a.   Why do you suppose there are five values that are shown as separate points and are labeled?

        Maybe because they are far away from most of the other values. It shows that more than half of the data are from about 12 to 27 Tootsie Pops.

    b.   Does knowing these data values change anything about your responses to Exercises 1 to 4 above?

        Not really, except maybe to say that only a few of the people could hold more than 30 Tootsie Pops; the rest held fewer than that. And only a few people could hold 10 or fewer Tootsie Pops.

Exercises 6–10 (15 minutes): Maximum Speeds

The goal of these exercises is not to compare the two data sets but rather to think about how the variability is different for birds and land animals. Note that two of the speeds are accurate to the hundredths place; the speed for the horse was probably measured at a racetrack. It is not clear how researchers were able to record such an accurate speed for the hummingbird. If preferred, round the data values for students.

In working with any data set, a good habit is to start by looking over the data values to see what might be unusual, different, or in some way interesting, which is the reason for the first question. When students describe the plots, encourage the use of fractions or percentages to talk about each of the four sections rather than words like *most* or *lots*.

For example, encourage statements such as $\frac{1}{4}$, or 25%, of the speeds were less than 76 mph.

©2015 Great Minds eureka-math.org
G6-M6-TE-B3-1.3.1-01.2016

Exercises 6–10: Maximum Speeds

The maximum speeds of selected birds and land animals are given in the tables below.

Bird	Speed (mph)
Peregrine falcon	242
Swift bird	120
Spine-tailed swift	106
White-throated needle tail	105
Eurasian hobby	100
Pigeon	100
Frigate bird	95
Spur-winged goose	88
Red-breasted merganser	80
Canvasback duck	72
Anna's hummingbird	61.06
Ostrich	60

Land Animal	Speed (mph)
Cheetah	75
Free-tailed bat (in flight)	60
Pronghorn antelope	55
Lion	50
Wildebeest	50
Jackrabbit	44
African wild dog	44
Kangaroo	45
Horse	43.97
Thomson's gazelle	43
Greyhound	43
Coyote	40
Mule deer	35
Grizzly bear	30
Cat	30
Elephant	25
Pig	9

Data sources: *Natural History Magazine*, March 1974, copyright 1974; The American Museum of Natural History; and James G. Doherty, general curator, The Wildlife Conservation Society; http://www.thetravelalmanac.com/lists/animals-speed.htm; http://en.wikipedia.org/wiki/Fastest_animals

As students answer the exercises, ask the following questions to help students connect their work to the outcomes:

- One of the fastest recorded speeds for a human was 27.79 mph for Usain Bolt during a 100-meter sprint in 2009. How does this human speed compare to the other land animals?

  □ *This human speed is similar to the fastest speeds of elephants and wildcats.*

6. As you look at the speeds, what strikes you as interesting?

   Answers will vary. Some students might suggest birds are really fast, especially the falcon. Others may notice that only two of the speeds have decimals. The speeds of specific animals might strike students as interesting.

7. Do birds or land animals seem to have the greatest variability in speeds? Explain your reasoning.

   It looks like the speeds of the birds vary a lot, as they go from 60 mph for some birds to 242 mph for others. The speeds of the land animals vary but not as much; they go from 9 mph to 75 mph.

8. Find the five-number summary for the speeds in each data set. What do the five-number summaries tell you about the distribution of speeds for each data set?

   Land animal five-number summary: Min = 9, Q1 = 32.5, Median = 43.97, Q3 = 50, Max = 75

   Bird five-number summary: Min = 60, Q1 = 76, Median = 97.5, Q3 = 105.5, Max = 242

   The summaries give me a sense of the range or span of the speeds (maximum − minimum speed) and how the speeds are grouped around the median.

©2015 Great Minds eureka-math.org
G6-M6-TE-B3-1.3.1-01.2016

9. Use the five-number summaries to make a box plot for each of the two data sets.

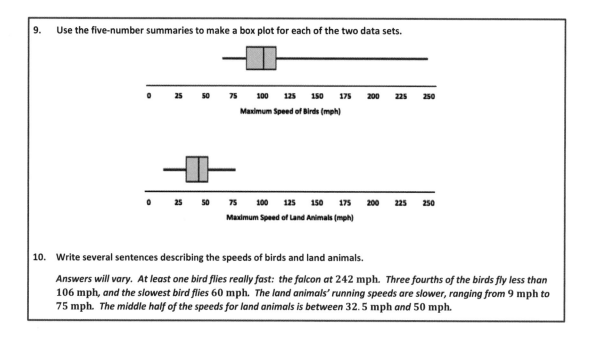

10. Write several sentences describing the speeds of birds and land animals.

Answers will vary. At least one bird flies really fast: the falcon at 242 mph. Three fourths of the birds fly less than 106 mph, and the slowest bird flies 60 mph. The land animals' running speeds are slower, ranging from 9 mph to 75 mph. The middle half of the speeds for land animals is between 32.5 mph and 50 mph.

Exercises 11–15 (12 minutes): What Is the Same, and What Is Different?

The focus in thinking about the three box plots in Exercises 11–13 should be on the IQR for each, noting that the minimum, median, and maximum in each box plot are the same. The middle half of the data is much more tightly packed around the median in the third plot. Students estimate the quartiles from the plots; if their answers vary a bit, that is okay because the emphasis is on the concept.

The spread of the middle half of the data is across the entire range (minimum to maximum) for the second plot. This could happen if there are 25% (or more) of the data values that are all equal to the minimum value in the data set and at least 25% (or more) of the data values that are equal to the maximum value in the data set. For example, consider the data set that consists of the following values: $2, 2, 2, 2, 5, 6, 7, 8, 9, 9, 9$. For this data set, the median is 6, the lower quartile is 2, and the upper quartile is 9. The lower quartile and the minimum are equal, and the upper quartile and the maximum are equal. This results in an odd-looking box plot like the Class 2 box plot in the exercises. As students answer the questions for these exercises, ask the following questions to help students connect their work to the outcomes:

- Are the IQR (Q3 − Q1) and the range (maximum − minimum), along with the statistics needed to compute them, enough to make a box plot? If not, what else do you need to know?

  □ *No. We also need to know the median.*

- About what fraction or percent of the data values will be between the quartiles?

  □ *About $\frac{1}{2}$ or 50% of the data values should be in the interval from the lower quartile to the upper quartile.*

- Is it possible for the lower quartile to be equal to the minimum value in a data set? What must be true in order for this to happen?

  □ *There would have to be a lot of values that are all equal to the minimum value. If there are at least 25% of the data values equal to the minimum value, the minimum and the lower quartile would be equal.*

Lesson 15:   More Practice with Box Plots

©2015 Great Minds eureka-math.org
G6-M6-TE-B3-1.3.1-01.2016

- Is it possible for the upper quartile to be equal to the maximum value in a data set? What must be true in order for this to happen?
  - □ *There would have to be a lot of values that are all equal to the maximum value. If there are at least 25% of the data values equal to the maximum value, the maximum and the upper quartile would be equal.*

Exercises 11–15: What Is the Same, and What Is Different?

Consider the following box plots, which show the number of correctly answered questions on a 20-question quiz for students in three different classes.

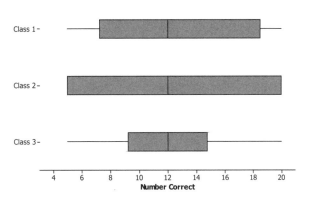

11. Describe the variability in the scores of each of the three classes.

    The range (max − min) is the same for all three classes, and so is the median, but the intervals that contain the middle half of the scores (the length of the box part of the box plot) are different. The third class has a small box, so the scores in the middle are close together. In Class 2, the minimum and lower quartile are the same score, and the maximum and upper quartile are also the same score, so lots of scores are piled at the ends of the range. The middle half of the scores in Class 1 are spread out more than Class 3 but not as much as Class 2.

    Teacher Note: The box plot for Class 2 may be difficult for students to interpret at first. If they have trouble, consider discussing the example provided earlier in the teacher notes that shows how it is possible that the minimum and the lower quartile might be equal and how the upper quartile and the maximum might be equal.

12.
    a. Estimate the interquartile range for each of the three sets of scores.

       Class 1 IQR = 10; Class 2 IQR = 15; Class 3 IQR = 6

    b. What fraction of students would have scores in the interval that extends from the lower quartile to the upper quartile?

       About one-half

©2015 Great Minds eureka-math.org
G6-M6-TE-B3-1.3.1-01.2016

c. What does the value of the IQR tell you about how the scores are distributed?

For Class 1, half of the scores are spread over an interval of width 10, and for Class 3, half of the scores are bunched together over an interval of width 5. For Class 2, the middle half of the data is spread over an interval of width 15, and in fact, because the quartiles are equal to the minimum and the maximum for Class 2, all of the data values are included in this interval with data values bunched up at the minimum and the maximum.

13. Which class do you believe performed the best? Be sure to use information from the box plots to back up your answer.

Answers will vary. A few sample answers are provided.

Class 3, as it has the smallest IQR. About half of the students scored close to the median score. Scores were more consistent for this class.

Approximately 25% of the students in Class 1 scored 18 or higher compared to 25% of the students in Class 3 who scored 15 or higher. Therefore, Class 1 performed the best.

In Class 2, several students must have scored near the top in order for the Q3 and maximum to be the same. Therefore, Class 2 performed the best.

14.

a. Find the IQR for the three data sets in the first two examples: maximum speed of birds, maximum speed of land animals, and number of Tootsie Pops.

Land animals: $50 - 32.5$ for an IQR of 17.5

Birds: $105.5 - 76$ for an IQR of 29.5

Tootsie Pops: $22 - 18$ for an IQR of 4

b. Which data set had the highest percentage of data values between the lower quartile and the upper quartile? Explain your thinking.

All of the data sets should have about half of the data values between the quartiles.

15. A teacher asked students to draw a box plot with a minimum value at 34 and a maximum value at 64 that had an interquartile range of 10. Jeremy said he could not draw just one because he did not know where to put the box on the number line. Do you agree with Jeremy? Why or why not?

Jeremy is correct since a box with a width of 10 could be drawn anywhere between the minimum and maximum values.

Closing (2 minutes)

- What are the values included in the five-number summary?
  - *The minimum, lower quartile, median, upper quartile, and the maximum are included in the five-number summary.*
- What does it mean when the "box" part of the box plot is very small?
  - *It means that the middle half of the data values are bunched up near the median and that the IQR is a small number.*

Exit Ticket (5 minutes)

©2015 Great Minds eureka-math.org
G6-M6-TE-B3-1.3.1-01.2016

Name _____   Date_____

Lesson 15: More Practice with Box Plots

Exit Ticket

Given the following information, create a box plot, and find the IQR.

For a large group of dogs, the shortest dog was 6 inches, and the tallest was 32 inches. One-half of the dogs were taller than 18 inches. One-fourth of the dogs were shorter than 15 inches. The upper quartile of the dog heights was 23 inches.

```
    ┌──────────────────────────────────────────────────┐
    4   6   8  10  12  14  16  18  20  22  24  26  28  30  32  34
                        Dog Height (inches)
```

©2015 Great Minds eureka-math.org
G6-M6-TE-B3-1.3.1-01.2016

Exit Ticket Sample Solutions

Given the following information, create a box plot, and find the IQR.

For a large group of dogs, the shortest dog was 6 inches, and the tallest was 32 inches. One-half of the dogs were taller than 18 inches. One-fourth of the dogs were shorter than 15 inches. The upper quartile of the dog heights was 23 inches.

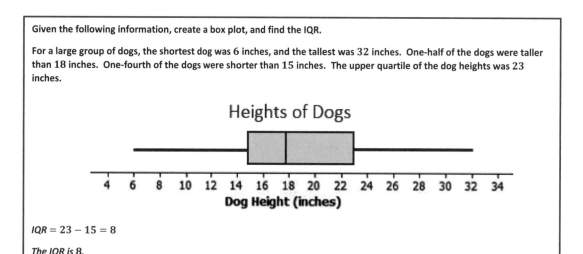

Heights of Dogs

$IQR = 23 - 15 = 8$

The IQR is 8.

Problem Set Sample Solutions

All students should be encouraged to do Problems 1 and 2 to be sure they understand the concepts developed in the lesson. Problem 4, part (b), should be discussed in some way as a whole class to raise awareness that medians are about counts and relative position of ordered data and not about the distance to the quartiles or the minimum or maximum.

1. The box plot below summarizes the maximum speeds of certain kinds of fish.

   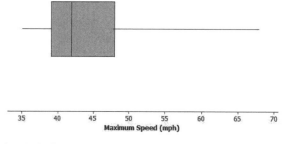

   Maximum Speed (mph)

   a. Estimate the values in the five-number summary from the box plot.

   Answers will vary. Min = 35 mph; Q1 = 39 mph; Median = 42 mph; Q3 = 48 mph; Max = 68 mph

   b. The fastest fish is the sailfish at 68 mph, followed by the marlin at 50 mph. What does this tell you about the spread of the fish speeds in the top quarter of the box plot?

   The Q3 is about 48, so all but one of the fish in the top quarter are between 48 mph and 50 mph.

   c. Use the five-number summary and the IQR to describe the speeds of the fish.

   The speeds of fish vary from 35 mph to 68 mph. The IQR is 9 mph; the middle half of the speeds are between 39 mph and 48 mph. Half of the speeds are less than 42 mph.

EUREKA MATH™

©2015 Great Minds eureka-math.org
G6-M6-TE-B3-1.3.1-01.2016

Note: Data for the box plot are provided below. These data do not appear in the student pages, but if time permits, share these data with students, and have them calculate the values in the five-number summary rather than estimating them from the given box plot.

Fish	Maximum Speed (mph)
Sailfish	68
Marlin	50
Wahoo	48
Tunny	46
Bluefin tuna	44
Great blue shark	43
Bonefish	40
Swordfish	40
Bonito	40
Four-winged flying fish	35
Tarpon	35

Data source: http://www.thetravelalmanac.com/lists/fish-speed.htm

2. Suppose the interquartile range for the number of hours students spent playing video games during the school week was 10. What do you think about each of the following statements? Explain your reasoning.

    a. About half of the students played video games for 10 hours during a school week.

    This may not be correct, as you know the width of the interval that contains the middle half of the times was 10, but you do not know where it starts or stops. You do not know the lower or upper quartile.

    b. All of the students played at least 10 hours of video games during the school week.

    This may not be correct for the same reason as in part (a).

    c. About half of the class could have played video games from 10 to 20 hours a week or from 15 to 25 hours.

    Either could be correct, as the only information you have is the IQR of 10, and the statement says "could be," not "is."

3. Suppose you know the following for a data set: The minimum value is 130, the lower quartile is 142, the IQR is 30, half of the data are less than 168, and the maximum value is 195.

    a. Think of a context for which these numbers might make sense.

    Answers will vary. For example, one possibility is the number of calories in a serving of fruit.

    b. Sketch a box plot.

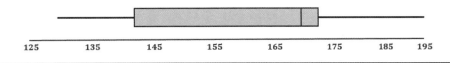

c.   Are there more data values above or below the median? Explain your reasoning.

The number of data values on either side of the median should be about the same: one-half of all of the data.

4.   The speeds for the fastest dogs are given in the table below.

Breed	Speed (mph)
Greyhound	45
African wild dog	44
Saluki	43
Whippet	36
Basanji	35
German shepherd	32
Vizsla	32
Doberman pinscher	30

Breed	Speed (mph)
Irish wolfhound	30
Dalmatian	30
Border collie	30
Alaskan husky	28
Giant schnauzer	28
Jack Russell terrier	25
Australian cattle dog	20

Data source: http://www.vetstreet.com/our-pet-experts/meet-eight-of-the-fastest-dogs-on-the-planet; http://canidaepetfood.blogspot.com/2012/08/which-dog-breeds-are-fastest.html

a.   Find the five-number summary for this data set, and use it to create a box plot of the speeds.

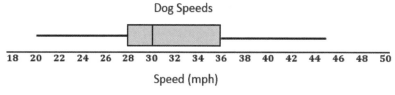

Dog Speeds

18 20 22 24 26 28 30 32 34 36 38 40 42 44 46 48 50

Speed (mph)

Min = 20, Q1 = 28, Median = 30, Q3 = 36, Max = 45

b.   Why is the median not in the center of the box?

The median is not in the center of the box because about $\frac{1}{4}$ of the speeds are between 30 and 36, and another $\frac{1}{4}$ are closer together, between 28 and 30.

c.   Write a few sentences telling your friend about the speeds of the fastest dogs.

Half of the dogs run faster than 30 mph; the fastest dog in the list is the greyhound with a speed of 45 mph. The slowest dog in the list is the Australian cattle dog with a speed of 20 mph. The middle 50% of the speeds are between 28 mph and 36 mph.

EUREKA
MATH™

©2015 Great Minds eureka-math.org
G6-M6-TE-B3-1.3.1-01.2016

Lesson 16: Understanding Box Plots

Student Outcomes

- Students summarize a data set using box plots, the median, and the interquartile range.
- Students use box plots to compare two data distributions.

Lesson Notes

The activities in this lesson engage students in thinking about everything they learned in the last several lessons about summarizing and describing data distributions. They consider graphical displays of numerical data—box plots and dot plots. They use quantitative measures of center (median) and variability (interquartile range) and describe overall patterns in the data with reference to the context.

If possible, students should have access to a graphing calculator or graphing software that allows them to construct box plots. These tools allow students to focus on what can be learned from the data rather than on figuring out the scale and plotting points. If technology is available, transfer the data sets to students in order to reduce time spent entering the data and also time spent tracking down entry errors.

Exercise 1 (10 minutes): Supreme Court Chief Justices

This exercise should only take a short time if students understood the concepts from the prior lessons. One common mistake is forgetting to order the data before finding the values in the five-number summary. If time permits, this exercise also provides an opportunity to make connections to social studies. Ask students if they know what cases are before the current Supreme Court, whether they think any data would be involved in those cases, and whether any of the analysis techniques might involve what they have been learning about statistics. Note that this discussion might extend the time necessary for the activity.

Ask the following question as students discuss the answers to the exercises in small groups:

- Why is it important to order the data before you find a median?
    - *The middle value, or median, is based on the order of the data.*

©2015 Great Minds eureka-math.org
G6-M6-TE-B3-1.3.1-01.2016

Exercise 1: Supreme Court Chief Justices

1. The Supreme Court is the highest court of law in the United States, and it makes decisions that affect the whole country. The chief justice is appointed to the court and is a justice the rest of his life unless he resigns or becomes ill. Some people think that this means that the chief justice serves for a very long time. The first chief justice was appointed in 1789.

The table shows the years in office for each of the chief justices of the Supreme Court as of 2013:

Name	Number of Years	Year Appointed
John Jay	6	1789
John Rutledge	1	1795
Oliver Ellsworth	4	1796
John Marshall	34	1801
Roger Brooke Taney	28	1836
Salmon P. Chase	9	1864
Morrison R. Waite	14	1874
Melville W. Fuller	22	1888
Edward D. White	11	1910
William Howard Taft	9	1921
Charles Evens Hughes	11	1930
Harlan Fiske Stone	5	1941
Fred M. Vinson	7	1946
Earl Warren	16	1953
Warren E. Burger	17	1969
William H. Rehnquist	19	1986
John G. Roberts	8	2005

Data source: http://en.wikipedia.org/wiki/List_of_Justices_of_the_Supreme_Court_of_the_United_States

Use the table to answer the following:

a. Which chief justice served the longest term, and which served the shortest term? How many years did each of these chief justices serve?

John Marshall had the longest term, which was 34 years. He served from 1801 to 1835. John Rutledge served the shortest term, which was 1 year in 1795.

b. What is the median number of years these chief justices have served on the Supreme Court? Explain how you found the median and what it means in terms of the data.

First, you have to put the data in order. There are 17 justices, so the median would fall at the 9th value (11 years) counting from the top or from the bottom. The median is 11. Approximately half of the justices served less than or equal to 11 years, and half served greater than or equal to 11 years.

c. Make a box plot of the years the justices served. Describe the shape of the distribution and how the median and IQR relate to the box plot.

The distribution seems to have more justices serving a small number of years (on the lower end). The range (max − min) is 33 years, from 1 year to 34 years. The IQR is $18 - 6.5 = 11.5$, so about half of the chief justices had terms in the 11.5-year interval from 6.5 to 18 years.

d. Is the median halfway between the least and the most number of years served? Why or why not?

The halfway point on the number line between the smallest number of years served, 1, and the greatest number of years served, 34, is 17.5, but because the data are clustered in the lower end of the distribution, the median, 11, is to the left of (smaller than) 17.5. The middle of the interval from the smallest to the largest data value has no connection to the median. The median depends on how the data are spread out over the interval.

©2015 Great Minds eureka-math.org
G6-M6-TE-B3-1.3.1-01.2016

Exercises 2–3 (10 minutes): Downloading Songs

These exercises illustrate how box plots can be useful for large data sets. The five-number summary provides a way to think about the location of the smallest 25% of the data, the middle 50% of the data, and the largest 25% of the data. The questions in the exercises ask students to think about these percentages as well as their fraction equivalents.

- Why is a distribution with a lot of data values harder to describe than one with few values?
  - *It is more difficult to find the values of the median, Q1 and Q3.*

- Can you easily find the median from the data distribution in Exercise 2? Why or why not?
  - *It is not easy to find the median in Exercise 2 because there are a lot of data points.*

- In what situations might box plots be really useful?
  - *Box plots are particularly useful when comparing two or more data sets.*

Exercises 2–3: Downloading Songs

2. A broadband company timed how long it took to download 232 four-minute songs on a dial-up connection. The dot plot below shows their results.

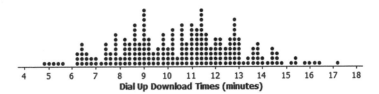

Dial Up Download Times (minutes)

a. What can you observe about the download times from the dot plot?

The smallest time was a little bit less than 5 minutes, and the largest is a little bit more than 17 minutes. Most of the times seem to be between 8 to 13 minutes.

b. Is it easy to tell whether or not 12.5 minutes is in the top quarter of the download times?

You cannot easily tell from the dot plot.

c. The box plot of the data is shown below. Now, answer parts (a) and (b) above using the box plot.

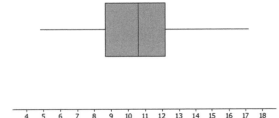

Dial Up Download Times (minutes)

Answer for part (a) based on the box plot: About half of the times are above 10.6 minutes. The distribution is roughly symmetric around the median. About half of the times are between 8.7 minutes and 12.2 minutes.

Answer for part (b) based on the box plot: 12.5 is above Q3, so it was in the top quarter of the data.

©2015 Great Minds eureka-math.org
G6-M6-TE-B3-1.3.1-01.2016

d.   What are the advantages of using a box plot to summarize a large data set? What are the disadvantages?

With lots of data, the dots in a dot plot overlap, and while you can see general patterns, it is hard to really get anything quantifiable. The box plot shows at least an approximate value for each of the five-number summary measures and gives a pretty good idea of how the data are spread out.

The disadvantage of box plots is that the specific values in the data set are not given.
Teacher note: It may be useful to have a brief class discussion of the advantages/disadvantages of dot plots and box plots. You can use the dot plot in part (a) and the box plot in part (b) to facilitate this discussion.

3.   Molly presented the box plots below to argue that using a dial-up connection would be better than using a broadband connection. She argued that the dial-up connection seems to have less variability around the median even though the overall range seems to be about the same for the download times using broadband. What would you say?

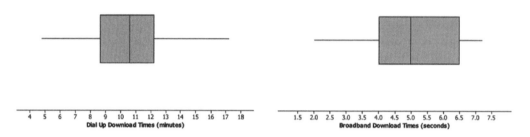

The scales are different for the two plots, and so are the units, so you cannot just look at the box plots. The time using broadband is centered near 5 seconds to download the song while the median for dial-up is almost 11 minutes for a song. This suggests that broadband is going to be faster than dial-up.
Teacher note: This is an important point. Make sure that students understand the importance of using the same scale if box plots are being constructed to compare two data distributions.

Exercises 4–5 (18 minutes): Rainfall

Students are asked to compare the variability that can be observed in dot plots of two different data sets. Students then use the data to make box plots and think about the distinction between comparing data distributions using dot plots and comparing using box plots. Working in pairs might help students sort out the ideas involved in the work and help them learn to communicate their thinking.

Ask students the following questions as they answer the questions in these exercises:

▪   Before looking at the graphs carefully, which city would you expect to have the most variability in the amount of precipitation? Explain your thinking.

The answer to this question is based on students having some knowledge of the two cities. If they are not aware of the cities, a short discussion about the location of each city and the general weather patterns of these cities might be considered. If time permits, locate each city on a map, and talk about what might influence the amount of precipitation in each city based on location and what type of precipitation (rain or snow) each city would have. Understanding data distributions usually involves understanding the context of the data.

▪   Notice that the horizontal scales are the same in both dot plots. Is this important? Why or why not?
    □   *Having the same scales is important if the two distributions are to be accurately compared. It is also important to have the same scales when comparing the box plots.*

©2015 Great Minds eureka-math.org
G6-M6-TE-B3-1.3.1-01.2016

Exercises 4–5: Rainfall

4. Data on the average rainfall for each of the twelve months of the year were used to construct the two dot plots below.

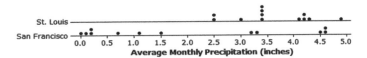

a. How many data points are in each dot plot? What does each data point represent?

   There are 12 data points in the St. Louis dot plot. There are also 12 data points in the San Francisco dot plot.
   Each data point represents the average monthly precipitation in inches for one month.

b. Make a conjecture about which city has the most variability in the average monthly amount of precipitation and how this would be reflected in the IQRs for the data from both cities.

   San Francisco has the most variability in the average monthly amount of precipitation. It should have the largest IQR of the two cities.

c. Based on the dot plots, what are the approximate values of the interquartile ranges (IQRs) for the average monthly precipitations for each city? Use the IQRs to compare the cities.

   The answers that follow are based on estimates from the dot plot. Students might get slightly different values. For St. Louis, the IQR is $4.2 - 3.2 = 1$; for San Francisco, the IQR is $3.9 - 0.2 = 3.7$. About the middle half of the monthly precipitation amounts in St. Louis are within 1 inch of each other. In San Francisco, the middle half of the monthly precipitation amounts are within about 4 inches of each other.

d. In an earlier lesson, the average monthly temperatures were rounded to the nearest degree Fahrenheit. Would it make sense to round the amount of precipitation to the nearest inch? Why or why not?

   Answers will vary. Possible answers include: It would not make sense because the numbers are pretty close together, or yes, it would make sense because you would still get a good idea of how the precipitation varied. If you rounded to the nearest inch, the IQR for San Francisco would be 4 because three of the values round to 0, and three of the values round to 5. The IQR for St. Louis would be 1 because most of the values round to 3 or 4. In both cases, that is pretty close to the IQR found in part (c).

5. Use the data from Exercise 4 to answer the following.

   a. Make a box plot of the monthly precipitation amounts for each city using the same scale.

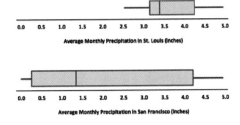

   b. Compare the percent of months that have above 2 inches of precipitation for the two cities. Explain your thinking.

   In St. Louis, the average amount of precipitation each month is always over 2 inches, while this happens, at most, for half of the months in San Francisco because the median amount of precipitation is just above 1 inch.

c. How does the top 25% of the average monthly precipitations compare for the two cities?

The top 25% of the precipitation amounts in the two cities are spread over about the same interval (about 4 to 5 inches). St. Louis has a bit more spread; the top 25% in St. Louis are between 4.2 inches and 4.8 inches, while the top 25% in San Francisco are all very close to 4.5 inches.

d. Describe the intervals that contain the smallest 25% of the average monthly precipitation amounts for each city.

In St. Louis, the smallest 25% of the monthly averages are between about 2.5 inches and 3.0 inches; in San Francisco, the smallest averages are much lower, ranging from 0 to 0.2 inches.

e. Think about the dot plots and the box plots. Which representation do you think helps you the most in understanding how the data vary?

Answers will vary. Some sample answers are provided below.

The dot plot because we can see individual values.

The box plot because it just shows how the data are spread out in each of the four sections.

Note: The data used in this problem are displayed in the table below.

Average Precipitation (inches)

	Jan.	Feb.	Mar.	Apr.	May	June	July	Aug.	Sept.	Oct.	Nov.	Dec.
St. Louis	2.45	2.48	3.36	4.10	4.80	4.34	4.19	3.41	3.38	3.43	4.22	2.96
San Francisco	4.5	4.61	3.76	1.46	0.70	0.16	0	0.06	0.21	1.12	3.16	4.56

Data source: http://www.weather.com

Closing (2 minutes)

- When comparing two box plots, what is important about the scale?
  - □ *The scales for all box plots must be the same.*
- When are box plots the most useful to compare different data sets?
  - □ *Box plots are a good tool to compare large data sets.*

Exit Ticket (5 minutes)

©2015 Great Minds eureka-math.org
G6-M6-TE-B3-1.3.1-01.2016

Name _____   Date_____

Lesson 16: Understanding Box Plots

Exit Ticket

Data on the number of pets per family for students in a sixth-grade class are summarized in the box plot below:

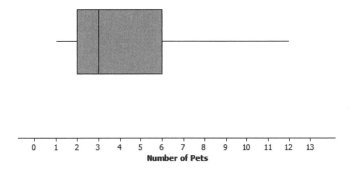

1. Can you tell how many families have two pets? Explain why or why not.

2. Given the box plot above, which of the following statements are true? If the statement is false, modify it to make the statement true.

   a. Every family has at least one pet.

   b. About one-fourth of the families have six or more pets.

   c. Most of the families have three pets.

   d. About half of the families have two or fewer pets.

   e. About three-fourths of the families have two or more pets.

Lesson 16:   Understanding Box Plots   **199**

©2015 Great Minds eureka-math.org
G6-M6-TE-B3-1.3.1-01.2016

Exit Ticket Sample Solutions

Data on the number of pets per family for students in a sixth-grade class are summarized in the box plot below:

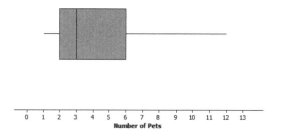

1. Can you tell how many families have two pets? Explain why or why not.

    You cannot tell from the box plot. You only know that the lower quartile (Q1) is 2 pets. You do not know how many families are included in the data set.

2. Given the box plot above, which of the following statements are true? If the statement is false, modify it to make the statement true.

    a. Every family has at least one pet.

        True

    b. About one-fourth of the families have six or more pets.

        True

    c. Most of the families have three pets.

        False, because you cannot determine the number of any specific data value. Revise to "You cannot determine the number of pets most families have."

    d. About half of the families have two or fewer pets.

        False. Revise to "About half of the families have three or fewer pets."

    e. About three-fourths of the families have two or more pets.

        True

©2015 Great Minds eureka-math.org
G6-M6-TE-B3-1.3.1-01.2016

EUREKA
MATH™

Problem Set Sample Solutions

All students should do Problems 1 and 2. Problem 4 could be an extension, making connections to previous work on the mean.

---

1. The box plots below summarize the ages at the time of the award for leading actress and leading actor Academy Award winners.

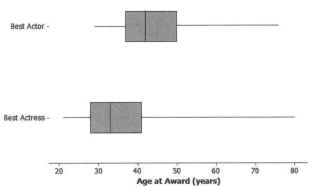

    Data source: http://en.wikipedia.org/wiki/List_of_Best_Actor_winners_by_age_at_win
    http://en.wikipedia.org/wiki/List_of_Best_Actress_winners_by_age_at_win

    a. Based on the box plots, do you think it is harder for an older woman to win an Academy Award for best actress than it is for an older man to win a best actor award? Why or why not?

        Answers will vary. Students might take either side as long as they give an explanation for why they made the choice they did that is based on the box plots.

    b. The oldest female to win an Academy Award was Jessica Tandy in 1990 for *Driving Miss Daisy*. The oldest actor was Henry Fonda for *On Golden Pond* in 1982. How old were they when they won the award? How can you tell? Were they a lot older than most of the other winners?

        Henry Fonda was 76, and Jessica Tandy was 80. I know this because those are the maximum values. You cannot tell if there were actors or actresses that were nearly as old.

    c. The 2013 winning actor was Daniel Day-Lewis for *Lincoln*. He was 55 years old at that time. What can you say about the percent of male award winners who were older than Daniel Day-Lewis when they won their Oscars?

        He was in the upper quarter and one of the older actors. Fewer than 25% of the male award winners were older than Daniel Day-Lewis.

    d. Use the information provided by the box plots to write a paragraph supporting or refuting the claim that fewer older actresses than actors win Academy Awards.

        Overall, the box plot for actresses starts about 10 years younger than actors and is centered around a lower age than the box plot for actors. The median age for actresses who won the award is 33, and for actors it is 42. The upper quartile is also lower for actresses, 41, compared to 49 for actors. The range for actresses' ages is larger, $80 - 21 = 59$, compared to the range for actors, $76 - 29 = 47$. About $\frac{3}{4}$ of the actresses who won the award were younger than the median age for the men.

©2015 Great Minds eureka-math.org
G6-M6-TE-B3-1.3.1-01.2016

2. The scores of sixth and seventh graders on a test about polygons and their characteristics are summarized in the box plots below.

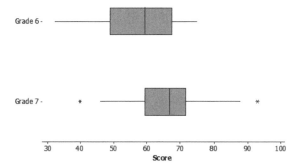

a. In which grade did the students do the best? Explain how you can tell.

Three-fourths of the seventh-grade students did better than half of the sixth graders. You can tell by comparing Q1 for Grade 7 to the median for Grade 6. Therefore, the seventh-grade students performed the best.

b. Why do you think two of the data values in Grade 7 are not part of the line segments?

The highest and lowest scores were pretty far away from the other scores, so they were marked separately.

c. How do the median scores for the two grades compare? Is this surprising? Why or why not?

The median score in Grade 7 was higher than the median in Grade 6. This makes sense because the seventh graders should know more than the sixth graders.

d. How do the IQRs compare for the two grades?

The middle half of the Grade 7 scores were close together in a span of about 11 with the median around 66. The middle half of the Grade 6 scores were spread over a larger span, about 17 points from about 50 to 67.

3. A formula for the IQR could be written as $Q3 - Q1 = IQR$. Suppose you knew the IQR and the Q1. How could you find the Q3?

$Q3 = IQR + Q1$. *Add the lower quartile to the IQR.*

4. Consider the statement, "Historically, the average length of service as chief justice on the Supreme Court has been less than 15 years; however, since 1969 the average length of service has increased." Use the data given in Exercise 1 to answer the following questions.

a. Do you agree or disagree with the statement? Explain your thinking.

The mean number of years as chief justice overall is about 13. The mean number of years since 1969 is about 14.7. Even though the mean has increased, it does not seem like a big difference because there have only been three justices since then to cover a span of 44 years (and three times 13 is 39, so not enough to really show an increasing trend).

b. Would your answer change if you used the median number of years rather than the mean?

The median overall was 11 years; the median since 1969 was 17 years, which is considerably larger. This seems to justify the statement.

Lesson 16:   Understanding Box Plots

©2015 Great Minds eureka-math.org
G6-M6-TE-B3-1.3.1-01.2016

Mathematics Curriculum

Topic D

Summarizing and Describing Distributions

6.SP.B.4, 6.SP.B.5

Focus Standards:	6.SP.B.4	Display numerical data in plots on a number line, including dot plots, histograms, and box plots.
	6.SP.B.5	Summarize numerical data sets in relation to their context, such as by:
		a. Reporting the number of observations.
		b. Describing the nature of the attribute under investigation, including how it was measured and its units of measurement.
		c. Giving quantitative measures of center (median and/or mean) and variability (interquartile range and/or mean absolute deviation), as well as describing any overall pattern and any striking deviations from the overall pattern with reference to the context in which the data were gathered.
		d. Relating the choice of measures of center and variability to the shape of the data distribution and the context in which the data were gathered.
Instructional Days:	6	
Lesson 17:	Developing a Statistical Project (E)[1]	
Lesson 18:	Connecting Graphical Representations and Numerical Summaries (P)	
Lesson 19:	Comparing Data Distributions (P)	
Lesson 20:	Describing Center, Variability, and Shape of a Data Distribution from a Graphical Representation (P)	
Lesson 21:	Summarizing a Data Distribution by Describing Center, Variability, and Shape (E)	
Lesson 22:	Presenting a Summary of a Statistical Project (E)	

[1]Lesson Structure Key: **P**-Problem Set Lesson, **M**-Modeling Cycle Lesson, **E**-Exploration Lesson, **S**-Socratic Lesson

Topic D: Summarizing and Describing Distributions

203

In Topic D, students integrate what they have learned about graphical and numerical data summaries in previous topics. They match dot plots and histograms to numerical measures of center and variability. Students estimate means and medians from graphical representations of data distributions. They also estimate mean absolute deviation (MAD) and interquartile range (IQR) from graphical representations based on an understanding of data distributions in terms of shape, center, and variability. Two of the lessons in this topic (Lessons 17 and 22) allow students to experience the four-step process described at the beginning of this module through the completion of a project. In this project, students experience the four-step investigative process by (1) formulating a statistical question, (2) designing and implementing a plan to collect data, (3) summarizing collected data graphically and numerically, and (4) using the data to answer the question posed.

©2015 Great Minds eureka-math.org
G6-M6-TE-B3-1.3.1-01.2016

Lesson 17: Developing a Statistical Project

Student Outcomes

- Students formulate a statistical question and a plan to collect data to answer the question.
- Given a statistical question, students use data to construct appropriate graphical and numerical summaries.
- Students use graphical and numerical summaries to answer a statistical question.

Lesson Notes

The following agenda provides an overview of the content of this exploration lesson.

> Part 1: Review of Statistical Questions
>
> Part 2: A Review of a Statistical Investigation
>
> Part 3: Developing Statistical Questions

In this lesson, students implement the four-step investigative process using questions discussed in previous lessons. Students then choose their own statistical questions and provide a plan to collect data to answer their questions. After their plans have been approved, students collect and organize their data and proceed to summarize the data using graphical and numerical summaries, which are then used in the following lessons. The activity in this lesson is designed to provide a review of the four-step process used to carry out a statistical study.

Students are expected to provide a daily update regarding their progress in collecting and summarizing the data they propose in this lesson. Students should have completed the numerical and graphical summaries before they start Lesson 21. Lesson 21 reviews the four steps and directs students to create a poster (or an outline for a presentation) based on their questions, the data collected, and the numerical and graphical summaries. During Lesson 22, students explain their statistical projects to their classmates or invited guests.

Exploratory Challenge

Review of Statistical Questions (8 minutes)

The following questions were presented throughout the module. Have students discuss in small groups what the questions have in common and why multiple questions use the word *typical*.

Exploratory Challenge

Review of Statistical Questions

Statistical questions you investigated in this module included the following:

- How many hours of sleep do sixth graders typically get on a night when there is school the next day?
- What is the typical number of books read over the course of 6 months by a sixth grader?
- What is the typical heart rate of a student in a sixth-grade class?
- How many hours does a sixth grader typically spend playing a sport or a game outdoors?

©2015 Great Minds eureka-math.org
G6-M6-TE-B3-1.3.1-01.2016

- What are the head circumferences of adults interested in buying baseball hats?
- How long is the battery life of a certain brand of batteries?
- How many pets do students have?
- How long does it take students to get to school?
- What is a typical daily temperature in New York City?
- What is the typical weight of a backpack for students at a certain school?
- What is the typical number of french fries in a large order from a fast food restaurant?
- What is the typical number of minutes a student spends on homework each day?
- What is the typical height of a vertical jump for a player in the NBA?

What do these questions have in common?

All of these questions are statistical questions because they can be answered by collecting data, and there is variability in the data.

Why do several of these questions include the word *typical*?

Answers will vary. Students may focus on the idea that typical *suggests finding a single number that summarizes the data collected to answer the statistical question.*

Two discussion questions are posed to highlight the characteristics of a statistical question that were initially developed in Lesson 1 and continued throughout the lessons of this module.

- What is common about these questions?

If necessary, remind students that answering each of these questions requires data. It is also anticipated that the data would vary, making them statistical questions.

  - *All of the questions could be answered by data that will vary.*
- Why do several of these questions include the word *typical*?

  - *Answering statistical questions often involves describing a data distribution. Often, we are interested in finding a single value that describes what is typical of the values in a data set.*

Remind students that asking what value is typical for a group is a statistical question, whereas asking about the value of a single observation or about a single individual is not a statistical question because it is not a question that would be answered by collecting data that vary.

- Which questions presented would be answered by collecting data that are categorical, and which would be answered by collecting data that are numerical?

  - *All of the questions presented would be answered by collecting data that are numerical.*

Ask students to think of a statistical question that would involve collecting categorical data. Consider examples such as "If our school were to select a school color that would be used in making T-shirts, what color would students prefer?" In this case, the data collected would be categorical.

- You will be completing your own statistical investigation. When it is time to think of your own question, remember that it should be a statistical question that would result in collecting numerical data.

A Review of a Statistical Investigation (15 minutes)

To provide students an opportunity to see the entire four-step process, review the steps in a statistical study using one or more of the questions they studied in the previous lessons (listed previously in this lesson). A table to structure the discussion of the first three steps of the process is provided in the student lesson. First, encourage students to select at least one of the statistical questions given and write it in the first row of the table. Next, students should recall the data collected to answer this question and to think about how the data might have been collected. Third, review the types of numerical summaries and graphs that were introduced in the lessons. Generally, students are expected to start with a graphical summary of the data. Then, based on the shape of the data distribution, the mean and MAD or the median and IQR would be used to describe center and spread. Finally, have students use the summaries to answer the statistical question. Again, reviewing one of the investigations from a previous lesson provides an opportunity to connect a conclusion to the other three steps.

MP.4

The following table is a completed example that uses the question, "How many hours of sleep do sixth graders typically get on a night when there is school the next day?"

> **A Review of Statistical Investigation**
>
> Recall from the very first lesson in this module that a statistical question is a question answered by data that you anticipate will vary.
>
> Let's review the steps of a statistical investigation.
>
> Step 1: Pose a question that can be answered by data.
>
> Step 2: Collect appropriate data.
>
> Step 3: Summarize the data with graphs and numerical summaries.
>
> Step 4: Answer the question posed in Step 1 using the numerical summaries and graphs.
>
> The first step is to pose a statistical question. Select one of the questions investigated in this module, and write it in the following Statistical Study Review Template.
>
> The second step is to collect the data. In all of these investigations, you were given data. How do you think the data for the question you selected in Step 1 were collected? Write your answer in the summary below for Step 2.
>
> The third step involves the various ways you summarize the data. List the various ways you summarized the data in the space for Step 3.

> *Scaffolding:*
>
> Depending on students' confidence with this process, the teacher can decide if the entire class picks the same question to discuss (the discussion is easier to follow along) or if each group picks its own question to discuss.

Statistical Study Review Template

Step 1: Pose a statistical question.

How many hours of sleep do sixth graders typically get on a night when there is school the next day? (Lesson 3)

Step 2: Collect the data.

Students from a sixth-grade class might have been asked to indicate how many hours they slept. The data would consist of the answers from all of the students.

Step 3: Summarize the data.

The first summary was to organize the data in a dot plot. This data set indicated a nearly symmetrical data distribution. Numerical summaries of the mean and the MAD or the median and IQR would provide a description of the typical number of hours of sleep for sixth-grade students and a measure of how much variability there was in the sleep times.

Step 4: Answer the question.

From the data, we can see that the typical sixth grader gets about 8.5 hours of sleep when there is school the next day because this is the mean of the data. The MAD is only 1 hour, so there is not a lot of variability in the data.

Before completing the fourth and final step, students may need to look back at the lesson where the question was presented. Although it may be difficult to answer the statistical question in this setting, it is important to point out the different types of numerical and graphical summaries that can be used for this final step. Describing a data distribution in terms of shape, center, and spread or, depending on the shape of the data distribution, calculating the mean and MAD or the median and IQR of the data often provides an answer to the statistical question.

 Using the questions presented earlier in this lesson, complete as many of these summaries as necessary in order for students to understand what is expected of them in completing a statistical project.

Make sure students understand that each lesson was built around a statistical question and that data were then summarized using graphs and the measures of center and variability. The process of collecting the data, however, was not a step students implemented in previous lessons. This lesson adds this new and important step into the investigative process. In general, collecting data is done by asking students in the class to respond to the questions. In some cases, students may pose a question that could involve collecting data from other students in the school or from other friends or family connections. Consider encouraging some students to obtain data from an appropriate website. Monitor the website choice by asking students to clearly indicate the site they plan to use. Check out the site to make sure students are getting appropriate data. A good site that was referenced in several lessons is the website of the American Statistical Association and its Census at School project (http://www.amstat.org/education/pdfs/Census_at_School-flyer.pdf).

Often, students at this grade level do not appreciate data. They may formulate a question that is unclear to those who are expected to answer it; for example, "How many hours of sleep do you get?" Several students answering that question would want to know what day of the week they should use. Help students clearly state their questions to avoid possibly collecting inaccurate data. Finally, be sure to screen the questions to make sure they are appropriate.

Ideas for students to consider have been provided previously in this lesson. Students could select one of these questions in their own statistical projects. Review the winning posters from the American Statistical Association's poster competition (www.amstat.org/education/posterprojects/index.cfm) for additional ideas.

©2015 Great Minds eureka-math.org
G6-M6-TE-B3-1.3.1-01.2016

Other contexts to suggest during a discussion with students include the following:

- Number of languages spoken by teachers at your school
- Height of students at your school (would require a sample of students, as not every student attending the school could be included in the data collection)
- Number of words in the sentences of a Dr. Seuss book
- Number of siblings for students in the school (would require a sample of students)

As indicated with some of the above suggestions, students may select a question that would require selecting a sample. Obtaining a good sample is an important part of statistical investigation. Students are introduced to random sampling and random samples in Grade 7. For this project, however, challenge students to make sure that they consider ways in which a good representation of the population is collected. Although introducing students to a definition of *random samples* is not expected, students should be challenged to think about collecting a representative sample in order to answer their statistical questions.

Developing Statistical Questions (15 minutes)

Developing Statistical Questions

Now it is your turn to answer a statistical question based on data you collect. Before you collect the data, explore possible statistical questions. For each question, indicate the data that you would collect and summarize to answer the question. Also, indicate how you plan to collect the data.

Think of questions that could be answered by data collected from members of your class or school or data that could be collected from recognized websites (such as the American Statistical Association and the Census at School project). Your teacher will need to approve both your question and your plan to collect data before data are collected.

As a class, explore possibilities for a statistical investigation. Record some of the ideas discussed by your class using the following table.

Possible Statistical Questions	What data would be collected, and how would the data be collected?

©2015 Great Minds eureka-math.org
G6-M6-TE-B3-1.3.1-01.2016

After discussing several of the possibilities for a statistical project, prepare a statistical question and a plan to collect the data. After your teacher approves your question and data collection plan, begin collecting the data. Carefully organize your data as you begin developing the numerical and graphical summaries to answer your statistical question. In future lessons, you will be directed to begin creating a poster or an outline of a presentation that will be shared with your teacher and other members of your class.

Complete the following to present to your teacher:

1. The statistical question for my investigation is:

2. Here is how I propose to collect my data. (Include how you are going to collect your data and a clear description of what you plan to measure or count.)

Closing (2 minutes)

- In order to complete your statistical investigation, do you need to formulate a statistical question that results in numerical or categorical data?

    □   *For this project, I need to collect numerical data in order to create different numerical and graphical summaries of my data.*

Lesson Summary

A statistical investigation involves a four-step investigative process:

- Pose questions that can be answered by data.
- Design a plan for collecting appropriate data, and then use the plan to collect data.
- Analyze the data.
- Interpret results and draw valid conclusions from the data to answer the question posed.

Exit Ticket (5 minutes)

©2015 Great Minds eureka-math.org
G6-M6-TE-B3-1.3.1-01.2016

Name _____ Date _____

Lesson 17: Developing a Statistical Project

Exit Ticket

1. What is a statistical question?

2. What are the four steps in a statistical investigation?

©2015 Great Minds eureka-math.org
G6-M6-TE-B3-1.3.1-01.2016

Exit Ticket Sample Solutions

> 1. **What is a statistical question?**
>
>   *A statistical question is one that can be answered by collecting data and where there is variability in the data.*
>
>
> 2. **What are the four steps in a statistical investigation?**
>
>   *Step 1: Pose a statistical question.*
>   *Step 2: Collect data.*
>   *Step 3: Summarize the data.*
>   *Step 4: Answer the statistical question posed.*

Problem Set Sample Solutions

> **Your teacher will outline steps you are expected to complete in the next several days to develop this project. Keep in mind that the first step is to formulate a statistical question. With one of the statistical questions posed in this lesson or with a new one developed in this lesson, describe your question and plan to collect and summarize data. Complete the process as outlined by your teacher.**

A formal Problem Set has not been added to this lesson. However, teachers are encouraged to design a Problem Set based on students' progress during this lesson. The following options are possible ideas for designing a Problem Set. Teacher discretion in organizing the project is important.

Option 1: Students who struggled with completing the four-step table developed around one of the questions used in this lesson should be encouraged to select a different question and complete the table for this second question. The first three steps provide students with a structure for connecting a question to a plan for collecting and then summarizing data. These steps were illustrated in the previous lessons; however, in this lesson, students need to bring the steps together. Once students understand these steps for a given question, they are ready to formulate their own questions and data collection plans.

Option 2: Students provide a question and a data collection plan to the teacher for review as outlined in the lesson. Direct students to complete the four-step table for their questions and plans. Using the table provided in this lesson is an excellent way for students to organize their progress, plus it provides a good record for the teacher to understand how students are thinking at the beginning of this project. For students ready to begin this process, direct them to provide a summary of their statistical questions, a plan for collecting the data, and a summary of the data they anticipate to collect. Although these steps were discussed in the lesson, organizing this into a table similar to the one presented in the lesson provides a summary of student progress. Periodically ask students during the next several days for an update on their progress by providing a summary of the table used in this lesson.

Option 3: For students going beyond the questions outlined in the lesson, they need to provide specific descriptions of what they plan to research and how they plan to collect the data. For example, if a student proposed to explore research on honeybees, make sure the student clearly indicates the statistical question (or the question to be answered by data that are anticipated to vary), where she plans to obtain the data, and how she plans to summarize the data. A brief written report or summary of student progress might constitute a workable Problem Set option for students at this level.

©2015 Great Minds eureka-math.org
G6-M6-TE-B3-1.3.1-01.2016

Lesson 18: Connecting Graphical Representations and Numerical Summaries

Student Outcomes

- Students demonstrate an understanding of graphical representations (dot plots and histograms) and numerical summaries by matching numerical summaries to graphical representations of distributions.

Lesson Notes

In the final lessons of this module, students deepen their understanding of the graphical representations and numerical summaries that they have learned in the module. As students apply their knowledge in a variety of contexts, have them think about the statistical question that they posed in the previous lesson. As they see different numerical summaries and graphical representations, they can think about how they might summarize the data they are collecting for their project.

Students may find this lesson challenging. It may be helpful to have a short discussion as each new context is introduced to make sure that students are comfortable with the context before asking them to work on the exercises related to that context. If time becomes an issue in this lesson, consider moving Exercises 10–11 and/or Exercise 12 to the Problem Set.

Classwork

Example 1 (3 minutes): Summary Information from Graphs

Review dot plots and histograms. Important points that should be included in the review include the following:

- Dot plots and histograms are both graphical displays of a data distribution.
- You can learn a lot from looking at a graphical display of a data distribution. In particular, you can get a sense of what a typical value is and how much the data values tend to differ from one another.
- Numerical summary measures (such as the mean and MAD or the median and the IQR) complement graphical displays.
- Summary measures can be estimated from graphical displays or can be calculated more precisely from the data.

©2015 Great Minds eureka-math.org
G6-M6-TE-B3-1.3.1-01.2016

Example 1: Summary Information from Graphs

Here is a data set of the ages (in years) of 43 participants who ran in a 5-kilometer race.

20	30	30	35	36	34	38	46
45	18	43	23	47	27	21	30
32	32	31	32	36	74	41	41
51	61	50	34	34	34	35	28
57	26	29	49	41	36	37	41
38	30	30					

Here are some summary statistics, a dot plot, and a histogram for the data:

Minimum $= 18$, Q1 $= 30$, Median $= 35$, Q3 $= 41$, Maximum $= 74$; Mean $= 36.8$, MAD $= 8.1$

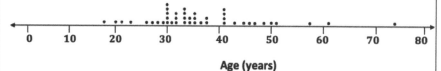

Age (years)

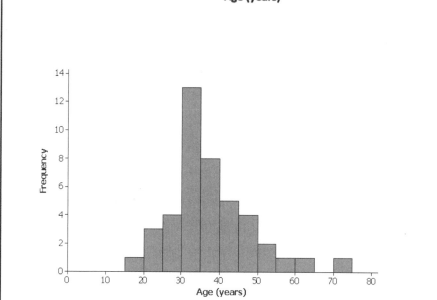

> *Scaffolding:*
>
> Recall that a dot plot includes a dot on a scale or number line for each value in a data set. Dots are stacked on top of one another when the same data value occurs more than once. Recall also that a histogram uses intervals of equal width on the horizontal scale and has a vertical scale that corresponds to either frequency or relative frequency. For each interval, the area of the bar is proportional to the number of observations in the interval, so the taller the bar, the greater the number of observations in that interval.

Exercises 1–7 (7 minutes)

Pose these questions one at a time. Encourage students to discuss the answers in small groups, and then discuss possible answers as part of a whole-class discussion.

Exercises 1–7

1.   Based on the histogram, would you describe the shape of the data distribution as approximately symmetric or as skewed? Would you have reached this same conclusion looking at the dot plot?

Both graphs show a slightly skewed right data distribution.

©2015 Great Minds eureka-math.org
G6-M6-TE-B3-1.3.1-01.2016

2. If there had been 500 participants instead of just 43, would you use a dot plot or a histogram to display the data?

    Dot plots do not work as well for large data sets, so with 500 ages, I would probably use a histogram to display the data distribution.

3. What is something you can see in the dot plot that is not as easy to see in the histogram?

    When using the histogram, we cannot determine the exact minimum or maximum age—for example, we only know that the minimum age is between 15 and 20 years of age. Also, we can only approximate the median (we cannot figure out the exact median value from a histogram).

    Since the dot plot provides us with a dot for each observation, we can see the actual data values. With the dot plot, we can see that the minimum is 18. The median is the 22nd observation (since there are 43 observations), and the 22nd dot counting from left to right is 35 (we cannot be that precise with the histogram). We can also see that the oldest runner (74) appears to be a more extreme departure from the rest of the data in the dot plot.

4. Do the dot plot and the histogram seem to be centered in about the same place?

    Yes. As both graphs are based on the same data, they should generally communicate the same information regarding center.

5. Do both the dot plot and the histogram convey information about the variability in the age distribution?

    Yes, as both graphs are based on the same data, they should generally communicate the same information regarding variability. However, as mentioned earlier, the oldest runner (74) appears to be a more extreme departure from the rest of the data in the dot plot. This does not show up as much in the histogram.

6. If you did not have the original data set and only had the dot plot and the histogram, would you be able to find the value of the median age from the dot plot?

    Yes. See the response to Exercise 3.

7. Explain why you would only be able to estimate the value of the median if you only had a histogram of the data.

    The median is the 22nd ordered observation in this data set since there are 43 observations. Counting from left to right, we know that the first 21 observations are in the first 4 intervals: 15–20 (1 value), 20–25 (3 values), 25–30 (4 values), and 30–35 (13 values). Cumulatively, we have encountered the lowest 21 observations by the time we are finished with the 30–35 interval. So, the 22nd value must be in the next interval, which is 35–40 years of age. We just cannot determine the exact value from the histogram.

Exercises 8–12 (25 minutes): Graphs and Numerical Summaries

Pose the questions to students one at a time. Allow for more than one student to offer an answer for each question, encouraging a brief discussion (e.g., lasting approximately two minutes).

Note: In some cases, the questions have more than one reasonable answer, and some answers may not be exact.

©2015 Great Minds eureka-math.org
G6-M6-TE-B3-1.3.1-01.2016

Exercises 8–12: Graphs and Numerical Summaries

8. Suppose that a newspaper article was written about the race. The article included the histogram shown here and also said, "The race attracted many older runners this year. The median age was 45." Based on the histogram, how can you tell that this is an incorrect statement?

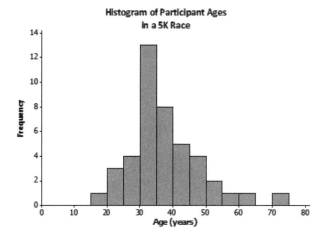

Histogram of Participant Ages in a 5K Race

Several answers are possible.

From the histogram, it appears that less than half of the runners are 45 or older (or alternatively, more than half of the runners are younger than 45).

The value of the median is in the 35–40 age interval.

9. One of the histograms below is another correctly drawn histogram for the runners' ages. Select the correct histogram, and explain how you determined which graph is correct (and which one is incorrect) based on the summary measures and dot plot.

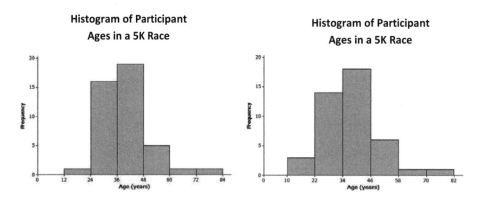

Histogram of Participant Ages in a 5K Race

Histogram of Participant Ages in a 5K Race

One of the objectives of this question is to reinforce the idea that there is more than one way to draw a proper histogram for a distribution. This question is especially detail oriented because students need to carefully reconcile components of the histogram with the data set given in Example 1. The histogram on the right is the correct one because it is consistent with the dot pot/data. Most notably, the histogram on the right correctly shows there are 3 runners in the 10–22 age group, while the left histogram shows only 1 runner in the 12–24 age group (and there are actually 4 runners in that interval). Other intervals in the left histogram do not match the dot plot/data (e.g., the 48–60 group), so several answers are possible.

EUREKA
MATH™

©2015 Great Minds eureka-math.org
G6-M6-TE-B3-1.3.1-01.2016

10. The histogram below represents the age distribution of the population of Kenya in 2010.

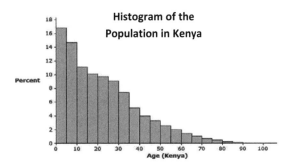

Histogram of the
Population in Kenya

a.   How do we know from the graph above that the first quartile (Q1) of this age distribution is between 5 and 10 years of age?

Since a histogram should display information that is consistent with summary measures, we are seeking a data value such that 25% of the distribution is at or below that value. While the 0–5 age group represents approximately the lowest 17%, the next group (age 5–10) appears to account for approximately the next 15% of the distribution. This means that about 17% is below 5 and about 32% is below 10. So, the 25% mark would be somewhere between 5 and 10 years.

b.   Someone believes that the median age in Kenya is about 30. Based on the histogram, is 30 years a good estimate of the median age for Kenya? Explain why it is or why it is not.

The median does not appear to be 30 years of age. Specifically, the 50ᵗʰ percentile estimated by adding approximate percentages (and/or visually assessing the point at which the area seems split evenly) appears to be in the 15–20 age group.

11. The histogram below represents the age distribution of the population of the United States in 2010. Based on the histogram, which of the following ranges do you think includes the median age for the United States: 20–30, 30–40, or 40–50? Why?

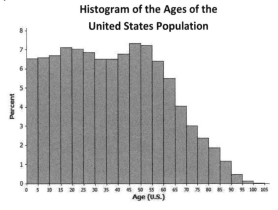

Histogram of the Ages of the
United States Population

Using similar arguments as described in the response to Exercise 10 part (b), the median appears to be in the 30–40 age group, most likely in the 35–40 interval.

EUREKA
MATH™

©2015 Great Minds eureka-math.org
G6-M6-TE-B3-1.3.1-01.2016

12. Consider the following three dot plots. Note: The same scale is used in each dot plot.

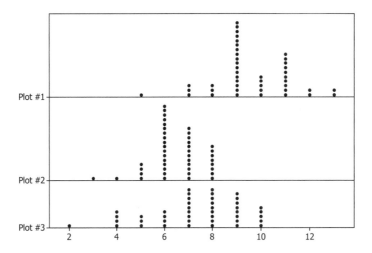

a. Which dot plot has a median of 8? Explain why you selected this dot plot over the other two.

Plot 3—It is the only distribution visually centered near 8, and one can tell that the 22nd ordered observation (the median in this case) is 8.

b. Which dot plot has a mean of 9.6? Explain why you selected this dot plot over the other two.

Plot 1—This dot plot is the only dot plot for which there could be a mean value as high as 9.6. It is the only dot plot with values of 11, 12, and 13, and there are several of these values.

c. Which dot plot has a median of 6 and a range of 5? Explain why you selected this dot plot over the other two.

Plot 2—It is the only dot plot that appears to be centered at 6. It is also the only dot plot with a range of 5 (each of the other dot plots has a range of 8).

Closing (5 minutes)

- What kinds of information about a data distribution can be seen in a graphical display that isn't conveyed by just a numerical measure of center or spread?
  - *Clustering, aspects of shape, extremeness of certain values, etc.*
- If dot plots can provide us with a way of figuring out exact (or nearly exact) observation values, why do we not always use dot plots to show a data distribution? What is a situation where a histogram might provide a better visual summary of the distribution or where a dot plot might not work well?
  - *A dot plot may be cumbersome for large data sets—like the population distribution of an entire country!*

Exit Ticket (5 minutes)

©2015 Great Minds eureka-math.org
G6-M6-TE-B3-1.3.1-01.2016

Name _____   Date_____

Lesson 18: Connecting Graphical Representations and Numerical Summaries

Exit Ticket

1. Many states produce maple syrup, which requires tapping sap from a maple tree. However, some states produce more pints of maple syrup per tap than other states. The following dot plot shows the pints of maple syrup yielded per tap in each of the 10 maple syrup–producing states in 2012.

Maple Syrup Yield per Tap by State (10 States - 2012 USDA Summary)

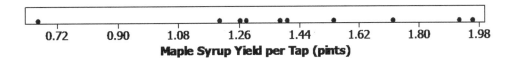

Maple Syrup Yield per Tap (pints)

Which *one* of the three sets of summary measures below could be correct summary measures for the data set displayed in the dot plot? For each choice that you eliminate, give at least one reason for eliminating it as a possibility.

a. Minimum = 0.66, Q1 = 1.26, Median = 1.385, Q3 = 1.71, Maximum = 1.95, Range = 2.4; Mean = 1.95, MAD = 0.28

b. Minimum = 0.66, Q1 = 1.26, Median = 1.71, Q3 = 1.92, Maximum = 1.95, Range = 1.29; Mean = 1.43, MAD = 2.27

c. Minimum = 0.66, Q1 = 1.26, Median = 1.385, Q3 = 1.71, Maximum = 1.95, Range = 1.29; Mean = 1.43, MAD = 0.28

©2015 Great Minds eureka-math.org
G6-M6-TE-B3-1.3.1-01.2016

2. Which *one* of the three histograms below could be a histogram for the data displayed in the dot plot in Problem 1? For each histogram that you eliminate, give at least one reason for eliminating it as a possibility.

a.

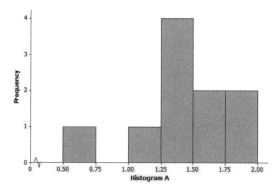

b.

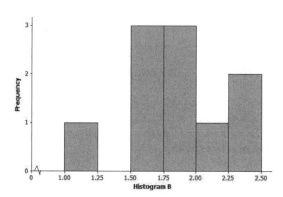

c.

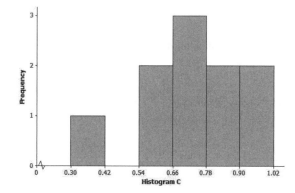

EUREKA
MATH™

©2015 Great Minds eureka-math.org
G6-M6-TE-B3-1.3.1-01.2016

Exit Ticket Sample Solutions

Note: Students are only expected to provide one reason for eliminating a choice in Problems 1 and 2.

---

1. Many states produce maple syrup, which requires tapping sap from a maple tree. However, some states produce more pints of maple syrup per tap than other states. The following dot plot shows the pints of maple syrup yielded per tap in each of the 10 maple syrup–producing states in 2012.

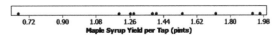

Maple Syrup Yield per Tap by State (10 States - 2012 USDA Summary)

Maple Syrup Yield per Tap (pints)

Which *one* of the three sets of summary measures below could be correct summary measures for the data set displayed in the dot plot? For each choice you eliminate, give at least one reason for eliminating it as a possibility.

a. Minimum $= 0.66$, Q1 $= 1.26$, Median $= 1.385$, Q3 $= 1.71$, Maximum $= 1.95$, Range $= 2.4$;
Mean $= 1.95$, MAD $= 0.28$

b. Minimum $= 0.66$, Q1 $= 1.26$, Median $= 1.71$, Q3 $= 1.92$, Maximum $= 1.95$, Range $= 1.29$;
Mean $= 1.43$, MAD $= 2.27$

c. Minimum $= 0.66$, Q1 $= 1.26$, Median $= 1.385$, Q3 $= 1.71$, Maximum $= 1.95$, Range $= 1.29$;
Mean $= 1.43$, MAD $= 0.28$

The correct answer is (c).

Choice (a) would not work because the range is too large. For the data set, the difference between maximum and minimum is only 1.29 pints. Also, the mean would not be that close to (or the same as) the maximum value in this case.

Choice (b) would not work because a median value of 1.71 would be too high. By estimating the dot values, we see that the 5th and 6th ordered observations (the median for a data set of 10 items) are near 1.4. Also, the MAD is much too large because the range of the data set is only 1.29 pints.

2. Which *one* of the three histograms below could be a histogram for the data displayed in the dot plot in Problem 1? For each histogram that you eliminate, give at least one reason for eliminating it as a possibility.

The correct answer is histogram (a).

Histograms (b) and (c) are for data sets with similar shape features to the correct graph (histogram (a)), but the range and distribution of values do not match the data set in the dot plot. For example, histogram (b) would not be valid, as it is based on 3 data values of 2 pints or more, and there are no values that large in the original dot plot. Also, the smallest value in histogram (b) is at least 1 pint, and the actual data set contains a value less than 1 pint. Histogram (c) is based on values that are smaller than many of those in the dot plot; in fact, all of the values in histogram (c) are less than 1.02 pints, and nearly all of the 10 observations in the actual data set are greater than 1.02.

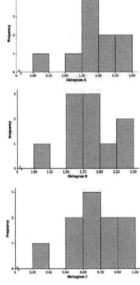

©2015 Great Minds eureka-math.org
G6-M6-TE-B3-1.3.1-01.2016

Problem Set Sample Solutions

1. The following histogram shows the amount of coal produced (by state) for the 20 largest coal-producing states in 2011. Many of these states produced less than 50 million tons of coal, but one state produced over 400 million tons (Wyoming). For the histogram, which *one* of the three sets of summary measures could match the graph? For each choice that you eliminate, give at least one reason for eliminating the choice.

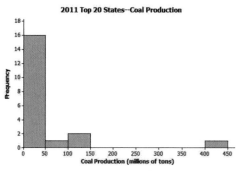

2011 Top 20 States—Coal Production

Source: U.S. Coal Production by State data as reported by the National Mining Association from http://www.nma.org/pdf/c_production_state_rank.pdf, accessed May 5, 2013

a. Minimum $= 1$, Q1 $= 12$, Median $= 36$, Q3 $= 57$, Maximum $= 410$; Mean $= 33$, MAD $= 2.76$

b. Minimum $= 2$, Q1 $= 13.5$, Median $= 27.5$, Q3 $= 44$, Maximum $= 439$; Mean $= 54.6$, MAD $= 52.36$

c. Minimum $= 10$, Q1 $= 37.5$, Median $= 62$, Q3 $= 105$, Maximum $= 439$; Mean $= 54.6$, MAD $= 52.36$

The correct answer is (b).

Choice (a) would not work because Q3 (the average of the 15th and 16th ordered observations) must be less than 50 since both the 15th and 16th ordered observations are less than 50. The mean is most likely greater than (not less than) the median given the skewed right nature of the distribution and the large outlier. The MAD value is most likely much larger than 2.76 given the presence of the outlier and its distance from the cluster of remaining observations.

Choice (c) would not work. Since there are 20 observations, the median (the average of the 10th and 11th ordered observations) must be less than 50, since both the 10th and 11th ordered observations are less than 50. Likewise, the Q3 (the average of the 15th and 16th ordered observations) must be less than 50, since both the 15th and 16th observations are less than 50. The mean is most likely greater than (not less than) the median given the skewed right nature of the distribution and the large outlier.

2. The heights (rounded to the nearest inch) of the 41 members of the 2012–2013 University of Texas Men's Swimming and Diving Team are shown in the dot plot below.

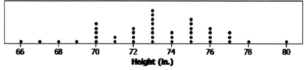

Height (in.)

Data Source: http://www.texassports.com accessed April 30, 2013

a. Use the dot plot to determine the 5-number summary (minimum, lower quartile, median, upper quartile, and maximum) for the data set.

Min $= 66$, Q1 $= 71$, Median $= 73$, Q3 $= 75$, and Max $= 80$

©2015 Great Minds eureka-math.org
G6-M6-TE-B3-1.3.1-01.2016

b. Based on this dot plot, make a histogram of the heights using the following intervals: 66 to < 68 inches, 68 to < 70 inches, and so on.

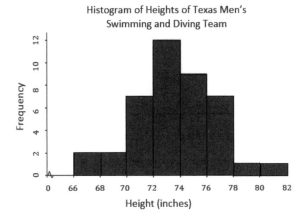

Histogram of Heights of Texas Men's Swimming and Diving Team

3. Data on the weight (in pounds) of 143 wild bears are summarized in the histogram below.

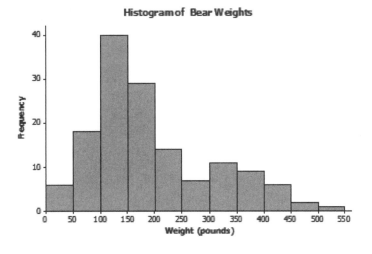

Histogram of Bear Weights

Which *one* of the three dot plots below could be a dot plot of the bear weight data? Explain how you determined which the correct plot is.

Dot plot 1 is the correct choice. Dot plot 2 does not have the same shape as the data distribution shown in the histogram, and it is centered to the right of where the histogram is centered. Although dot plot 3 has the same shape as the distribution shown in the histogram, it is not centered in the same place as the histogram.

©2015 Great Minds eureka-math.org
G6-M6-TE-B3-1.3.1-01.2016

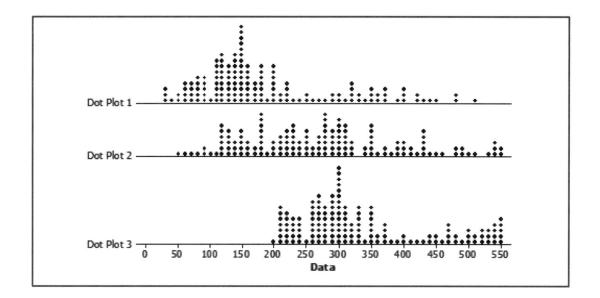

©2015 Great Minds eureka-math.org
G6-M6-TE-B3-1.3.1-01.2016

Lesson 19: Comparing Data Distributions

Student Outcomes

- Given box plots, students comment on similarities and differences in data distributions.

Classwork

As students work through this lesson, encourage them to think about the data they have collected for their projects and to think about how they might summarize that data using both numerical summaries and graphical displays.

Lesson 18 was about understanding data distributions and seeing how graphical displays and numerical summaries are used to learn about important characteristics of a data distribution. In this lesson, the focus is on comparing two or more data distributions. As students work though this lesson, each time they encounter a new example that presents them with data distributions, encourage them to think about how the distributions are similar and how they are different and what this means in the context of the example.

Have students read the following paragraphs.

> Suppose that you are interested in comparing the weights of adult male polar bears and the weights of adult male grizzly bears. If data were available on the weights of these two types of bears, they could be used to answer questions such as the following:
>   Do adult polar bears typically weigh less than adult grizzly bears?
>   Are the weights of adult polar bears similar to each other, or do the weights tend to differ a lot from bear to bear?
>   Are the weights of adult polar bears more consistent than the weights of adult grizzly bears?
>
> These questions could be answered most easily by comparing the weight distributions for the two types of bears. Graphs of the data distributions (such as dot plots, box plots, or histograms) that are drawn side by side and that are drawn to the same scale make it easy to compare data distributions in terms of center, variability, and shape.
>
> In this lesson, when two or more data distributions are presented, think about the following:
>   How are the data distributions similar?
>   How are the data distributions different?
>   What do the similarities and differences tell you in the context of the data?

Example 1 (3 minutes): Comparing Groups Using Box Plots

Review box plots and five-number summaries. Remind students of the following important points.

- A box plot provides a useful summary of a distribution, and certain summary measures (such as median, quartiles, IQR) can be obtained or estimated from the box plot.
- When box plots are shown together (using the same scale), visual differences between the box plots correspond to quantitative differences between the corresponding summary measures of the distributions.

Example 1: Comparing Groups Using Box Plots

Recall that a *box plot* is a visual representation of a five-number summary. The box part of a box plot is drawn so that the width of the box represents the IQR. The distance from the far end of the line on the left to the far end of the line on the right represents the range.

If two box plots (each representing a different distribution) are drawn side by side using the same scale, it is easy to compare the values in the five-number summaries for the two distributions and to visually compare the IQRs and ranges.

Here is a data set of the ages of 43 participants in a 5-kilometer race (shown in a previous lesson).

20	30	30	35	36	34	38	46
45	18	43	23	47	27	21	30
32	32	31	32	36	74	41	41
51	61	50	34	34	34	35	28
57	26	29	49	41	36	37	41
38	30	30					

Here is the five-number summary for the data: Minimum = 18, Q1 = 30, Median = 35, Q3 = 41, Maximum = 74.

There was also a 15-kilometer race. The ages of the 55 participants in that race appear below.

47	19	30	30	36	37	35	39
19	49	47	16	45	22	50	27
19	20	30	32	32	31	32	37
22	81	43	43	54	66	53	35
22	35	35	36	28	61	26	29
38	52	43	37	38	43	39	30
58	30	48	49	54	56	58	

Does the longer race appear to attract different runners in terms of age? Below are side-by-side box plots that may help answer that question. Side-by-side box plots are two or more box plots drawn using the same scale. What do you notice about the two box plots?

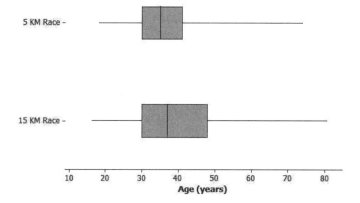

Both the range and the IQR are larger for the longer race, which means there is more variability in the ages for the long race than in the ages for the short race.

EUREKA MATH™

©2015 Great Minds eureka-math.org
G6-M6-TE-B3-1.3.1-01.2016

Exercises 1–6 (10 minutes)

In some cases, the questions have more than one correct answer. Answers may not be exact when students are estimating values of summary measures from the box plots.

Students work individually. If time allows, discuss answers as a class.

Exercises 1–6

1. Based on the box plots, estimate the values in the five-number summary for the ages in the 15-kilometer race data set.

    Minimum = 16, Q1 = 30, Median = 37, Q3 = 48, and Maximum = 81

2. Do the two data sets have the same median? If not, which race had the higher median age?

    The two data sets do not have the same median; the 15 km race has a slightly higher median: 37 years of age compared to 35 years of age for the 5 km race.

3. Do the two data sets have the same IQR? If not, which distribution has the greater spread in the middle 50% of its distribution?

    The two data sets do not have the same IQR; the 15 km race has a slightly higher IQR: 18 years of age compared to 11 years of age for the 5 km race. The ages of runners in the middle 50% for the 15 km race are more spread out.

4. Which race had the smaller overall range of ages? What do you think the range of ages is for the 15-kilometer race?

    The 5 km race had the smaller range of ages: 56 compared to 65 for the 15 km race.

5. Which race had the oldest runner? About how old was this runner?

    The 15 km race had the oldest runner at 81 years of age. The oldest runner for the 5 km race was only 74.

6. Now, consider just the youngest 25% of the runners in the 15-kilometer race. How old was the youngest runner in this group? How old was the oldest runner in this group? How does that compare with the 5-kilometer race?

    For the 15 km race, the youngest 25% of the runners had ages between the minimum and Q1. The youngest runner was 16 years old because this was the minimum for this distribution. The oldest runner in this group was 30 years old or younger because Q1 was 30. For the 5 km race, this youngest runner was 18 years old, and the oldest runner in the bottom 25% was 30 years old or younger (both distributions have the same Q1).

Exercises 7–12 (20 minutes): Comparing Box Plots

Pose the questions to students one at a time. Allow for more than one student to offer an answer for each question, encouraging a brief (two-minute) discussion.

In some cases, the questions have more than one correct answer. Answers may not be exact when students are estimating values of summary measures from the box plots. Note: Non-baseball-related questions with similar objectives appear in the Problem Set.

Lesson 19:   Comparing Data Distributions   227

©2015 Great Minds eureka-math.org
G6-M6-TE-B3-1.3.1-01.2016

Exercises 7–12: Comparing Box Plots

In 2012, Major League Baseball had two leagues: an American League of 14 teams and a National League of 16 teams.
Jesse wondered if American League teams have higher batting averages and on-base percentages. (Higher values are
better.) Use the following box plots to investigate. (Source: http://mlb.mlb.com/stats/sortable.jsp, accessed
May 13, 2013)

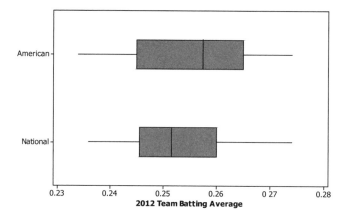

7. Was the highest American League team batting average very different from the highest National League team
    batting average? Approximately how large was the difference, and which league had the higher maximum value?

    *The highest batting averages for both leagues appear to be around 0.274. (This value must be estimated from the
    box plot, so other answers that are close to 0.274 are acceptable.)*

8. Was the range of the American League team batting averages very different or only slightly different from the range
    of the National League team batting averages?

    *They appear to be only slightly different, with the American League range being slightly higher. The American
    League minimum (0.234) is slightly lower than the National League minimum (0.236), and both leagues appear to
    have the same maximum.*

9. Which league had the higher median team batting average? Given the scale of the graph and the range of the data
    sets, does the difference between the median values for the two leagues seem to be small or large? Explain why
    you think it is small or large.

    *The American League has the higher median batting average at about 0.258, while the median batting average for
    the National League median is about 0.252. In answering the second part of this question, make sure that students
    look at the difference in the medians. Students might say that they think this is a small difference because 0.006 is
    a small number. However, a better answer would consider the scale and the range of the data. The difference of*
    0.006 *is roughly* $\dfrac{1}{6}$ *of the range for the National League, which suggests that the difference may be large enough to
    be considered meaningful.*

Lesson 19:   Comparing Data Distributions

©2015 Great Minds eureka-math.org
G6-M6-TE-B3-1.3.1-01.2016

10. Based on the box plots below for on-base percentage, which three summary values (from the five-number summary) appear to be the same or virtually the same for both leagues?

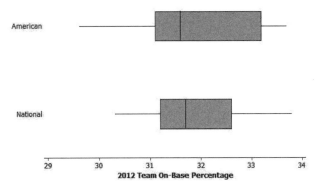

The Q1, median, and maximum appear to be roughly the same.

11. Which league's data set appears to have less variability? Explain.

The National League data set appears to have less variability, as it has a smaller IQR and smaller range.

12. Recall that Jesse wondered if American League teams have higher batting averages and on-base percentages. Based on the box plots given above, what would you tell Jesse?

Answers will vary.

It does look like the American League teams tend to have higher team batting averages. The median and upper quartile for the American League team batting average box plot are greater than the median and upper quartile for the National League. However, there is at least one team in the American League with a team batting average that is lower than every team in the National League, and there is at least one team in the National League that has a team batting average that is about the same as the American League team with the highest batting average.

For on-base percentage, the median and lower quartile and the maximum are about the same for both leagues. So it does not really look like it would be reasonable to say that the American League teams tend to have higher team on-base percentages than National League teams.

©2015 Great Minds eureka-math.org
G6-M6-TE-B3-1.3.1-01.2016

Closing (5 minutes)

- What kinds of information about a quantitative data distribution might not be presented well if we only use box plots?
    - *Clustering, some aspects of shape, and number of observations*
- What other kinds of graphs might be placed side by side to visually communicate the similarities and differences between data distributions?
    - *Side-by-side dot plots would be effective for this, assuming the same scale is used.*

Lesson Summary

When comparing the distribution of a quantitative variable for two or more distinct groups, it is useful to display the groups' distributions side by side using graphs drawn to the same scale. This makes it easier to describe the similarities and differences in the distributions of the groups.

Exit Ticket (7 minutes)

©2015 Great Minds eureka-math.org
G6-M6-TE-B3-1.3.1-01.2016

Name _____   Date_____

Lesson 19: Comparing Data Distributions

Exit Ticket

Hay is used to feed animals such as cows, horses, and goats. Almost $\frac{1}{3}$ of the hay grown in the United States comes from just five states. Is this because these states have more acres planted in hay, or could it be because these states produce more hay per acre than other states? The following box plots show the distribution of hay produced (in tons) per acre planted in hay for three different regions: 22 eastern states, 14 midwestern states, and 12 western states.

Source: *United States Department of Agriculture National Agricultural Statistics Service Crop Production 2012 Summary*, ISSN: 1057-7823, p. 75, accessed May 5, 2013

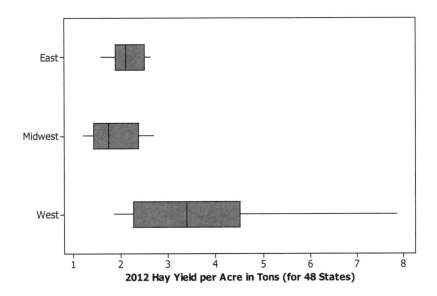

2012 Hay Yield per Acre in Tons (for 48 States)

1. Which of the three regions' data sets has the least variability? Which has the greatest variability? To explain how you chose your answers, write a sentence or two that supports your choices by comparing relevant summary measures (such as median and IQR) or aspects of the graphical displays (such as shape and variability).

©2015 Great Minds eureka-math.org
G6-M6-TE-B3-1.3.1-01.2016

2. True or false: The western state with the smallest hay yield per acre has a higher hay yield per acre than at least half of the midwestern states. Explain how you know this is true or how you know this is false.

3. Which region typically has states with the largest hay yield per acre? To explain how you chose your answer, write a sentence or two that supports your choice by comparing relevant summary measures or aspects of the graphical displays.

EUREKA
MATH

©2015 Great Minds eureka-math.org
G6-M6-TE-B3-1.3.1-01.2016

Exit Ticket Sample Solutions

Hay is used to feed animals such as cows, horses, and goats. Almost $\frac{1}{3}$ of the hay grown in the United States comes from just five states. Is this because these states have more acres planted in hay, or could it be because these states produce more hay per acre than other states? The following box plots show the distribution of hay produced (in tons) per acre planted in hay for three different regions: 22 eastern states, 14 midwestern states, and 12 western states.

Source: *United States Department of Agriculture National Agricultural Statistics Service Crop Production 2012 Summary*, ISSN: 1057-7823, p. 75, accessed May 5, 2013

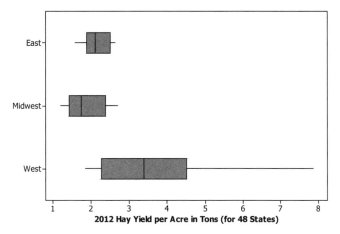

2012 Hay Yield per Acre in Tons (for 48 States)

1. Which of the three regions' data sets has the least variability? Which has the greatest variability? To explain how you chose your answers, write a sentence or two that supports your choices by comparing relevant summary measures (such as median and IQR) or aspects of the graphical displays (such as shape and variability).

    The East data set has the least variability, as it has the smallest range and the smallest IQR. The West data set has the greatest variability, as it has the largest range and the largest IQR.

2. True or false: The western state with the smallest hay yield per acre has a higher hay yield per acre than at least half of the midwestern states. Explain how you know this is true or how you know this is false.

    This is true; the minimum value of the West data set is higher than the median value of the Midwest data set. Therefore, this minimum value for the West must be higher than at least half of the midwestern states' values.

3. Which region typically has states with the largest hay yield per acre? To explain how you chose your answer, write a sentence or two that supports your choice by comparing relevant summary measures or aspects of the graphical displays.

    The West typically has states with the largest hay yield per acre. Over half of the western states have hay yields that are higher than any yield in either of the other two regions. Also, some western yields are more than two times the largest eastern and midwestern yields.

Lesson 19:   Comparing Data Distributions

233

©2015 Great Minds eureka-math.org
G6-M6-TE-B3-1.3.1-01.2016

Problem Set Sample Solutions

Before students begin the Problem Set, consider allowing time for them to work on their projects. If students have not collected data, then provide assistance in completing that process. If students have collected data, then provide them time to create numerical or graphical summaries of the data (dot plots, box plots, or histograms). Assign only one or two of the problems in the Problem Set if the time is needed for completion of the project.

1. College athletic programs are separated into divisions based on school size, available athletic scholarships, and other factors. A researcher wondered if members of swimming and diving programs in Division I (usually large schools that offer athletic scholarships) tend to be taller than the swimmers and divers in Division III programs (usually smaller schools that do not offer athletic scholarships). To begin the investigation, the researcher creates side-by-side box plots for the heights (in inches) of 41 male swimmers and divers at Mountain Vista University (a Division I program) and the heights (in inches) of 10 male swimmers and divers at Eaglecrest College (a Division III program).

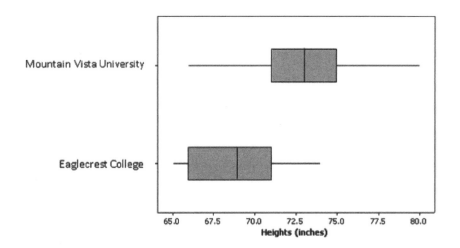

a. Which data set has the smaller range?

    Eaglecrest College has the smaller range.

b. True or false: A swimmer who had a height equal to the median for the Mountain Vista University would be taller than the median height of swimmers and divers at Eaglecrest College.

    True

c. To be thorough, the researcher will examine many other colleges' sports programs to further investigate the claim that members of swimming and diving programs in Division I are generally taller than the swimmers and divers in Division III. But given the graph above, in this initial stage of her research, do you think that the claim might be valid? Carefully support your answer using summary measures or graphical attributes.

    Based on just these two teams, it looks like the claim may be correct. A large portion of the Mountain Vista University distribution is higher than the maximum value of the Eaglecrest College distribution. The median value for the Mountain Vista University appears to be 4 inches higher than the median value of the Eaglecrest College distribution.

©2015 Great Minds eureka-math.org
G6-M6-TE-B3-1.3.1-01.2016

2. Data on the weights (in pounds) of 100 polar bears and 50 grizzly bears are summarized in the box plots shown below.

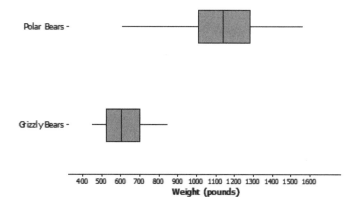

a. True or false: At least one of the polar bears weighed more than the heaviest grizzly bear. Explain how you know.

    True. The lower quartile and the median weight for the polar bears were greater than the maximum weight for the grizzly bears, so at least 75% of the polar bears weighed more than the heaviest grizzly bear.

b. True or false: Weight differs more from bear to bear for polar bears than for grizzly bears. Explain how you know.

    True. The weights of the grizzly bears are more compact than the weights of the polar bears. The grizzly bear weight distribution has a smaller range and IQR than the polar bear weight distribution.

c. Which type of bear tends to weigh more? Explain.

    Polar bears tend to have greater weights. The median weight for grizzly bears is much smaller than the median polar bear weight, and about half of the grizzly bear weight distribution is lower than the minimum weight for the polar bears.

©2015 Great Minds eureka-math.org
G6-M6-TE-B3-1.3.1-01.2016

3. Many movie studios rely heavily on viewer data to determine how a movie will be marketed and distributed. Recently, previews of a soon-to-be-released movie were shown to 300 people. Each person was asked to rate the movie on a scale of 0 to 10, with 10 representing "best movie I have ever seen" and 0 representing "worst movie I have ever seen."

Below are some side-by-side box plots that summarize the ratings by gender and by age.

For 150 women and 150 men:

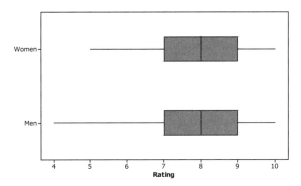

For 3 age groups:

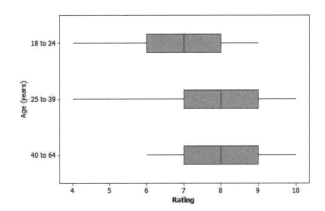

a. Does it appear that the men and women rated the film in a similar manner or in a very different manner? Write a few sentences explaining your answer using comparative information about center and variability.

    It appears that the men and women rated the film in a very similar manner: The box plots show the same quartile values, the same medians, and the same maximums. The only difference is that the minimum rating from a man was slightly lower than the minimum rating from a woman.

b. It appears that the film tended to receive better ratings from the older members of the group. Write a few sentences using comparative measures of center and spread or aspects of the graphical displays to justify this claim.

    For the two oldest age groups, the Q1, median, Q3, and maximum values are all higher than the 18–24 counterparts. In fact, the Q1 value for each of these two older groups equals the median rating of the youngest group, and the median value for each of these two older groups equals the Q3 rating of the youngest group. Additionally, while the two oldest groups have similar distributions, the minimum score of the oldest group was much higher than the minimum value of the 25–39 group. This means that none of the 40–64 respondents rated the movie with a score as low as a 4 (as was the case in the 25–39 age group).

EUREKA
MATH™

©2015 Great Minds eureka-math.org
G6-M6-TE-B3-1.3.1-01.2016

Lesson 20: Describing Center, Variability, and Shape of a Data Distribution from a Graphical Representation

Student Outcomes

- Given a frequency histogram, students estimate the values of the mean and mean absolute deviation (MAD) or the median and interquartile range (IQR).

Lesson Notes

In this lesson, students integrate knowledge from earlier lessons in this module. Remind students of what they have done in previous lessons. In each lesson of this module, students created and interpreted graphical displays of data, including dot plots, box plots, and histograms. If actual data are provided and the data set is not too large, a dot plot is an informative way to display the data distribution. If the data set is large, a histogram is generally used to display the data distribution. Histograms can be challenging for students at this grade level. A histogram provides a display of the data distribution, but the shape of a histogram can sometimes depend on the intervals used to construct the histogram. It is important to investigate the shape of the data distribution because the shape influences the choice of numerical summaries—the mean and MAD are used for data distributions that are approximately symmetric, and the median and IQR are used for data distributions that are skewed.

In this lesson, students consider a histogram of the length of yellow perch in the Great Lakes region. The data presented in this lesson are based on various scientific research studies of yellow perch during the 1990s. The yellow perch is a valuable resource for the fishing industry, as well as a food source for several other species of fish and wildlife. Before students analyze the data, share with them that the histogram is part of the yellow perch story that they uncover in this lesson. Although the sample presented in this lesson has been simplified for students, it is consistent with actual data that were particularly disturbing to scientists researching the yellow perch. The histogram was constructed using data on the length of yellow perch. Length is important because the length of a yellow perch is used to estimate the age of the fish. As a result, the histogram indicates that most of the fish were older or adult fish. It would be preferable for the younger fish to represent a larger proportion of the population of yellow perch. If the frequencies for intervals representing the younger fish are less than the frequencies for intervals representing older fish, then in time there will be fewer and fewer fish, possibly even indicating that the yellow perch will not survive.

Classwork

Have students read the following paragraph.

> Great Lakes yellow perch are fish that live in each of the five Great Lakes and many other lakes in the eastern and upper Great Lakes regions of the United States and Canada. Both countries are actively involved in efforts to maintain a healthy population of perch in these lakes.

©2015 Great Minds eureka-math.org
G6-M6-TE-B3-1.3.1-01.2016

Example 1 (10 minutes): The Great Lakes Yellow Perch

Example 1: The Great Lakes Yellow Perch

Scientists collected data from many yellow perch because they were concerned about the survival of the yellow perch. What data do you think researchers might want to collect about these perch?

Answers will vary. Anticipate that students also suggest collecting data on physical characteristics of the fish, such as weight, length, etc. Some students may say they would look for evidence of disease. Students might also suggest collecting data on age, but this might be difficult to determine. As this lesson progresses, students see that it is possible to estimate the age of a perch from its length.

Scientists captured yellow perch from a lake in this region. They recorded data on each fish and then returned each fish to the lake. Consider the following histogram of data on the length (in centimeters) for a sample of yellow perch.

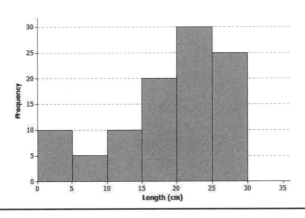

MP.1

- If researchers are interested in the ages of the perch in the lake, why do you think researchers might want to collect data on the length of the perch?
  - □ *Because the length might give us information about the fish's age.*
- How many fish captured had a length of 20 to 25 centimeters?
  - □ *Thirty fish captured had a length of 20 to 25 centimeters.*
- Do you know how many fish had a length of 22 centimeters? Why or why not?
  - □ *We only know that there were 30 fish with lengths in the 20 to 25 cm range, but we can't tell from just looking at the histogram exactly how many of them were 22 cm long.*

If needed, remind students that a histogram does not provide the frequency of a specific value, only the frequency for an interval of values.

- Why do you think the scientists were concerned about what they saw in the histogram of the lengths of yellow perch?
  - □ *Scientists were concerned because there were a lot less short fish than long fish, which could indicate that there are not many young yellow perch in the Great Lakes.*

Lesson 20:   Describing Center, Variability, and Shape of a Data Distribution from a
                          Graphical Representation

©2015 Great Minds eureka-math.org
G6-M6-TE-B3-1.3.1-01.2016

Exercises 1–11 (12 minutes)

Students work individually or in small groups as they answer the questions in these exercises. Discuss the answers to these questions as a group.

Exercises 1–11

Scientists were concerned about the survival of the yellow perch as they studied the histogram.

1. What statistical question could be answered based on this data distribution?

   Answers will vary. A possible statistical question would be, "What is a typical length of the Great Lakes yellow perch?"

2. Use the histogram to complete the following table:

Length of Fish in Centimeters (cm)	Number of Fish
$0 - < 5$ cm	10
$5 - < 10$ cm	5
$10 - < 15$ cm	10
$15 - < 20$ cm	20
$20 - < 25$ cm	30
$25 - < 30$ cm	25

3. The length of each fish in the sample was measured and recorded before the fish was released back into the lake. How many yellow perch were measured in this sample?

   100 fish were measured in this sample.

4. Would you describe the distribution of the lengths of the fish in the sample as a skewed distribution or as an approximately symmetric distribution? Explain your answer.

   The data distribution is a skewed distribution with the tail to the left.

5. What percentage of fish in the sample were less than 10 centimeters in length?

   15 of the 100 fish measured in this sample had a length of less than 10 centimeters, so 15% of the fish are less than 10 centimeters.

6. If the smallest fish in this sample was 2 centimeters in length, what is your estimate of an interval of lengths that would contain the lengths of the shortest 25% of the fish? Explain how you determined your answer.

   25% of the fish are represented in the first three intervals. If the smallest value in the first interval is known, then an estimate of the interval of the smallest 25% of the fish is 2 centimeters to 15 centimeters. I determined this by considering the histogram bars at the low end and looking for intervals that would represent 25 fish.

7. If the length of the largest yellow perch was 29 centimeters, what is your estimate of an interval of lengths that would contain the lengths of the longest 25% of the fish?

   In a similar way, there are 25 fish in the interval 25 to 30 centimeters in length. If the longest fish were measured at 29 centimeters, then an estimate of an interval containing the upper 25% would be 25 to 29 centimeters.

©2015 Great Minds eureka-math.org
G6-M6-TE-B3-1.3.1-01.2016

8. Estimate the median length of the yellow perch in the sample. Explain how you determined your estimate.

    To estimate the median length, I would identify a length for which approximately 50% of the fish would be above and approximately 50% of the fish would be below. Starting from the smallest lengths, an estimate of the median would be located within the 20 to 25 centimeters interval. The same interval would be identified if I started with the largest lengths. As the actual values of the lengths of the fish are not known, any estimate within that interval would be a good estimate. For example, an estimate of 23 centimeters would be a good estimate.

9. Based on the shape of this data distribution, do you think the mean length of a yellow perch would be greater than, less than, or the same as your estimate of the median? Explain your answer.

    Because the data distribution is skewed, the smaller lengths will pull an estimate of the mean to the left of the median. Therefore, an estimate of the mean would be less than the estimate of the median.

10. Recall that the mean length is the balance point of the distribution of lengths. Estimate the mean length for this sample of yellow perch.

    Answers will vary, but an estimate of a length in the 15 to 20 centimeters interval would show an understanding of this idea. For example, 17 or 18 centimeters would be a good estimate of the mean.

11. The length of a yellow perch is used to estimate the age of the fish. Yellow perch typically grow throughout their lives. Adult yellow perch have lengths between 10 and 30 centimeters. How many of the yellow perch in this sample would be considered adult yellow perch? What percentage of the fish in the sample are adult fish?

    85 fish are counted in the intervals that represent 10 to 30 centimeters. Therefore, 85% of the fish in this sample are estimated to be adult fish.

Example 2 (5 minutes): What Would a Better Distribution Look Like?

Example 2: What Would a Better Distribution Look Like?

Yellow perch are part of the food supply of larger fish and other wildlife in the Great Lakes region. Why do you think that the scientists worried when they saw the histogram of fish lengths given previously in Exercise 2.

The small percentage of short fish means that there are fewer young yellow perch than older yellow perch.

Sketch a histogram representing a sample of 100 yellow perch lengths that you think would indicate the perch are not in danger of dying out.

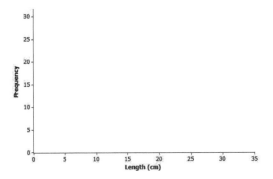

Answers will vary, but students' histograms should have a larger number of fish with short lengths.

©2015 Great Minds eureka-math.org
G6-M6-TE-B3-1.3.1-01.2016

Discuss the summary that was provided at the beginning of the teacher notes. A better distribution of fish would have more young fish. Because age is related to length, a better distribution would have more fish in the smaller length intervals. As the lengths (or ages) increased, the number of fish would be expected to decline. Allow students to sketch their own histogram shapes in response to the discussion question in this exercise. Point out that a histogram with the greater frequencies of fish in the smaller length intervals would be better.

Exercises 12–17 (8 minutes): Estimating the Variability in Yellow Perch Lengths

> **Exercises 12–17: Estimating the Variability in Yellow Perch Lengths**
>
> You estimated the median length of yellow perch from the first sample in Exercise 8. It is also useful to describe variability in the length of yellow perch. Why might this be important? Consider the following questions:
>
> 12. In several previous lessons, you described a data distribution using the five-number summary. Use the histogram and your answers to the questions in previous exercises to provide estimates of the values for the five-number summary for this sample:
>
>   Minimum (min) value $= 2$ *centimeters*
>
>   Q1 value $= 15$ *centimeters*
>
>   Median $= 23$ *centimeters*
>
>   Q3 value $= 25$ *centimeters*
>
>   Maximum (max) value $= 29$ *centimeters*
>
>   *Because students are estimating these values from a histogram, expect a variety of reasonable answers. Any values that are reasonably close to the values shown here should be considered acceptable.*
>
> 13. Based on the five-number summary, what is an estimate of the value of the interquartile range (IQR) for this data distribution?
>
>   *Based on the above estimates, an estimate of the interquartile range (IQR) would be as follows:*
> 25 *centimeters* $- 15$ *centimeters* $= 10$ *centimeters.*
>
>   *Actual student answers will vary depending on their answers to Exercise 12.*
>
> 14. Sketch a box plot representing the lengths of the yellow perch in this sample.
>
>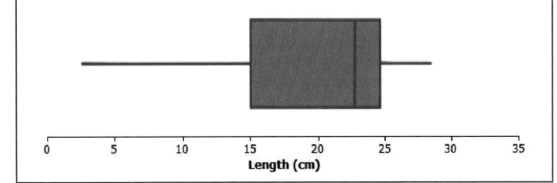

15. Which measure of center, the median or the mean, is closer to where the lengths of yellow perch tend to cluster?

For a skewed distribution, the median is closer to where the lengths of yellow perch tend to cluster.

16. What value would you report as a typical length for the yellow perch in this sample?

Encourage students to use the estimate of the median value in the previous questions as a typical value for the yellow perch.

17. The mean absolute deviation (or MAD) or the interquartile range (IQR) is used to describe the variability in a data distribution. Which measure of variability would you use for this sample of perch? Explain your answer.

When the median is selected as the measure of center for a typical value (because the distribution is not approximately symmetric), then the interquartile range would be selected as the measure of variability. In this case, 10 centimeters, or the IQR determined in Exercise 13, would be the measure of the variability.

Closing (5 minutes)

- What is the problem with the yellow perch length distribution shown in the histogram?

  □ *The limited number of yellow perch that are short implies there are not many young yellow perch in the Great Lakes.*

- What is a typical yellow perch length?

  □ *Because the length distribution was skewed, the median length of about 23 centimeters would be considered a typical length for yellow perch.*

- What would you use as a measure of the variability of yellow perch lengths?

  □ *Because the length distribution is skewed, you would use the interquartile range.*

Lesson Summary

Data distributions are usually described in terms of shape, center, and spread. Graphical displays such as histograms, dot plots, and box plots are used to assess the shape. Depending on the shape of a data distribution, different measures of center and variability are used to describe the distribution. For a distribution that is skewed, the median is used to describe a typical value, whereas the mean is used for distributions that are approximately symmetric. The IQR is used to describe variability for a skewed data distribution, while the MAD is used to describe variability for a distribution that is approximately symmetric.

Exit Ticket (5 minutes)

Name _____   Date_____

Lesson 20: Describing Center, Variability, and Shape of a Data Distribution from a Graphical Representation

Exit Ticket

1. Great Lake yellow perch continue to grow until they die. What does the histogram in Example 1 indicate about the ages of the perch in the sample?

2. What feature of the histogram in Example 1 indicates that the values of the mean and the median of the data distribution will not be equal?

3. Adult yellow perch have lengths between 10 and 30 centimeters. Would a perch with a length equal to the median length be classified as an adult or a pre-adult fish? Explain your answer.

Exit Ticket Sample Solutions

1. Great Lake yellow perch continue to grow until they die. What does the histogram in Example 1 indicate about the ages of the perch in the sample?

    The histogram indicates that most of the perch are in the intervals corresponding to the longest lengths. Because length is related to age, the histogram indicates that there are more older fish.

2. What feature of the histogram in Example 1 indicates that the values of the mean and the median of the data distribution will not be equal?

    The histogram indicates that the shape of the data distribution is skewed. For skewed distributions, the mean and the median are not equal.

3. Adult yellow perch have lengths between 10 and 30 centimeters. Would a perch with a length equal to the median length be classified as an adult or a pre-adult fish? Explain your answer.

    A perch equal to the median length would be classified as an adult fish. The median is estimated to be between 20 and 25 centimeters in length. Adult fish are 10 centimeters or more in length.

Problem Set Sample Solutions

Take students' progress on their projects into consideration when assigning problems from this Problem Set. Make sure that students understand the project expectations, and consider asking for a brief written summary of their progress or a sample of the graphs or numerical summaries of their data. If time is needed for students to work on their projects, assign a subset of the problems in the Problem Set.

Another sample of Great Lake yellow perch from a different lake was collected. A histogram of the lengths for the fish in this sample is shown below.

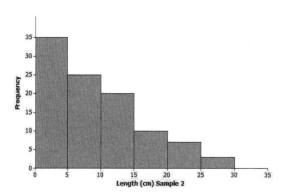

1. If the length of a yellow perch is an indicator of its age, how does this second sample differ from the sample you investigated in the exercises? Explain your answer.

    The second sample has more fish with lengths in the intervals corresponding to shorter lengths. Therefore, more of the fish are younger.

2. Does this histogram represent a data distribution that is skewed or that is nearly symmetrical?

    This distribution is also skewed. However, the tail of this distribution is to the right, or toward the longer lengths.

©2015 Great Minds eureka-math.org
G6-M6-TE-B3-1.3.1-01.2016

3. What measure of center would you use to describe a typical length of a yellow perch in this second sample? Explain your answer.

    Students should recommend the median of the data distribution as a description of a typical value of the length of the yellow perch because this distribution is skewed.

4. Assume the smallest perch caught was 2 centimeters in length, and the largest perch caught was 29 centimeters in length. Estimate the values in the five-number summary for this sample:

    Q1, Q3, and median values are not as clear cut in this distribution as in Exercise 4, so allow a wider range of acceptable answers.

    Minimum (min) value = 2 centimeters

    Q1 value = 4 centimeters (a value greater than 2 but within the interval of 0 to 5 centimeters)

    Median value = 7 centimeters (a value within the interval of 5 to 10 centimeters)

    Q3 value = 12 centimeters (a value within the interval of 10 to 15 centimeters)

    Maximum (max) value = 29 centimeters

5. Based on the shape of this data distribution, do you think the mean length of a yellow perch from this second sample would be greater than, less than, or the same as your estimate of the median? Explain your answer.

    An estimate of the mean would be greater than the median length because the values in the tail, or to the right of the median, pull the mean in that direction. Consider estimating the mean as the balance point of this distribution. (If students have problems with estimating the balance point, consider providing them with a representation similar to the representation used to introduce a balance point in earlier lessons. Use a ruler with coins (or weights) taped to locations that would represent a skewed distribution. This representation may help students sense the point of balance.)

6. Estimate the mean value of this data distribution.

    An estimate of the mean would be a value slightly larger than the median value. For example, a mean of 10 or 11 centimeters would be a reasonable estimate of a balance point.

7. What is your estimate of a typical length of a yellow perch in this sample? Did you use the mean length from Problem 5 for this estimate? Explain why or why not.

    Since the median was selected as the appropriate estimate of a measure of center, a value of 7 centimeters (or whatever students used to estimate the median) would be an estimate of a typical value for a yellow perch from this sample.

8. Would you use the MAD or the IQR to describe variability in the length of Great Lakes yellow perch in this sample? Estimate the value of the measure of variability that you selected.

    Students should use the IQR to describe the variability because the data distribution is skewed, and the median was used as a measure of a typical value. An estimate of the IQR based on the above estimates would be as follows: 12 centimeters − 4 centimeters = 8 centimeters.

©2015 Great Minds eureka-math.org
G6-M6-TE-B3-1.3.1-01.2016

Lesson 21: Summarizing a Data Distribution by Describing Center, Variability, and Shape

Student Outcomes

- Given a data set, students describe the data distribution using the mean and mean absolute deviation (MAD) or the median and the interquartile range (IQR).

Lesson Notes

This lesson provides an opportunity for students to summarize a given data set. As students work through this lesson, have them think about how what they are doing applies to the data that they have collected for their projects. In the Problem Set of this module, students are expected to summarize their project data (collected in Lesson 17) and construct a poster or an outline of a presentation. This lesson guides students through the four steps used to carry out a statistical study as a review and as preparation for the presentation in Lesson 22.

Classwork

Discussion (5 minutes)

Have students read the following information.

> Each of the lessons in this module is about data. What are data? What questions can be answered by data? How do you represent the data distribution so that you can understand and describe its shape? What does the shape tell us about how to summarize the data? What is a typical value of the data set? These and many other questions were part of your work in the exercises and investigations. There is still a lot to learn about what data tell us. You will continue to work with statistics and probability in Grades 7 and 8 and throughout high school, but you have already begun to see how to uncover the stories behind data.
>
> When you started this module, the four steps used to carry out a statistical study were introduced.
>
> Step 1:   Pose a question that can be answered by data.
>
> Step 2:   Collect appropriate data.
>
> Step 3:   Summarize the data with graphs and numerical summaries.
>
> Step 4:   Answer the question posed in Step 1 using the numerical summaries and graphs.
>
> In this lesson, you will carry out these steps using a given data set.

- Which steps of the process have you already completed as part of your project?
  - *We have already created a question and collected data, so we have completed the first two steps.*
- This lesson provides guidance on how to complete the final two steps of your statistical study.

©2015 Great Minds eureka-math.org
G6-M6-TE-B3-1.3.1-01.2016

- Before we look further into the process, make a prediction about the average annual rainfall in the state of New York.

  □ *Answers will vary. Anticipate a variety of answers, as students are not necessarily able to make a reasonable guess. If you are in a state other than New York, you can also ask if they think that New York gets more or less rainfall than your state.*

Exploratory Challenge (30 minutes): Annual Rainfall in the State of New York

Students work independently in completing a template that provides a structure for summarizing the rainfall data.

Students are given the annual rainfall in inches for New York from 1983 to 2012. The data were obtained from the National Climate Data Center. (If any students need data for their presentations discussed in the Problem Set, this site provides climate data for regions, cities, and states and could be a source to help students struggling to obtain data for their projects.)

Before students organize their summaries, discuss the context explained in the lesson. Make sure students understand what the data represent by highlighting the words *annual* and *rainfall*. Ask students why a statistical study of rainfall is important. For example, when a reporter says that a certain year was unusually rainy, on what basis was that claim made?

Direct students to study the template that is included with this lesson. Review the four steps involved in a statistical study. Indicate that during the next 25 minutes, they are expected to complete the template in order to organize their statistical summaries of the data.

Exploratory Challenge: Annual Rainfall in the State of New York

The National Climate Data Center collects data throughout the United States that can be used to summarize the climate of a region. You can obtain climate data for a state, a city, a county, or a region. If you were interested in researching the climate in your area, what data would you collect? Explain why you think these data would be important in a statistical study of the climate in your area.

Answers will vary. Anticipate that student responses will include things like temperature, amount of rainfall, number of sunny days per year, number of tornadoes per year, etc.

For this lesson, you will use yearly rainfall data for the state of New York that were compiled by the National Climate Data Center. The following data are the number of inches of rain (averaged over various locations in the state) for the years from 1983 to 2012 (30 years).

45	42	39	44	39	35	42	49	37	42	41	42	37	50	39
41	38	46	34	44	48	50	47	49	44	49	43	44	54	40

Use the four steps to carry out a statistical study using these data.

Step 1:   Pose a question that can be answered by data.

   What is a statistical question that you think can be answered with these data? Write your question in the template provided for this lesson.

Step 2:   Collect appropriate data.

   The data have already been collected for this lesson. How do you think these data were collected? Recall that the data are the number of inches of rain (averaged over various locations in the state) for the years from 1983 to 2012 (30 years). Write a summary of how you think the data were collected in the template for this lesson.

> Step 3: Summarize the data with graphs and numerical summaries.
>
> A good first step might be to summarize the data with a dot plot. What other graph might you construct? Construct a dot plot or another appropriate graph in the template for this lesson.
>
> What numerical summaries will you calculate? What measure of center will you use to describe a typical value for these data? What measure of variability will you calculate and use to summarize the variability of the data? Calculate the numerical summaries, and write them in the template for this lesson.
>
> Step 4: Answer your statistical question using the numerical summaries and graphs.
>
> Write a summary that answers the question you posed in the template for this lesson.

The following directions should be considered as students work through this lesson. Students work individually or in small groups as they complete the template.

Step 1: Pose a question that can be answered by data.

- What is a statistical question that you think can be answered with these data? Write your question in the template provided for this lesson.

It is important that students are reminded of the two most important parts of the definition of a *statistical question*. A statistical question is (1) a question that is answered by data and (2) a question that anticipates the data will vary. As students examine the data, point out to them that there is variability. Although students may use different wording in their statistical questions, it is anticipated that most students will form a question that essentially asks, "What is the typical annual rainfall in New York?"

Step 2: How do you think the data were collected?

- The data have already been collected for this lesson. How do you think these data were collected? Recall that the data are the number of inches of rain (averaged over various locations in the state) for the years from 1983 to 2012 (30 years). Write a summary of how you think the data were collected in the template for this lesson.

The data are provided in this lesson. This step is more challenging as they carry out their own statistical study because they need to explain the plan they developed to collect their data. For this lesson, allow students to speculate on how the National Climate Data Center might have collected these data. As the data represent the annual rainfall for the state of New York, the center had to collect rainfall totals from several reporting weather centers around the state. They calculated an average of those levels for each day of the year. At the end of the year, the National Climate Data Center added those daily results together. Students might be asked how a rainfall level is measured at a weather center. A rain gauge might be a good visual to share with students.

MP.4 Step 3: Construct graphs and calculate numerical summaries of the data.

- A good first step might be to summarize the data with a dot plot. What other graph might you construct? Construct a dot plot or another appropriate graph in the template for this lesson.

- What numerical summaries will you calculate? What measure of center will you use to describe a typical value for these data? What measure of variability will you calculate and use to summarize the variability of the data? Calculate the numerical summaries, and write them in the template for this lesson.

©2015 Great Minds eureka-math.org
G6-M6-TE-B3-1.3.1-01.2016

This step represents most of the work students are expected to do in this lesson. As a first step, encourage students who are not sure how to start summarizing the data to construct a dot plot. A blank grid is provided at the end of the Teacher Notes that can be duplicated for students who may need some structure in making a dot plot. This grid could also be used if any student decides to develop a box plot or a histogram of the data distribution.

Dot Plot of Annual Rainfall from 1983 to 2012

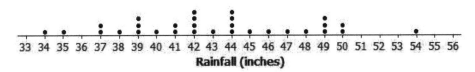

Students examine the dot plot and make decisions about the data distribution. For example, is the distribution approximately symmetric, or is the distribution skewed? This dot plot shows a data distribution that is approximately symmetric.

Based on the decision that the distribution is approximately symmetric, students should proceed to calculate the mean as a measure of center and the MAD as a measure of variability. Some students might also choose to investigate this distribution with a box plot to answer the question about the symmetry.

Box Plot of Annual Rainfall from 1983 to 2012

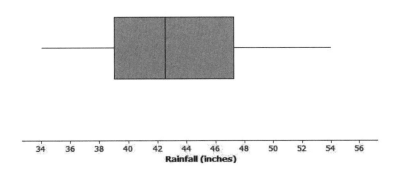

The box plot does not indicate a perfectly symmetrical distribution; however, it is approximately symmetric. The mean and the median of this data distribution are nearly equal to each other. Based on this decision, students should calculate the mean and the MAD.

The mean rainfall is 43 inches (to the nearest inch), and the mean absolute deviation (MAD) is 3.9 or 4 inches (to the nearest inch).

At the end of the Teacher Notes is a table that could be used for students who need structure in calculating the MAD. There are several steps in calculating the MAD, and some students may need help in organizing these steps.

Step 4: Answer your statistical question using the numerical summaries and graphs.

- Write a summary that answers the question you posed in the template for this lesson.

Lesson 21: Summarizing a Data Distribution by Describing Center, Variability, and Shape

249

©2015 Great Minds eureka-math.org
G6-M6-TE-B3-1.3.1-01.2016

This step asks students to write a short summary interpreting the graphs and numerical summaries. Students should connect this back to their statistical questions. Students would indicate that the typical rainfall for New York is about 43 inches per year. They would also indicate that a typical distance from the mean is about 4 inches.

Closing (5 minutes)

If time permits, revisit the original guesses students made about the annual rainfall for New York. Did students have a pretty good idea of the annual rainfall in New York? Discuss this question with students.

Lesson Summary

Statistics is about using data to answer questions. The four steps used to carry out a statistical study include posing a question that can be answered by data, collecting appropriate data, summarizing the data with graphs and numerical summaries, and using the data, graphs, and summaries to answer the statistical question.

Exit Ticket (5 minutes)

Consider a special type of Exit Ticket for this lesson. Since students are expected to complete a summary of the four-step process for an investigative study as part of their projects, use this opportunity to assess students' understanding of this process as it relates to the statistical questions and data they collected for their projects.

©2015 Great Minds eureka-math.org
G6-M6-TE-B3-1.3.1-01.2016

Name _____   Date_____

Lesson 21: Summarizing a Data Distribution by Describing Center, Variability, and Shape

Exit Ticket

Based on the statistical question you are investigating for your project, summarize the four steps you are expected to complete as part of the presentation of your statistical study.

Exit Ticket Sample Solutions

> **Based on the statistical question you are investigating for your project, summarize the four steps you are expected to complete as part of the presentation of your statistical study.**
>
> **Step 1:** *State my statistical question. My question is based on collecting data that will vary.*
>
> **Step 2:** *Devise a plan to collect data. I prepared a question to ask the students in my class. (Allow students to explain the question they asked, the responses they received, and the method they used for recording answers.)*
>
> **Step 3:** *Summarize my data. I prepared a dot plot of the responses to the question. My dot plot indicated that the responses to my question were skewed to the left; therefore, I used the median of the data distribution to describe my center and the IQR to describe the variability. (Allow for a summary of the specific median or mean and a specific summary of the variability as the MAD or IQR.)*
>
> **Step 4:** *Based on my graphs and numerical summaries, I answered my question.*

Problem Set Sample Solutions

The Problem Set for this lesson involves creating a poster or an outline for a presentation using the data collected in Lesson 17. The directions in the lesson indicate that students are expected to carry out the four steps either on their posters or an outline of their presentations. If students provided adequate summaries of the four-step process in the Exit Ticket, they could use this as a guide in completing the poster. Highlight the following:

For Step 1, students are expected to have a question clearly identified as their statistical question. The question should involve the data they collected. Students should have anticipated variability in the data.

For Step 2, students should indicate how they collected the data based on the plan proposed in Lesson 17. For example, for a question that investigates a typical height of students in the class, did every student state a height in inches, or was there a way to measure everyone's height? For a question that investigates how many books students read, did students ask members of their class how many books they read each month?

For Step 3, students include graphs and numerical summaries of the data. It is anticipated that students begin with a dot plot, but students might also construct a box plot or a histogram. Based on the shape of the distribution, students select appropriate numerical summaries—either the mean and the mean absolute deviation (MAD) or the median and the interquartile range (IQR). Posters or outlines should indicate what summaries were used and why.

For Step 4, students should have a concluding statement that answers the statistical question. Students should provide a brief description of their numerical summaries and graphs.

> **In Lesson 17, you posed a statistical question and created a plan to collect data to answer your question. You also constructed graphs and calculated numerical summaries of your data. Review the data collected and your summaries.**
>
> **Based on directions from your teacher, create a poster or an outline for a presentation using your own data. On your poster, indicate your statistical question. Also, indicate a brief summary of how you collected your data based on the plan you proposed in Lesson 17. Include a graph that shows the shape of the data distribution, along with summary measures of center and variability. Finally, answer your statistical question based on the graphs and the numerical summaries.**
>
> **Share the poster you will present in Lesson 22 with your teacher. If you are instructed to prepare an outline of the presentation, share your outline with your teacher.**

Lesson 21:   Summarizing a Data Distribution by Describing Center, Variability, and Shape

©2015 Great Minds eureka-math.org
G6-M6-TE-B3-1.3.1-01.2016

Additional Resource Materials

The following could be used to provide structure in constructing a dot plot, histogram, or box plot of the rainfall data. A similar type of grid (or graph paper) could be prepared for students as they complete the Problem Set. The grid provided for students should not include the units along the horizontal axis since that is part of what they are expected to do in preparing their summaries.

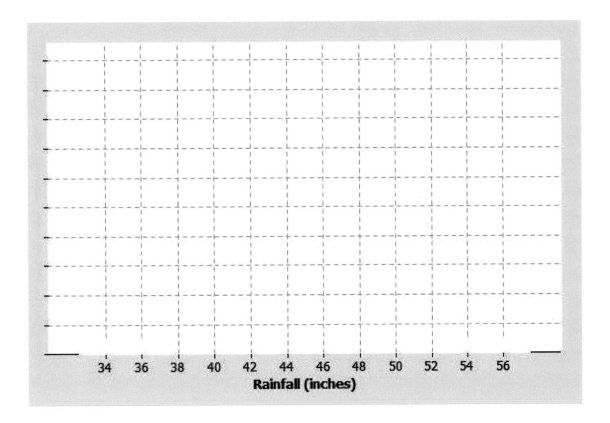

©2015 Great Minds eureka-math.org
G6-M6-TE-B3-1.3.1-01.2016

The following table could be used for students requiring some structure in calculating the mean absolute deviation, or MAD, for the rainfall data.

Data Value	Distance from the Mean
45	
42	
39	
44	
39	
35	
42	
49	
37	
42	
41	
42	
37	
50	
39	
41	
38	
46	
34	
44	
48	
50	
47	
49	
44	
49	
43	
44	
54	
40	

©2015 Great Minds eureka-math.org
G6-M6-TE-B3-1.3.1-01.2016

Lesson 22: Presenting a Summary of a Statistical Project

Student Outcomes

- Using data collected by students or data provided by the teacher (for cases in which collecting data was not possible), students communicate conclusions based on the data distribution.

Lesson Notes

This is an exploration lesson. In previous lessons, students posed a statistical question, developed a data collection plan, and collected and summarized data. In this lesson, each student has an opportunity to present a summary of his statistical study. Students should be reminded that their presentations should focus on the four-step investigative process. It is this process that defines a statistical study for students at this grade level.

If students carried out the process outlined in previous lessons, this lesson is a formal presentation day in which they either display and explain their posters or are provided a few minutes to explain their statistical studies. If there is not enough time for students to formally present their studies, organize a gallery walk. Hang posters around a classroom, and allow students to view as many as possible. Encourage students to take notes as they read the posters. Provide each student with a general template (see a suggested template at the end of this lesson) that can be used to summarize at least one poster as part of a whole-class discussion. Conclude the gallery walk with a short discussion of what they saw and what questions interested them. Ask students if there were any studies that surprised them. (Often a statistical study confirms a conjecture. There are times, however, that data lead to conclusions that were not expected.)

The audience for the presentations may vary. In most cases, the class is the audience. However, this type of project allows for other formats. It might be possible to use this day as an opportunity to invite parents, school administrators, or other available teachers to listen to the presentations.

Anticipate that problems will arise. In the event that there are students who did not complete Lesson 17 or were not able to collect data on their own, the posters or presentations can be based on data obtained from an outside source. It was pointed out in each of the lessons leading up to this presentation day that students were to advise their teachers about their progress. Students presenting a study based on data they did not collect should give proper credit to the source of that data on their posters or in their presentations.

Formal speaking is a comfortable and exciting experience for some students. For other students, it is an intimidating and possibly frightening experience. Teachers should use their best judgment in terms of organizing the formal presentations. If there are any students who need a little more structure in sharing their ideas, the following partially completed table could be provided to these students. Use it to help them organize their thoughts. The posters provide a format for students to present their ideas without formally presenting their studies.

Classwork

Exploratory Challenge (35 minutes): Presentation

A template for summarizing a statistical study in a poster or a presentation is provided at the end of this lesson. Discuss the template with students. If you have students do a gallery walk, students can use this template to summarize and evaluate the posters of other students. Ask each student to complete the summary for at least one poster other than his own. These summaries can then be used to structure a class discussion of the posters, highlighting how the various posters address the four-step process.

A statistical study involves the following four-step investigative process:

Step 1: Pose a question that can be answered by data.

Step 2: Collect appropriate data.

Step 3: Summarize the data with graphs and numerical summaries.

Step 4: Answer the question posed in Step 1 using the numerical summaries and graphs.

Now it is your turn to be a researcher and to present your own statistical study. In Lesson 17, you posed a statistical question, proposed a plan to collect data to answer the question, and collected the data. In Lesson 21, you created a poster or an outline of a presentation that included the following: the statistical question, the plan you used to collect the data, graphs and numerical summaries of the data, and an answer to the statistical question based on your data. Use the following table to organize your presentation.

Points to Consider:	Notes to Include in Your Presentation:
(1) Describe your statistical question.	*"My statistical question is …."*
(2) Explain to your audience why you were interested in this question.	*"I am interested in finding an answer to this question because …."*
(3) Explain the plan you used to collect the data.	*"My plan for collecting data to answer my question was …."* *"I was able to collect my data as planned." (If you were not able to collect the data, explain why.) Explain any challenges or unexpected reactions in collecting your data.*
(4) Explain how you organized the data you collected.	*"Let me explain how I organized my data and prepared my summaries."* *Students might use a table to summarize the data or organize data in a list that could be used to prepare a dot plot or a box plot.*
(5) Explain the graphs you prepared for your presentation and why you made these graphs.	*"I developed a dot plot to start my statistical study because …."*
(6) Explain what measure of center and what measure of variability you selected to summarize your study. Explain why you selected these measures.	*"I selected (the mean or the median) as the measure of center because …."*

Lesson 22:   Presenting a Summary of a Statistical Project

©2015 Great Minds eureka-math.org
G6-M6-TE-B3-1.3.1-01.2016

(7)	Describe what you learned from the data. (Be sure to include an answer to the question from Step (1) on the previous page.)	*"Let me tell you the answer to my statistical question ...."*

Evaluation of Posters

Given that students' work involves several steps, including displaying and organizing their work, it is recommended that a well-defined rubric be developed for evaluating this work. A sample rubric is available at the American Statistical Association's website: http://www.amstat.org/education/posterprojects/index.cfm.

Rubric designs are highly dependent on the process used to complete this project; therefore, the final rubric design should be a teacher decision. Assessment of the project should provide students with feedback regarding the statistical question, the collection of the data, the summary of the data using graphs and numerical summaries, and the conclusions reached in answering the statistical question.

Closing (2 minutes)

Encourage a discussion around the questions posed in the Exit Ticket, or if time is not available for a discussion, encourage students to write their responses.

Lesson Summary

Statistics is about using data to answer questions. The four steps used to carry out a statistical study include posing a question that can be answered by data, collecting appropriate data, summarizing the data with graphs and numerical summaries, and using the data, graphs, and numerical summaries to answer the statistical question.

Exit Ticket (8 minutes)

©2015 Great Minds eureka-math.org
G6-M6-TE-B3-1.3.1-01.2016

Name _____ Date_____

Lesson 22: Presenting a Summary of a Statistical Project

Exit Ticket

After you have presented your study, consider what your next steps are by answering the following questions:

1. What questions still remain after you concluded your statistical study?

2. What statistical question would you like to answer next as a follow-up to this study?

3. How would you collect the data to answer the new question you posed in Question 2?

EUREKA MATH

©2015 Great Minds eureka-math.org
G6-M6-TE-B3-1.3.1-01.2016

Template for Lesson 22: Summarizing a Poster

Step 1:   What was the statistical question presented on this poster?

Step 2:   How were the data collected?

Step 3:   What graphs and numerical summaries were used to summarize data?

Describe at least one graph presented on the poster. (For example, was it a dot plot? What was represented on the scale?) What numerical summaries of the data were included (e.g., the mean or the median)? Also, indicate why these particular numerical summaries were selected.

Step 4:   Summarize the answer to the statistical question.

©2015 Great Minds eureka-math.org
G6-M6-TE-B3-1.3.1-01.2016

Name _____   Date _____

1. A group of students were asked how many states they have visited in their lifetime. Below is a dot plot of their responses.

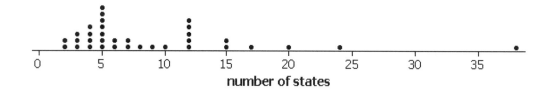

number of states

   a. How many observations are in this data set?

   b. In a few sentences, summarize this distribution in terms of shape, center, and variability.

   c. Based on the dot plot above and without doing any calculations, circle the best response below, and then explain your reasoning.

      A. I expect the mean to be larger than the median.
      B. I expect the median to be larger than the mean.
      C. The mean and median should be similar.

      Explain:

©2015 Great Minds eureka-math.org
G6-M6-TE-B3-1.3.1-01.2016

d. To summarize the variability of this distribution, would you recommend reporting the interquartile range or the mean absolute deviation? Explain your choice.

e. Suppose everyone in the original data set visits one new state over summer vacation. Without doing any calculations, describe how the following values would change (i.e., larger by, smaller by, no change—be specific).

Mean:

Median:

Mean Absolute Deviation:

Interquartile Range:

©2015 Great Minds eureka-math.org
G6-M6-TE-B3-1.3.1-01.2016

2. Diabetes is a disease that occurs in both young and old people. The histogram and box plot below display the ages at which 548 people with diabetes first found out that they had this disease.

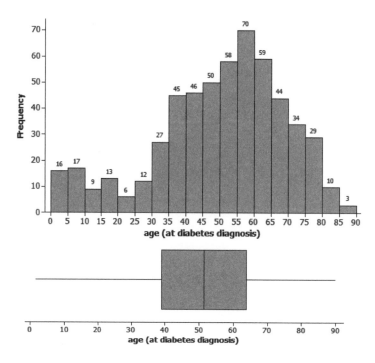

The American Diabetes Association has identified two types of diabetes:

- Type 1 diabetes is when the body does not produce insulin. Type 1 diabetes is usually first found in children and young adults (less than 20 years of age).

- Type 2 diabetes is when the body does not produce enough insulin and the cells do not respond to insulin. Type 2 diabetes is usually first found in older adults (50 years of age or older).

a. Explain how the histogram shows the two types of diabetes.

©2015 Great Minds eureka-math.org
G6-M6-TE-B3-1.3.1-01.2016

EUREKA
MATH™

b. Estimate the percentage of these 548 people who found out they had the disease before age 20. Explain how you made your estimate.

c. Suggest a statistical question that the box plot of the age data would allow you to answer more quickly than the histogram would.

d. The interquartile range for these data is reported to be 24. Write a sentence interpreting this value in the context of this study.

©2015 Great Minds eureka-math.org
G6-M6-TE-B3-1.3.1-01.2016

3. The following table lists the diameters (in miles) of the original nine planets.

Planet	Diameter (in miles)
Mercury	3,030
Venus	7,520
Earth	7,926
Mars	4,217
Jupiter	88,838
Saturn	74,896
Uranus	31,762
Neptune	30,774
Pluto	1,428

a. Calculate the five-number summary (minimum, lower quartile, median, upper quartile, and maximum) of the planet diameters. Be sure to include measurement units with each value.

Minimum:

Lower quartile:

Median:

Upper quartile:

Maximum:

b. Calculate the interquartile range (IQR) for the planet diameters.

EUREKA
MATH™

©2015 Great Minds eureka-math.org
G6-M6-TE-B3-1.3.1-01.2016

c. Draw a box plot of the planet diameters.

d. Would you classify the distribution of planet diameters as roughly symmetric or skewed? Explain.

e. Pluto was recently reclassified as a *dwarf plant* because it is too small to clear other objects out of its path. The mean diameter with all nine planets is 27,821 miles, and the MAD is 25,552 miles. Use this information to argue whether or not Pluto is substantially smaller than the remaining eight planets.

A Progression Toward Mastery

Assessment Task Item		STEP 1 Missing or incorrect answer and little evidence of reasoning or application of mathematics to solve the problem.	STEP 2 Missing or incorrect answer but evidence of some reasoning or application of mathematics to solve the problem.	STEP 3 A correct answer with some evidence of reasoning or application of mathematics to solve the problem OR an incorrect answer with substantial evidence of solid reasoning or application of mathematics to solve the problem.	STEP 4 A correct answer supported by substantial evidence of solid reasoning or application of mathematics to solve the problem.
1	**a** 6.SP.B.5a	Student does not use information in the dot plot.	Student counts 15 unique outcomes for the *number of states*.	Student counts 33 or 35 dots.	Student correctly counts 34 dots.
	b 6.SP.A.2	Student does not use information in the dot plot.	Student provides descriptions that are not consistent with the graph.	Student only addresses two of the main components of shape, center, and variability.	Student gives a complete description of each component. For example, "The distribution is skewed indicating many students visiting around 5 states, but another cluster indicates some students visiting around 12 states. Almost all of the students have visited fewer than 15 states, but one outlier has visited more than 35."
	c 6.SP.B.5d	Student only circles an incorrect response and does not provide justification.	Student circles A but does not justify the choice or circles B or C, but the justification is inconsistent. For example, "The median should be larger because there are some students who have visited a lot of states."	Student circles A, but the justification is incomplete or inconsistent. For example, "The mean will be larger because most of the data are between 0 and 10."	Student circles A and comments on how the skewness and/or outliers will pull the value of the mean to the right of the value of the median.

EUREKA MATH

©2015 Great Minds eureka-math.org
G6-M6-TE-B3-1.3.1-01.2016

	d **6.SP.B.5d**	Student does not address the choice of the measure of variability.	Student makes a choice but does not justify the response.	Student makes a choice, but the justification is inconsistent (e.g., the MAD because of the outlier).	Student chooses the interquartile range because of the presence of skewness and/or outliers.
	e **6.SP.A.3**	Student only indicates that there is not enough information to answer the question.	Student only addresses two of the four measures.	Student answers are not completely consistent with the mean and median measuring the center and the MAD and IQR measuring the spread.	Student correctly answers that the mean and median increase by one because everyone shifts the same amount. The MAD and IQR stay the same because everyone shifts the same amount.
2	**a** **6.SP.A.2**	Student does not utilize information from the histogram.	Student discusses the ages and the recommendation but does not connect to the histogram.	Student discusses observations below age 20 and above age 20 but does not address the distinctness of the two clumps of values around age 20.	Student focuses on the two clumps, with the valley between the clumps around the cited 20 years of age.
	b **6.SP.B.5a**	Student makes no use of the distribution (e.g., $\frac{20}{90}$).	Student uses the box plot and assumes half of the 25% below 40 years of age are below 20 years of age.	Student uses the histogram but makes a minor calculation error. The result is still consistent with the graph (e.g., below 20%).	Student uses the histogram and finds $\frac{16+17+9+13}{548} \approx 0.10$, or about 10%.
	c **6.SP.A.1**	Student fails to distinguish between the box plot and the histogram.	Student suggests a feature of the box plot but does not relate to a statistical question. For example, "How many people have diabetes?"	Student suggests a feature of the box plot, but the statistical question is vague or incomplete. For example, "Where are most of the ages?"	Student suggests a statistical question that relates to the quartiles or median. For example, "What is the median age at diagnosis?"
	d **6.SP.A.3**	Student only attempts to explain how the IQR is calculated and does so incorrectly.	Student does not interpret the IQR as a measure of the spread. For example, "Most people are diagnosed around 24 years."	Student addresses the IQR as a measure of the spread but does not provide an interpretation in context. For example, "$Q3 - Q1$."	Student correctly answers that the width of the middle 50% of the diagnosed ages is 24 years.
3	**a** **6.SP.B.5**	Student is not able to identify information correctly from the table.	Student does not sort the observations before making computations: 3,030, 77,23, 88,838, 31,268, and 1,428 miles.	Student sorts the data but performs minor calculation errors or only correctly finds 3 of the values.	Student sorts the data correctly: 1,428, 3,623.5, 7,926, 53,329, and 88,838 miles.

b 6.SP.B.5c	Student does not perform a calculation.	Student calculates $Q3 - Q2$ or $Q2 - Q1$ or reports a negative value.	Student reports correct values from part (a), but as a range, and does not calculate the difference in the values.	Student uses $Q3 - Q1$ using the values from part (a).
c 6.SP.B.4	Student does not construct a graph.	Student constructs a dot plot or histogram.	Student constructs and scales a graph, but the graph does not match the values reported in part (a).	Student correctly constructs and scales a graph using the values from part (a).
d 6.SP.A.2	Student does not justify the choice.	Student gives a reasonable response, but it is not based on a graph of the data or on the quartiles. For example, "A few planets are really large, so the data are skewed."	Student refers to the box plot and/or quartiles but draws an inconsistent conclusion (e.g., describes the correct box plot as symmetric or judges the distance between the quartiles as similar because the values are so large).	Student uses the box plot and judges the relative widths of the segments to answer the question.
e 6.SP.B.5	Student only uses the context and does not use the mean and MAD values.	Student compares Pluto's diameter to the mean without considering the MAD.	Student answers generically but does not relate to Pluto's value explicitly. For example, "Not all observations will fall within one MAD from the mean."	Student uses the difference between the mean and the MAD to determine that Pluto's diameter is just over one MAD away from the mean; thus, Pluto is not much smaller.

EUREKA MATH™

©2015 Great Minds eureka-math.org
G6-M6-TE-B3-1.3.1-01.2016

Name _____   Date _____

1. A group of students were asked how many states they have visited in their lifetime. Below is a dot plot of their responses.

number of states

a. How many observations are in this data set?

    34

b. In a few sentences, summarize this distribution in terms of shape, center, and variability.

    A typical number of states is 5, but there
    is a lot of variability (eg. 2 states to over 35 states).
    There were also 5 people who visited 12 states.
    The distribution is skewed with one very high value.

c. Based on the dot plot above and without doing any calculations, circle the best response below, and then explain your reasoning.

    (A.) I expect the mean to be larger than the median.
    B.   I expect the median to be larger than the mean.
    C.   The mean and median should be similar.

    Explain:

    The mean will get pulled higher by the student
    who has been to a lot more states.

d. To summarize the variability of this distribution, would you recommend reporting the interquartile range or the mean absolute deviation? Explain your choice.

> The interquartile range because we do have a few extreme values which would enlarge the MAD, or the mean absolute deviation.

e. Suppose everyone in the original data set visits one new state over summer vacation. Without doing any calculations, describe how the following values would change (i.e., larger by, smaller by, no change—be specific).

Mean:

> The mean would increase by one state.

Median:

> The median would increase by one state.

Mean Absolute Deviation:

> The MAD would not change.

Interquartile Range:

> The interquartile range would not change.

Module 6:   Statistics

©2015 Great Minds eureka-math.org
G6-M6-TE-B3-1.3.1-01.2016

EUREKA MATH

2. Diabetes is a disease that occurs in both young and old people. The histogram and box plot below display the ages at which 548 people with diabetes first found out that they had this disease.

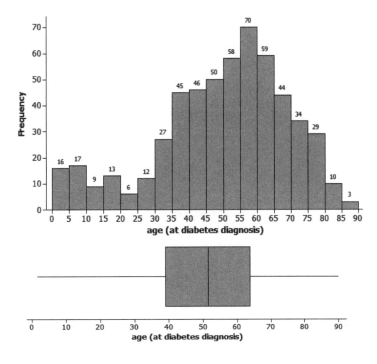

The American Diabetes Association has identified two types of diabetes:

- Type 1 diabetes is when the body does not produce insulin. Type 1 diabetes is usually first found in children and young adults (less than 20 years of age).

- Type 2 diabetes is when the body does not produce enough insulin and the cells do not respond to insulin. Type 2 diabetes is usually first found in older adults (50 years of age or older).

a. Explain how the histogram shows the two types of diabetes.

There are two "humps" in the distribution—
one to the left of 20 years and one
around 50-55 years.

©2015 Great Minds eureka-math.org
G6-M6-TE-B3-1.3.1-01.2016

b. Estimate the percentage of these 548 people who found out they had the disease before age 20. Explain how you made your estimate.

$$\frac{16 + 17 + 9 + 13}{548} = \frac{55}{548} \approx 0.10$$

About 10% of this sample (found by finding the sum of the bars below 20 and dividing by the number of people in the study).

c. Suggest a statistical question that the box plot of the age data would allow you to answer more quickly than the histogram would.

What is the median age at which people are diagnosed with diabetes?

d. The interquartile range for these data is reported to be 24. Write a sentence interpreting this value in the context of this study.

The "length" of the ages for the middle 50% of ages is 24 years, or the distance between the top 25% and the bottom 25% of ages is 24 years.

EUREKA
MATH

©2015 Great Minds eureka-math.org
G6-M6-TE-B3-1.3.1-01.2016

3. The following table lists the diameters (in miles) of the original nine planets.

Planet	Diameter (in miles)
Mercury	3,030
Venus	7,520
Earth	7,926
Mars	4,217
Jupiter	88,838
Saturn	74,896
Uranus	31,762
Neptune	30,774
Pluto	1,428

a. Calculate the five-number summary (minimum, lower quartile, median, upper quartile, and maximum) of the planet diameters. Be sure to include measurement units with each value.

Minimum:

1,428 miles

1,428, 3,030, 4,217, 7,520,
(7,926) 30,774, 31,762, 74,896, 88,838

Lower quartile:

3,030 miles + 4,217 miles = 7,247 miles
7,247 miles ÷ 2 = 3,623.5 miles

Median:

7,926 miles

Upper quartile:

31,762 miles + 74,896 miles = 106,658 miles
106,658 miles ÷ 2 = 53,329 miles

Maximum:

88,838 miles

b. Calculate the interquartile range (IQR) for the planet diameters.

53,329 miles − 3,623.5 miles = 49,705.5 miles

©2015 Great Minds eureka-math.org
G6-M6-TE-B3-1.3.1-01.2016

c.   Draw a box plot of the planet diameters.

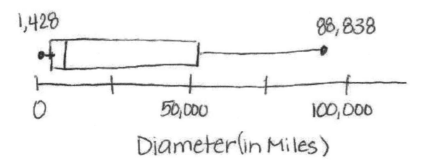

1,428   88,838

0   50,000   100,000

Diameter (in Miles)

d.   Would you classify the distribution of planet diameters as roughly symmetric or skewed? Explain.

Skewed because the box to the right of the median stretches out much further than the box to the left of the median.

e.   Pluto was recently reclassified as a *dwarf plant* because it is too small to clear other objects out of its path. The mean diameter with all nine planets is 27,821 miles, and the MAD is 25,552 miles. Use this information to argue whether or not Pluto is substantially smaller than the remaining eight planets.

Pluto is 1,428 miles in diameter.
Mean - MAD = 27,821 miles - 25,552 miles = 2,269 miles
Pluto is a little more than one mean absolute deviation from the mean. As a result, Pluto is not substantially smaller.

Module 6:   Statistics

©2015 Great Minds eureka-math.org
G6-M6-TE-B3-1.3.1-01.2016

EUREKA MATH